Flying Saucers

Reflection of the sun in horizontal ice plates floating in the air.

FLYING SAUCERS

DONALD H. MENZEL

Professor of Astrophysics, Harvard University

HARVARD UNIVERSITY PRESS · CAMBRIDGE · 1953

Library of Congress Catalog Card Number 52–12419
Printed in the United States of America

To my good friend
SAM BASS WARNER
former Register of Copyrights
and now publisher of
THE SHORE LINE TIMES
Guilford, Connecticut

PREFACE

In this book I have tried to answer the question "What Are The Flying Saucers?" No single answer suffices, because the apparitions stem from not one but many dozens of causes. Most of the reports refer to reflections from material objects: distant planes, jet aircraft, vapor trails, miscellaneous balloons, newspapers, kites, birds, peculiar clouds, spider webs, insects, feathers, and so on. Searchlights playing on thin layers of cloud or mist account for many of the records. Venus, Jupiter, various stars, bright fireballs, and even the moon shining through broken clouds, have been frequently identified as flying saucers. According to the U. S. Air Force, about 80 per cent of all sightings possess natural explanations, like those listed above.

I shall use the phrase "true flying saucer" to refer to the 20 per cent that the Air Force lists as unexplained. And in this sense I have adopted the thesis that: flying saucers are real; people have seen them; they are not what people thought they saw.

I present evidence to show that this mysterious residue consists of the rags and tags of meteorological optics: mirages, reflections in mist, refractions and reflections by ice crystals. Some phenomena are probably related to the aurora; others are unusual forms of shooting stars. A few — like the great saucer of 1882 — probably represent natural phenomena that we still do not fully understand.

Experimental devices in development by various armed services account for not more than two or three out of a thousand sightings, and thus are unimportant for sustaining the saucer scare. Atomic experimentation is also guiltless in this respect. Saucers are not weapons or devices sent by Russia or any other foreign power.

Above all, there is not the slightest evidence to support the popular fantasy that saucers are interplanetary space ships, manned by beings from beyond the earth, however much some people want to believe in this unscientific, highly publicized interpretation of saucers. To them I am the man who shot Santa Claus. One devotee of the saucer cult wrote me: "Dr. Menzel — I wish that one of those space ships would land on top of Observatory Hill, and that a squad of the Little Men would seize you, put you in their ship and take you away to Venus. Then, maybe you'd believe!" Well — maybe I would!

I wish to make a few special acknowledgments — to my wife for efficient research on the flying saucers of history; to my daughter, Elizabeth, for special assistance on Chapters 11 and 13; and to Joseph D. Elder of the Harvard University Press for many valuable editorial suggestions. My aunt, Marie C. Menzel, has helped in many ways. To Steve White, editor of _Look_, I am indebted for many stimulating conferences. A. C. Nelson and F. Broman of the University of Denver provided the basic material for Chapter 12. Ralph Haynes of Widener Library and Catherine Hanley of Phillips Library have helped in the literature search. V. Schaefer of the General Electric Company made many useful comments and also provided illustrations. Although the sources of illustrations are detailed elsewhere, I must thank B. and T. Duell, J. F. Chappell, Charles F. Brooks, and J. Robert Hamilton for their very special assistance on illustrations. Helmut Landsberg gave me valuable advice on problems of meteorological optics. Ed King of Duxbury read the manuscript and made helpful suggestions. Luigi Jacchia kindly provided a translation of the Reinzer book. Martha Mastrangello, Bettina Hansen, and Velma Adams assisted with the typing, editing, and proofreading. _Look_ and _Time_ have given permission for use of illustrations and quotations from articles prepared for them.

D. H. M.

CONTENTS

SOURCES OF ILLUSTRATIONS

The frontispiece and Figs. 39 and 40 are from photographs by the Signal Corps Engineering Laboratory.

Figures 1, 5, 25, 29, and 47 are from photographs by J. F. Chappell, Lick Observatory, Mount Hamilton, California.

Figures 2 and 34 are by courtesy of Charles F. Brooks, Blue Hill Meteorological Observatory, Harvard University.

Figures 3, 18, 19, 30, 31, 33, 65, 66, 67, 68, and 69 are from drawings by J. R. Hamilton.

Figure 4 is from a photograph by W. Ray Allen, High Altitude Observatory, Climax, Colorado.

Figure 6 is from a United Press photograph.

Figures 7, 52, 53, 54, and 56 are from photographs by A. Rothstein, courtesy of Look.

Figure 8 is by courtesy of Anthony D. Keogh and Amrum H. Katz.

Figure 9 was drawn from official Air Force figures.

Figure 10 is from a sketch by J. R. Capron, published in The London, Edinburgh, and Dublin Philosophical Magazine and Journal of Science, series 5, vol. 15 (1883).

Figures 11, 35, 36, 38, 58, 78, and 79 are from drawings by T. Duell from 16th- and 17th-century broadsides.

Figures 13, 14, 15, 16, 17, 21, 37, 60, 70, 71, 72, and 73 are from Franz Reinzer, Meteorologia Philosophico-Politica (Augsburg, 1709).

Figure 20 is by courtesy of the Museum of Fine Arts, Boston.

Figure 26 is from a photograph by Vincent J. Schaefer, General Electric Research Laboratory, Schenectady, New York.

Figure 27 is from a photograph by Walter Orr Roberts, High Altitude Observatory, Climax, Colorado.

Figure 32 is by courtesy of B. and T. Duell.

Figures 41 and 50 are from James Glaisher, Camille Flammarion, Wilfrid de Fonvielle, and Gaston Tissandier, Travels in the Air (London, 1871).

Figure 49 is from Frédéric Zürcher and Elie Margollé, Meteors, Aerolites, Storms, and Atmospheric Phenomena (translated by William Lackland, New York, 1876).

Figures 51, 74, and 75 are by courtesy of Look.

Figure 55 is from a photograph by J. Coyne, courtesy of Time, Inc.

Figures 61 and 62 are from photographs by Störmer.

Figure 64 is from a photograph by the High Altitude Observatory, Climax, Colorado.

Figure 76 is by courtesy of F. L. Whipple, Harvard Observatory.

Figure 80 is from a painting by W. Kranz, based on another painting by C. Brioschi and on a sketch by an eyewitness.

Figure 81 is from a drawing by Gustave Hahn, published in the Journal of the Royal Astronomical Society of Canada *(1913), redrawn by J. R. Hamilton.*

Figure 82 is from D. H. Menzel, Elementary Manual of Radio Propagation *(New York: Prentice-Hall, 1948).*

Figures 85 and 86 are from the United Artists motion picture "Destination Moon."

Figure 87 is from a drawing by R. J. Trumpler, Lick Observatory, Mount Hamilton, California.

Figure 88(a) is from a photograph by E. E. Barnard, Yerkes Observatory, Williams Bay, Wisconsin.

Figures 88(b,c) are from photographs by W. H. Wright, Lick Observatory, Mount Hamilton, California.

Figure 89 is copyright by Hugo Gernsback, Radio-Electronics Magazine, New York.

Flying Saucers

1

The saucers start to fly

▀▀▀

Throughout the ages, apparitions of one kind or another have plagued the human race. Primitive people the world over have generally believed in the existence of demons, ghosts, elves, goblins, dragons, sea serpents — to mention just a few of the more common fantasies.

People believed in such things either because they themselves had seen them or because they knew someone else who had seen them. Most of these mythical creatures are as out of date as a side-saddle at a rodeo. We no longer believe in ghosts — or in dragons, either. And we would regard anyone who did as perhaps being a bit "touched" — or at least very superstitious. And yet these apparitions have all played some useful role in history, if only as the simplest available explanation for some otherwise mysterious happening.

And now we are seeing flying saucers! What are they? And how do they fly? Are they real? Or will they go the way of dragons?

Saucers have been seen in the daytime, flashing like silver in the sunlight. Others have been seen at night, luminous globes or disk-shaped blobs of light. Sometimes they stand still, at other times they move or veer with tremendous speeds. Estimates of size have varied all the way from a few feet to several hundred feet in diameter, with 50 feet being somewhere near the average. Saucers have been seen from the ground and from planes. Some saucers have skimmed along the horizon; others have soared to great heights.

In the early days of the scare, the saucers caused, directly or indirectly, at least two plane crashes and several deaths. As the sightings of these mysterious objects increased, especially in the neighborhood of our highly secret atomic laboratories in the Western deserts, authorities clamped down a lid of secrecy upon everything associated with the phenomenon.

According to the allocation of responsibilities in the Department of Defense, anything that flies falls under the jurisdiction of the U. S. Air Force. Saucers fly. In consequence, the Air Force received one of the toughest assignments ever given to a government agency: coördination and investigation of thousands of reports, all the way from Seattle to the border of the Iron Curtain.

The mysterious character of the phenomena appeared to demand secrecy. But the restrictions and red tape of military classification, however necessary, have long delayed the solution of the problem. Scientists who might easily have provided the key that would unlock the secrets of the saucers did not receive detailed information — information necessary for a serious study of the whole problem. Second, the restrictions placed on the saucer projects served only to deepen the fear of an already frightened public.

Rumors flew like the saucers. Suggested identifications included weather balloons, distant airplanes, meteors, kites, wind-blown newspapers, hallucinations, a secret plane called "The Flying Wing," searchlights on clouds, a Russian device sent to spy out our atomic secrets or to promote confusion through some form of psychological warfare, "skyhook" balloons, semiïnvisible clouds, or *craft from interplanetary space!*

Of all the possibilities, it was the last that struck the public imagination. Here was Jules Verne brought up to date! Space craft from Venus, or perhaps from Mars, controlled, according to some reports, by miniature beings 26 inches high! Little men whose powerful physiques could withstand the tremendous buffeting that the flying saucers would give them. Little men who allegedly wore no buttons on their clothes. Little men, supposedly investigating the earth because they had seen our atomic-bomb blasts and were concerned whether or not the bombs constituted a menace to interplanetary peace.

Most scientists will agree that interplanetary travel is by no means an impossibility. Actually it seems nearer of accomplishment today than simple aviation was back in Jules Verne's time. And if we can put a ship into space, why should not other beings from other planets be able to do likewise? The saucers seem to be the answer.

Several books and countless magazine articles have argued that the flying saucers represent some type of space ship. Most of the authors have disclaimed having any inside information. They draw their conclusions from such data as they have available, put together in a form best calculated to support the interplanetary hypothesis, and overlook or dismiss evidence to the contrary.

Here and there one will find an inference that the Air Force — or perhaps the Atomic Energy Commission — is suppressing information that would fully substantiate the claims that interplanetary saucers are "real." The authors claim that these government agencies are the villains in the piece. From purely selfish motives, rather than because of international security, so the argument goes, they have suppressed information about the saucers, including several known to have landed or crashed. The reasons given, such as a desire to keep the secrets for military use only, are nebulous and unconvincing.

My studies of the sun take me frequently to Colorado and New Mexico, and I was at the Holloman Air Base, near Alamogordo, New Mexico, at the height of the flying-saucer scare. One morning I had glimpsed what seemed to be several saucers moving overhead — until I focused my eyes more clearly and recognized the objects as weather balloons. That afternoon, I expressed my belief that most of the saucers could be thus explained. But others in the group — including several well-known scientists — indicated that there was probably more to the saucer story than that.

Early that evening, I had my second attack of saucers. I was in the back seat of an automobile, being driven toward Alamogordo and admiring the full moon as it rose over Sacramento Peak toward the east. A few degrees north of the moon, I noticed what seemed to be a bright star, and then a second star appeared not far from the first. Casually, I assumed that they were Castor and Pollux in the constellation Gemini. Then, very suddenly, I realized that Gemini was a winter object; the two stars had to be something else.

Like most astronomers, I am always hopeful of finding a nova — a star that has exploded and thus become exceptionally bright. I rapidly opened the window of the car for a better look. To my surprise, I could bring neither of these objects into clear focus, although nearby Antares was quite sharp.

Both hazy disks shone with a slightly bluish light. They were, in a sense, "flying" simply because they were elevated. Suddenly alive to the fact that I was seeing something unusual, I asked the driver to stop. We climbed out of the car just in time to see the saucers literally fade away as mysteriously as they had appeared. I reported the occurrence in detail to the Air Force.

Had it not been for the current flying-saucer publicity, I should probably not have given the phenomenon a second thought. Under the actual circumstances, I have long wondered what it was that I actually saw. The simpler and more obvious explanations, like wisps of clouds, or distant searchlights, did not seem acceptable. But at no time did I have even the slightest suspicion that the objects were of interplanetary origin.

I recently found a reference in an old book by Edward J. Lowe, an English meteorologist, who mentioned a similar phenomenon observed as long ago as 1838 — similar except for the fact that he saw four instead of two ghostly images flying near the moon.

Perhaps I shall be expected, at this point, to explain exactly what I saw that evening in New Mexico. I am sorry to say that I cannot explain the phenomenon in every detail, but I do have certain ideas on the subject which seem to be entirely reasonable.

I shall explain those ideas, but first let me say what I do *not* believe. I do *not* believe that what I saw, or anything anyone else has reported seeing, were missiles or messengers or vehicles from Venus, the moon, or Mars, or space. I do *not* believe they were missiles or messengers or vehicles from Russia or any other foreign country. I do *not* believe that the exploding of the atomic bomb was in any way a direct cause of the saucers.

In all of nature I cannot think of anything more terrifying than an unexpected stroke of lightning with its accompanying clap of thunder. But lightning would be even more terrifying if we did not understand it — if, for example, we thought that some pagan god or supernatural force beyond our control were threatening us with his displeasure.

A total eclipse of the sun or the moon might scare us even more than does a lightning flash if we did not know how and why it occurs, and when to expect it.

We can enjoy the colorful beauty of the rainbow arching across the sky, because we know that it is a natural phenomenon and not an apparition heralding some exceptional catastrophe on earth.

Thunder and lightning, eclipses, or the rainbow are relatively simple phenomena in terms of modern science. True, some aspects of a great storm may be terrifying. A cloudburst can produce a destructive flood. A lightning bolt will cause damage or even death where it strikes, unless brought under control by the simple lightning rod. But any fear that we may experience during a violent storm stems from knowledge rather than from ignorance. Astronomers can foretell to the nearest second how and where a total eclipse will occur. And we would consider childish anyone who screamed with fright during an eclipse or who beat upon a dishpan in an attempt to halt the event or to frighten away the dragons supposedly devouring the sun. Yet is our own attitude toward the flying saucers any more rational?

I admit that strange sights do appear in the sky — more, indeed, than the average man realizes. I have myself, on more than one occasion, seen a cross flaming in the sky, a cross centered on the sun with its arms glowing in rainbow colors. An apparition prophesying the end of the world? No! Just a pattern of light caused by clouds of ice crystals far above the surface of the earth.

There are three reasons why I am, perhaps, more familiar with unusual sights in the sky than is the average person. First of all, as an astronomer, I am more conscious of the heavens. I probably look upward more often than most people do, and also I am more sensitive to the presence of any occurrence the least bit unusual. Second, when any interesting atmospheric phenomenon occurs in the sky, from a simple halo around the sun or moon to a brilliant display of the aurora borealis, the local newspapers have developed the habit of calling me, to help them interpret what is going on. Thus I manage to see some unusual sights that I would otherwise miss. Third, and perhaps most important of all, I have studied textbooks of optical meteorology and know how light rays from the sun, moon, and stars travel through the earth's atmosphere.

Light does not always travel in a straight line. Clouds, water droplets, ice crystals (tiny snowflakes), or even dust intercept the down-coming light and can change both its quality and its direction. I have seen white clouds brilliantly edged with rainbow hues. I have seen "mock suns" or "mock moons" glowing like silver on either side of the real sun or moon. (However, the extra moons that I saw in the New Mexican desert were not of this variety.) I have seen a red rainbow, a rainbow with all of the other colors missing. I have seen a rainbow at night. I have seen the sun surmounted by a pillar of fire.

These optical sights are somewhat unusual, but they are understandable. They require no beings from interplanetary space to produce them.

All my study has convinced me that nature is fundamentally simple — though rarely perfect and complete. If we see a rainbow, some portions of the arc may be missing. Sometimes we view only a small segment of the bow, because the raindrops fall in a local shower.

And when we come to the more complicated phenomena produced by crystals of ice, we discover a wide variation about the simple or perfect picture. Sometimes the ice crystals have the form of long needles; at other times they assume the form of starlike plates. Sometimes they are steady and at others strongly agitated. That bows, halos, and mock suns produced by different types of crystal bear any resemblance to one another is most surprising.

To understand flying saucers we shall have to discuss in some detail the different types of optical tricks that the atmosphere and its contents can play upon our eyes. But the things we see are natural optical *phenomena*, not optical illusions. The illusion, if any, comes from our psychological impression and mental interpretation of the phenomenon.

Flying saucers are real — as real as a rainbow, and no more dangerous. Men have recorded them throughout history; even the Bible refers to them. But note one specific point: the objects identified as "saucers" comprise not one but at least five different types. A saucer seen during the daytime is not the same as one seen at night. A saucer seen from an airplane may differ appreciably from a saucer seen from the ground. Failure to recognize this simple fact has been one of the basic stumbling blocks that has long postponed our discovering what the saucers really are.

The current saucer epidemic started in a simple and unheralded manner. On 24 June 1947, Kenneth Arnold, a businessman from Boise, Idaho, was making a routine flight from Chehalis to Yakima, Washington, in a private plane. The official Air Force report recounts Arnold's story in some detail.

Just as he neared Mount Ranier and was admiring the grandeur of the second highest peak in the continental United States, he saw with a start what appeared to be a chain of unfamiliar aircraft flying close to the mountain.

"I could see their outline quite plainly against the snow as they approached the mountain," he said. "They flew very close to the mountain tops, directly south to southeast down the hogback of the range, flying like geese in a diagonal chainlike line, as if they were linked together.

"They were approximately 20 or 25 miles away, and I couldn't see a tail on them. I watched for about three minutes — a chain of saucerlike things at least five miles long, swerving in and out of the high mountain peaks. They were flat like a piepan and so shiny they reflected the sun like a mirror. I never saw anything so fast."

Arnold estimated that the objects were slightly smaller than a DC-4 that happened to be conveniently near at hand for purposes of comparison. He clocked the speed at about 1200 miles an hour, although this figure seems to be inconsistent with the length of time that he estimated them to be in view. From his previous statement, they could scarcely have traveled more than 25 miles during the 3 minutes that he watched. This gives about 500 miles an hour, which is still a figure large enough to be startling.

Arnold, on arrival at his destination, naturally reported what he had seen — and thus touched off what eventually proved to be a chain reaction that has attained fantastic proportions. The saucer story caught the public eye, and, although papers tended at first to scoff at or ridicule the tale, as the reports of other sightings increased, the saucers became front-page news everywhere.

Arnold himself, feeling keenly the criticism of the press, stated, "They can call me Einstein, Flash Gordon, or just a screwball, but I am absolutely certain of what I saw." He further said that no matter what else he might see in the sky in the future, "even if it were a ten-story building flying through the air," he would shut his eyes and completely disregard it.

Arnold's story, coupled with the other incidents, was of such a nature as to demand some sort of official investigation. And here, as stated earlier, the U. S. Air Force stepped into the picture. They set up "Project Saucer" to investigate sightings in general and to study the various phenomena from different angles. Professor J. Allen Hynek, astrophysicist of Ohio State University, became consultant, to advise on the possible astronomical character of these incidents. His report stated that the Arnold experience could not possibly be attributed to any reasonable known astronomical phenomenon and finally concluded, "It appears probable that whatever objects were observed were traveling at subsonic speeds and may therefore have been some sort of known aircraft."

Although what Arnold saw has remained a mystery until this day, I simply cannot understand why the simplest and most obvious explanation of all has been overlooked. The basic clues are in Arnold's original words: "Down the hogback of the range . . . as if they were linked together . . . a chain of saucerlike things . . . like a piepan and so shiny they reflected the sun like a mirror." He mentions the outline seen against the snow of the mountain.

For the interpretation we have one or more closely related possibilities. But it does seem to me that the association of the saucers with the hogback is perhaps the most significant feature of all. This observation serves to fix their distance and approximate size, and roughly confirms Arnold's estimate of their apparent speed.

I have spent considerable time in the high Rocky Mountains in Colorado. From the High Altitude Observatory of Harvard University and University of Colorado at Climax, Colorado, I have occasionally watched through binoculars or a small telescope the billowing blasts of snow, ballooning up from the tops of the ridges. For the air along any mountain range is often highly turbulent. These rapidly shifting, tilting clouds of snow would reflect the sun like a mirror. And the rocking surfaces would make the chain sweep along something like a wave, with only a momentary reflection from each crest.

There is another possibility. On a calm, clear day the earth's atmosphere may contain one or more sharp layers of haze or dust.

Fig. 1. Storm clouds developing from air rising over a hogback.

Such a layer is almost invisible if we are below or above it. But it will be extremely marked to any plane flying close to it. Fog or haze can, under certain conditions, reflect the sun in almost mirror fashion.

A layer of this kind may well have been present during Arnold's famous flight. But, over the jagged range, it would have been tilted, torn, and twisted by the violent air circulation, so that it could have produced the observed effect. Perhaps some condensation arising from the turbulence may have contributed to the reflectivity of the cloud.

I feel certain that turbulence over the ridge, the sort of air currents that make a plane rock uncomfortably as it travels over rugged country, was in the main responsible for Arnold's saucers. But whether the apparent metallic glint came from billows of snow or billows of haze we do not have enough evidence at the moment to decide.

I can find no evidence that anyone has considered seriously the foregoing explanation of what Arnold saw. My good friend and colleague, the distinguished Navy physicist, Dr. Urner Liddel, has independently suggested that reflections in fog or mist may account for many of the saucers. And the only reason I have seen given for the rejection of this hypothesis is its apparent inability to explain also the green fireballs that mystify observers on the desert of New Mexico. To my mind, this procedure is just about as sensible as refusing to eat a hot dog merely because bananas, which have a similar shape, do not happen to agree with you. Actually the green fireballs are an entirely different phenomenon.

That this mystery should have continued is all the more surprising in view of the fact that the official Air Force releases state that "only a few days after Arnold's sighting, a disk was reported seen over his home town of Boise — 'a half-circle in shape, clinging to a cloud and just as bright and silvery looking as a mirror caught in the rays of the sun.'"

How any person familiar with meteorological optics could have missed the significance of this incident, I do not know! It was a sundog or mock sun.

The evidence seems to indicate that the Air Force lumped the flying saucers into one of three general classifications: mistaken objects like planes, balloons, or kites; fireballs, meteors, or an occasional glimpse of the planet Venus; hallucinations in general. Thus they gave no serious consideration to the possible effects of mist, ice crystals, or mirages, which phenomena, singly or jointly, I believe are the basic cause of most of the unexplained objects that deserve to be called "real saucers" or "bona fide saucers."

2

Flying saucers seen from the air

▄▄▄

As Kenneth Arnold's spectacular description of the mysterious flying disks spread over the country, additional reported sightings swept the nation, flooding eastward like a tidal wave. Like Arnold's, most of these early reports concerned daylight observations. To see a flying saucer, apparently all one had to do was look at the sky for a reasonable length of time, and then a saucer would obligingly skim into view.

The story caused some wonderment in London and other foreign capitals when it broke. A friend of mine, a leading British scientist, commented on the gullibility of the American public with respect to these hallucinations.

"Just wait," I told him. "It won't be long before a special brand of British saucers will be on the market." And sure enough, within several weeks, sightings from England and other places abroad began to pour in. Apparently the saucers did not recognize national boundaries!

The fact that some of these sightings were from Finland and Sweden, close to the Iron Curtain, caused some concern in high circles. These incidents led to a stricter security regulation, because there was a remote possibility that the phenomena might in some way be from activity behind the Iron Curtain. The proximity of some of the sightings to Russian-controlled Peenemunde, the old German rocket center, was also disquieting.

The mere existence of the saucer scare led newspapers to publicize nationally events that otherwise might have remained purely local — for example, the observation of a fireball of unusual brightness. These objects are common, especially when referred to an area as large as the entire United States. Under normal circumstances, only the most brilliant of such displays would be news. The attention of the American public, thus focused on nighttime apparitions, shortly reported luminous disks whizzing singly or in groups across the sky.

Most of the objects proved to be bright meteors — mere shooting stars. These lights that streak across the sky result from collision of the earth with tiny fragments of rock or metal, which exist in considerable abundance in interplanetary space — debris left over from creation. Friction in the earth's atmosphere heats such a particle to the point where it becomes luminous and vaporizes. There is nothing at all mysterious about such objects, at least nothing mysterious in the flying-saucer sense.

But now reports began to filter in of strange lights seen flying across the desert at night. These reports were never fully released, because the sightings lay so close to the White Sands Proving Ground and the Holloman Air Base in New Mexico, where scientists working for the Department of Defense test rockets and guided missiles. Also, many sightings occurred in the neighborhood of Los Alamos, New Mexico, one of our great laboratories used for the development of atomic energy.

One of the earliest nighttime reports that seemed to fall into some category of flying saucers came in August 1947. Two airline pilots for a Bethel, Alabama, company saw a big black cigar-shaped body silhouetted against the evening sky. It might well have passed for one of the familiar lenticular clouds (Fig. 2), except for the fact that it moved. In fact, the object seemed to be dead ahead, and they avoided collision only by swerving sharply, during which time the object crossed directly in front of them. The pilots then tried to follow the dark body which sped on before them, outdistancing them despite the fact that they were flying at a rate of 175 miles per hour. Four minutes later it vanished. Their report says that the object resembled "a C-54 without motors, wings, or visible means of propulsion — smooth surfaced and streamlined."

This report has in it several remarkable features which in themselves are hidden clues to the nature of the object. One of these, of course, is its cigar-shaped form and the fact that here we encounter the reverse of a report that might have been given later at night. The object was *dark*, silhouetted against the *bright* horizon. A few hours later, under conditions otherwise similar, the object might have appeared luminous against a black sky.

I believe that what the flyers saw was a mirage. Few persons, except those familiar with the details of meteorological optics, realize how frequently mirages occur. Many persons do not know what a mirage is or what can cause it. First, let me say that a mirage is something real, not a hallucination like a pink elephant. Nor is it an optical illusion. Light may depart appreciably from its nearly straight-line path when exceptional temperature conditions occur in the lower atmosphere, as, for example, when an intensely

Fig. 2. A lenticular cloud, often mistaken for a flying saucer.

hot or extremely cold layer of air lies close to the earth's surface. The air acts as a sort of lens to bring a distant light source into focus. The lens is imperfect, so that the world seen through it is distorted and unfamiliar; it is a little like looking through someone else's spectacles. No wonder one sees weird things — even flying saucers. This brief description of a mirage will have to serve until we again consider the question in more detail, in a later chapter.

The effect that the Alabama flyers saw was compounded out of a raising of land into the sky and a lowering of sky into the land. The black object that resembled a C-54 was a mirage of the distant landscape, the darkened surface of the earth "lifted" as if by magic to form an island in the sky. But the form, size, and position of this island are very sensitive indeed to the position of the observer. If he moves, the image may dart in a counter direction. And as he tries to run it down the image itself will appear smaller and smaller, finally vanishing into the distance. There is nothing really mysterious about the report, unless it is the fact that its interpretation has remained a mystery for nearly five years.

The Air Force has, with good reason, generally regarded the airline pilots as the most reliable observers of all. These men are highly skilled and possess both judgment and integrity. They are not likely to make a report merely for the sensation it will cause. They will relate their impressions honestly and to the best of their ability. Any mistakes they may make are at least honest ones.

A number of the objects sighted from planes conform reasonably well to the detailed description that two Eastern Airlines pilots, Captains C. S. Chiles and John B. Whitted, gave of a strange object that they encountered in the skies near Montgomery, Alabama, at 2:45 A.M., 23 July 1948. The moon, shining through broken clouds, provided good illumination.

The pilots described the object as "a wingless aircraft, 100 feet long, cigar-shaped, and about twice the diameter of a B-29 with no protruding surfaces."

"We saw it at the same time and asked each other, 'What in the world is this?'" Chiles remarked.

"Whatever it was, it flashed down toward us and we veered to the left. It veered to its left and passed us about 700 feet to our right and above us. Then, as if the pilot had seen us and had wanted to avoid us, it pulled up with a tremendous burst of flame from the rear and zoomed into the clouds, its prop wash or jet wash rocking our DC-3."

The craft appeared to possess neither wings nor fins, but both of the pilots gained the impression that the plane was illuminated inside, for an intense glare, like that from burning magnesium, radiated from what seemed to be windows in the cabin of the craft.

"We saw no occupants," Chiles affirmed. "From the side of the craft came an intense, fairly dark blue glow that ran the entire length of the fuselage — like a blue fluorescent factory light. The exhaust was a red-orange flame, with a lighter color predominant around the outer edges." This flame extended 30 to 50 feet behind the object and deepened in intensity as the craft swung upward. Chiles estimated that its speed was about one-third faster than that of the average jet.

I should assume that this report, confirmed by several similar descriptions, went far to establish in the minds of the general public as well as of Air Force investigators that the saucers were solid objects and some form of flying craft, humanly manned.

Observers from the ground at Robbins Air Force Base, Macon, Georgia, had seen some object "trailing varicolored flames" about an hour before; the impression arose that the two sightings referred to the same object.

One might put down to imagination the rocking of the DC-3 by "prop wash or jet wash." After all, the DC-3 was in the process of veering and the excited pilots might well have ascribed part of the acceleration and deceleration that they were experiencing in their own craft to some external force that was really nonexistent. But one could not in any way question that the men had reported something unusual, something that was a real flying saucer.

Several days later a widely circulated story claimed that a high-speed rocket had broken loose from White Sands and, running out of control, was responsible for the object seen by Chiles and Whitted. The suggestion was completely fantastic and subsequent investigation proved that there was no foundation of truth in the report.

Mr. and Mrs. Tom Rush of Jackson, Mississippi, reported a somewhat similar "wingless aircraft" as they swung in for a landing at Jackson on 1 January 1949. The object was "cigar-shaped" and crossed 500 feet ahead of them. A check showed that there was no known aircraft in the region.

On 20 January 1951, Captain Lawrence W. Vinther of Mid-Continent Airlines took off in a DC-3 to locate a mysterious light that had been reported above the field by the control tower. Suddenly the light loomed dead ahead, then swerved and passed about 200 feet above the plane. A moment later the startled pilot discovered that the "thing" had now reversed course and was flying parallel to the DC-3, about 200 feet away. The moon was shining brightly and the object, according to Captain Vinther and his co-pilot, James F. Bachmeier, was cigar-shaped, with wings. A white glow outlined the lower surface of the plane but there was no observable glow from the exhaust. The object dropped lower and finally disappeared.

R. S. Lambert, Supervisor of Educational Broadcasts for the Canadian Broadcasting Company, has reported a number of similar sightings in Canada. Over North Bay, on 12 April 1951, two airmen observed a flying disk that came to a dead stop and then suddenly reversed direction and disappeared "at a terrific speed." The color of the disk was "bright amber." Remember that phrase, "bright amber," because we shall pick it up again in a later chapter.

The Canadian Air Force, I am told, is fully as concerned with these mysterious objects as the U. S. Air Force. They also have recently set up a board to investigate these objects and determine their nature.

One of the most startling and frightening incidents in all of flying-saucer history occurred on the night of 1 October 1948, when National Guard Lieutenant George F. Gorman reported a 27-minute dogfight that he had with a flying saucer over Fargo, North Dakota. Gorman had been on a routine F-51 patrol flight and was returning to his base. As he started to land, Gorman sighted what he took to be the tail light of a plane a thousand yards or so distant. He checked with the Tower and received the information that no other airplane was nearby, except for a Piper Cub, which showed plainly. So Gorman moved in for a closer look at the light.

He reported: It was from six to eight inches in diameter, clear white and completely round, with a sort of fuzz at the edges. It was blinking on and off. As I approached, however, the light suddenly became steady and pulled into a sharp left bank. I thought that it was making a pass at the Tower.

I dived after it and brought my manifold pressure up to 60 inches, but I couldn't catch up with the thing. It started gaining altitude and again made a left bank.

I put my 51 into a sharp turn and tried to cut the light off in its turn. By then we were at about 7,000 feet. Suddenly it made a sharp right turn and we headed straight at each other. Just when we were about to collide I guess I got scared.

I went into a dive and the light passed over my canopy at about 500 feet. Then it made a left circle about 1,000 feet above, and I gave chase again.

Gorman continued the dogfight, struggling between near collision and distant chase. The ball of light dodged and parried like a skilled boxer. It seemed to be directed by human intelligence, although its small size precluded the possibility that this "saucer" was itself manned by a being within it. Instead, those who have wished to interpret this phenomenon in interplanetary terms have made it a sort of super guided missile, controlled by one of the super saucers hovering invisibly somewhere out of sight, far above the scene of combat.

Indeed, the behavior of the thing convinced Gorman, who had been a pilot instructor for French military students during World War II, that it was controlled by "thought." He added, "I am also convinced that the object was governed by the laws of inertia because its acceleration was rapid but not immediate and, although it was able to turn fairly tight at considerable speed, it still followed a natural curve."

Certainly the ball could outmaneuver Gorman's F-51. "When I attempted to turn with the object I blacked out temporarily due to excessive speed," Gorman noted. "I am in fairly good physical condition and I do not believe that there are many if any pilots who could withstand the turn and speed effected by the light, and remain conscious."

The official Air Force release that refers to this incident makes the following statement, whose meaning I have not been able to grasp: "From a psychological aspect, the Gorman incident raised the question, 'Is it possible for an object without appreciable shape or known aeronautical configuration to appear to travel at variable speeds and maneuver intelligently?'"

An observer from the ground, watching Gorman's dogfight, reported that he could see a light of some fast-moving object. This report gave additional weight, if any was needed, to Gorman's statement. Unfortunately, the report omits significant data that would help in the unraveling of this mystery.

However, the behavior of this mysterious light ball toying with Gorman's plane struck a responsive note somewhere. Digging deeply into confidential Air Force files, the investigators reviewed certain peculiar incidents that antedated the Arnold sighting by several years. During the latter stages of World War II, allied aircraft frequently reported the presence of glowing balls of light that tended to accompany the planes on their bombing missions. Observed over both Germany and Japan, these mysterious light blobs, which seemingly hitch-hiked just for the ride, would fly along docilely, as long as the pilot made no effort to get rid of them. However, if he tried any dodging technique, these balls of fire would fly right in front of the plane, and put on an exhibition of shadow boxing not dissimilar to that displayed by Gorman's sphere of light. The airmen of World War II called these objects "fireball fighters" or, more commonly, "foo fighters."

To my mind, the similarity of Gorman's object to the foo fighters seems entirely reasonable. The official Air Force releases, however, state that "the most reasonable explanation for the reported 'balls of light' is that they were suspended from balloons or some other means of support not visible at night, and that the violent maneuvers sometimes reported in these cases were due to optical illusion." By clinging to the idea of "hallucination" or gross "exaggeration," the official investigators were either avoiding coming to grips with the issue, or else they themselves were becoming frightened. Of all possible explanations, the idea that balls of light suspended from balloons could account for the observations is completely at variance with the reports. I should rather accept the alternative that the objects were interplanetary saucers.

And many thinking persons doubtless concluded that if the best answer that the official investigators could come up with was "balloon-supported lights" something must be wrong about the whole business.

Thus the Air Force release, designed to ease the public's mind, had just the opposite effect. Within a few months of the press memorandum of 27 April 1949, three books on the subject appeared.[1] All of them argued for the interplanetary-saucer solution and all of them implied, either directly or indirectly, that the National Defense establishment was concealing something — concealing something, that is, besides its own ignorance as to what the flying saucers really were.

"But why," an Air Force officer recently pointed out to me, "should we conceal information about interplanetary saucers if we have proof that they really exist? If we could just take a few Congressmen and Senators out to that mysterious base in New Mexico and show them a true flying saucer and the bodies of the little men that someone reported had crashed there, we should have no trouble at all with our appropriations. And if these objects are even a fraction of the menace that some of the saucer devotees imply, we Colonels would all be Major Generals in no time!"

I think that Gorman was right when he stated that the foo fighter seemed to be controlled by thought. However, the thought that controlled it was his own. But the object was only light reflected from a distant source by a whirlpool of air over one wing of the plane. The fact that the foo-ball sightings increased toward the end of World War II signifies that more of our planes had by then been damaged in combat or by antiaircraft fire. The patches on the wings are not always perfect and the flow of air over them can be quite turbulent. The reflectivity of the air whirl may be increased by the formation of fog or even ice crystals within it. Ice crystals floating in the air can reflect a distinct source of light as in a mirror and thus a bright image can seem to accompany a plane in its flight.

Special circumstances are necessary, but the phenomenon fortunately is rare enough that we can call on these unusual conditions to explain the occurrences. We may not be able to account for every detail; the impressions of the observer are hazy and leave many gaps.

Arnold's original sighting had been on 24 June 1947. For a few months afterward, reports of sightings assumed enormous proportions. But by the end of that year the number was dwindling and in all probability the saucer scare would have completely faded away had it not been for a tragedy that struck on 7 January 1948. Observers from Godman Air Force Base, Fort Knox, Kentucky, saw from the ground an unidentified object that resembled "an ice-cream cone topped with red." The report is well confirmed by both military and civilian observers. The Godman Tower requested that four National Guard F-51 planes investigate the phenomenon. Let us refer again to the official Air Force release.

Three of the planes closed in on the object, and reported it to be metallic and of "tremendous size." One pilot described it as "round like a teardrop and at times almost fluid."

The Flight Leader, Captain Thomas F. Mantell, contacted the Godman Tower with an initial report that the object was traveling at half his speed at 12 o'clock high.

"I am closing in now to take a good look," he radioed. "It is directly ahead of me and still moving at about half my speed . . . The thing looks metallic and of tremendous size.

"It's going up now and forward as fast as I am . . . That's 360 miles per hour," Captain Mantell reported from his F-51. "I'm going up to 20,000 feet and if I am no closer, I'll abandon chase."

The time was 1515 hours [3:15 P.M.].

That was the last radio contact made by Mantell with the Godman Tower.

Later that day his body was found in the wreckage of his plane near Fort Knox.

Five minutes after Mantell disappeared from his formation, the two remaining planes returned to Godman. A few minutes later one resumed the search . . . covering territory 100 miles to the south as high as 33,000 feet . . . but found nothing.

Subsequent investigation revealed that Mantell had probably blacked out at 20,000 feet from lack of oxygen and had died of suffocation before the crash.

The mysterious object which the flyer chased to his death was first identified as the planet Venus. However, further probing showed the elevation and azimuth readings of Venus and the object at specified time intervals did not coincide.

It is still considered "unidentified."

On the same day, about two hours later, several watchers over Lockbourne Air Force Base, Columbus, Ohio, observed an unusual sky phenomenon. They described it as "round or oval, larger than a C-47 and traveling in level flight faster than 500 miles per hour." They followed the object visually from the Lockbourne Observation Tower for more than twenty minutes. Observers said that it glowed from white to amber, leaving an amber exhaust trail five times its own length. It moved like an elevator and at one time appeared to touch the ground. No sound was heard. Finally, the object faded and lowered toward the horizon.

I should, perhaps, call particular attention to the fact that the Columbus apparition occurred near sunset and endured some few minutes thereafter. And perhaps we should not make too much of the inconsistency that a body in level flight at 500 miles per hour would traverse 167 miles in 20 minutes. How, then, could it have remained in view so long?

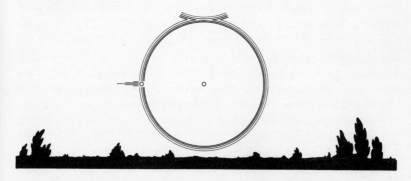

Fig. 3. A halo surrounding the sun, with a sundog or mock sun at the left. Such a sundog may have the appearance of an ice-cream cone topped with red, like the apparition reported at Godman Air Force Base. For more highly developed halos see Chapters 10 and 15.

But what was it that Mantell had really chased? Had the disk attacked him and wrecked his plane? The Air Force report gave no more information than that cited above. Official silence on the question stimulated the ready imaginations of those not familiar with routine military procedure. Ugly rumors began to fly, such as exceptional damage to Mantell's plane or even that Mantell himself had been "riddled with bullets." Even though there was no evidence whatever to support these scare stories, denial by the Air Force would have only made matters worse, absolutely convincing frightened individuals that the Air Force was really concealing the facts about saucers. Thus, from this unusual incident and useless tragedy, the flying-saucer scare took a new lease on life, which has continued until this day.

Captain Mantell was chasing a bona fide saucer, if my interpretation of what he saw is correct. The clue lies in the shape and color of the object: a luminous ice-cream cone "topped with red." Color in the sky is significant, especially as early as 3:00 in the afternoon. Sunset may tint clouds with many shades of red, but red in the middle of the afternoon, especially on a midwinter day, suggests only one thing to the scientist familiar with meteorological optics. The patch of light, with little question, was what we ordinarily term a "mock sun," caused by ice crystals in cirrus clouds that lay even higher than Mantell's plane was able to reach (Fig. 3). This mock sun and attached halos could have produced an effect similar to the one described. And it would also fully account for the fact that Mantell was never able to close in on it. Chasing one of these mock suns or "sundogs," as they are sometimes called, is just like chasing the rainbow. It races on ahead at the same speed that you are moving yourself. Sometimes it displays colors; at other times it appears silvery.

Some of those who read my initial story as released in *Look* or *Time* have offered objections. One writes: "Could you convince Captain Mantell's mother that her son was so stupid as to chase a mirage until he blacked out and crashed?" Let me repeat that the mirage or mock sun looks quite as real as the ordinary sun. Captain Mantell was apparently not familiar with mock suns, but ignorance of such a phenomenon is not stupidity. Even if he had heard of such strange images, the saucer scare has conditioned the minds of all of us to see saucers at the slightest provocation.

I shall leave until a later chapter a full discussion of the optical effects that ice crystals can produce in the atmosphere. But why, I ask, has this identification of Mantell's object taken so long? No wonder that a jittery and imaginative American public, faced with a statement that the Air Force still considers the object "unidentified," begins to imagine frightening things — like interplanetary saucers!

3

Flying saucers seen from the ground

Although the flying-saucer scare began with observations from an airplane, people soon found that they could see saucers equally well from the ground — maybe not exactly the same kind of saucer, but nonetheless satisfying to the imagination.

The reports rapidly accumulated — of single saucers and multiple saucers, daytime saucers and nighttime saucers, saucers seen near the horizon and saucers seen high in the sky, saucers that floated and saucers that moved with a speed beyond human comprehension.

On the very day that Arnold recorded his famous "pieplates" from Mount Ranier, Lieutenant Governor Donald S. Whitehead of Idaho saw a mysterious object that looked something like a comet, hanging low in the Western sky. Rotation of the earth eventually seemed to carry it below the horizon. We still cannot say whether this evening object was a variety of saucer or whether it was the planet Saturn or Mercury seen, as Dr. J. Allen Hynek of Ohio State University later claimed, through a haze of cirrus clouds. Nevertheless, this report seemed to substantiate the earlier incident and started the people making their own observations from ground-based stations.

Saucers ranging through all colors of the spectrum — red, orange, yellow, green, or blue — in addition to silver, gray, or black, were disporting themselves in the heavens. Air Force officers, observing from the special testing base at Muroc, California, claimed that they had seen a series of disks flashing by at speeds greater than 300 miles per hour. Policemen from Portland, Oregon, noted disks that "wobbled, disappeared and reappeared," strongly resembling "shiny chromium hubcaps."

On the very day of the original Arnold incident, a Portland prospector named Fred M. Johnson reported that he had seen "a strange reflection in the sky." As he examined the phenomenon more closely, he recognized half a dozen or so disks, about 30 feet in diameter. He watched them with his telescope for nearly a minute while they "banked in the sun." Through the telescope he could see that they had tails and did not seem to be flying in any regular formation; they made no noise. His place of observation was a mile above sea level in the Cascade Mountains of Oregon. Johnson stated that, at the time he made his report, he had not yet heard of the Arnold story, which indeed had scarcely been released.

One minor detail added by Johnson singled out his report from many other similar sightings that occurred later. He stated that as long as he could see the disks the needle of his compass-watch "weaved wildly from side to side." The behavior of the saucers, according to this report, is distinctive enough to label them as probably a true sighting. Bright reflections from patches of clouds were the most likely cause.

The chance association of a wobbling compass needle with the appearance of the saucers fired the imaginations of many who later dragged magnetism boldly into the picture, as a possible motive power for saucers in general. A good compass is a fairly delicate mechanism to handle and the needle wobbles on the slightest provocation. We do not know whether Johnson's telescope contained magnetic material or not, but in any case the excitement engendered by the appearance of these peculiar objects, plus Johnson's haste in trying to observe them with his telescope, could easily have made his hand tremble. In my opinion, therefore, the reported magnetic disturbance did not exist and had nothing whatever to do with the observed phenomena.

Nevertheless, the authors of several books and articles stress this particular event as showing that the saucers fly on magnetic tracks from star or planet to earth and that the men behind the saucers have learned how to control this magnetic force in some way unknown to us.

I should be the last person to insist that we earthlings know all there is to know about magnetism and that no further discoveries are possible. Although I can see no possible method for harnessing magnetic fields so as to derive useful motive power from them, I would not want to say that it is absolutely beyond question. But magnetic lines of force are not moving like the ropes of a ski tow. They are not material chains to which a saucer can attach itself and be dragged along. In fact, the lines have no more objective existence than lines of latitude and longitude, or the contour lines that designate altitude. They are, however, a convenient fiction for describing certain of the properties of magnetic fields. They can be thought of as behaving something like the rubber bands of a slingshot. Before we can use the rubber as a source of power, to shoot a rock or a bean, we must first stretch the bands by doing actual work on them. The rubber bands will not stretch themselves.

Similarly, we have no hope of harnessing magnetic fields as a substitute for some other source of power, be it coal, electricity, gasoline, or uranium. But if someone *should* find a way of utilizing magnetic fields, certainly it would not be along the lines suggested in any of the pseudo-scientific records that pretend to explain how saucers may employ the magnetic field for motive power. The accompanying descriptions are generally so much mumbo jumbo, like an alchemist's recipe for turning base metal into gold, despite the fact that the writers sometimes season them with a dash of good science, paraphrased from some elementary textbook of electricity and magnetism. These methods would be no more effective as a source of power than filling the gas tank of your car with water from the garden hose.

It is, perhaps, not too surprising that most of the daytime saucer reports have generally been traced to some definite object other than the conventional or bona fide saucer. Kites, weather balloons, clouds, and distant planes have accounted for many of these sightings.

A man sitting in the park on a calm summer afternoon scarcely realizes how intense the winds aloft may be. They may be blowing in gales stronger than 60 miles an hour, with different layers moving in opposite directions. Objects such as newspapers or kites can be caught in an occasional whirlwind and lifted to great heights, where they may fly for hundreds of miles before they again reach the ground. Weather balloons, which are often released in clusters rather than singly, are not at all uncommon. Moreover, all such objects look disklike when viewed against the sky. And it is extremely hard for even the experienced observer to recognize them for what they really are.

Dr. Vincent Schaefer, of the General Electric Company, Schenectady, New York, writes: "Only a few months ago one of the boys in our weather room called me to look at a peculiar object hovering under the base of a cumulus cloud. It seemed to be maneuvering in a peculiar manner. With a telescope we found it to be a very large piece of paper flopping around in an ascending current of warm air, presenting first its edge and then its full dimensions as it fluttered in the ascending air. While I watched it, the paper suddenly disappeared as it entered the cloud at an altitude greater than 5,000 feet above the ground. Without the careful analysis we should doubtless have had another saucer to add to the bulging clutter in Air Force files."

In addition to the ordinary weather balloons, certain scientists, notably physicists and students of meteorology, have occasionally employed an even larger balloon, known as the "skyhook," to carry heavy instruments to great heights. Such an object, seen over Denver, Colorado, on the afternoon of 29 June 1950, caused a real flurry of saucer rumors. Shortly afterward, however, the object moved westward over Climax, Colorado, where W. Ray Allen of the staff of the High Altitude Observatory took a photograph of it through a telescope (Fig. 4). It was very clearly a "skyhook" balloon, and publication of Allen's photographs in the Denver newspapers quieted the saucer rumor. The Navy physicist, Dr. Urner Liddel, affirmed that many of the saucer reports could probably be traced to these "skyhook" balloons, which attain great heights and often fly enormous distances before they explode and fall back to the ground. Some of these balloons, in fact, have crossed the Atlantic.

As for the frequency of sightings in the West and Southwest, a large part of the effect stems from the extreme clarity of the atmosphere in these regions. Those who live on the Eastern seaboard practically never see a really blue sky. Even on the clearest days, the heavens retain a milky tinge that is most apparent when we look toward the sun, where the brilliant glare of light reflected from dust and haze practically blinds us.

In the Far West, especially at high altitudes, the skies are blue, almost a purple-blue, and this blueness extends right up to the edge

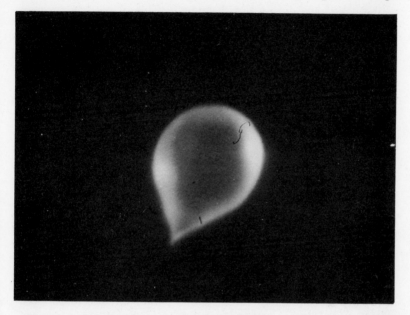

Fig. 4. A skyhook balloon that had been reported as a flying saucer. Photographed with a 5-inch telescope at the High Altitude Observatory of Harvard University and University of Colorado, Climax, Colorado, 4:30 P.M., 29 June 1950.

of the sun. On the best days, if you hold your thumb overhead so that it just eclipses the sun and no more, you will not even suspect that the sun is hiding behind it. Try a similar experiment in the East and the dazzling glare will almost blind you. Of course my comments about sky clarity do not extend to the smog-infested regions of some of our greatest Western cities. They refer, rather, to mountainous areas of the West and Southwest. In fact, that is why I established solar observatories there, one at Climax, Colorado, at an altitude of 11,500 feet and the other at Sacramento Peak, New Mexico, at an altitude of 9,200 feet.

These clear skies make it possible for us to view the planet Venus in the daytime, as well as the "skyhook" balloons. Few people seem to realize that Venus, when at greatest brilliance, is plainly visible to the naked eye during broad daylight. This planet has, on more than one occasion, produced its series of sensations. Rapidly moving cirrus clouds overlying the planet may cause the object to appear to be in rapid motion. Many persons cannot readily focus their eyes on a distant object, especially when it is elevated above the horizon. They see only a bright blur in the sky and report another flying saucer.

The rumor that certain individuals charged with the military security of Los Alamos attempted to shoot down the planet Venus in August 1945 was exaggerated. No shots were fired, but the people did get very excited. Just what they were afraid of, I have been unable to ascertain.

Most of the reports of daytime saucers that remain, after we have eliminated the spurious objects, are of one or more silvery objects seen in the sky. Many stories mention a characteristic "wobble," and sometimes several saucers seem to be chained together. Often they will hover for some minutes and then either slowly disappear or rapidly accelerate and vanish within two or three seconds. Occasionally the saucers dart back and forth with tremendous speed, though sometimes the motion is "aimless." A majority of such objects lie some distance from the zenith and many of them are to be found within a few degrees of the horizon.

One of the more startling apparitions occurred on 10 July 1947, in southern New Mexico. An astronomer who remains unidentified, other than by the fact that his wife and two teen-age daughters accompanied him, was driving westward in his car, at about 4:50 in the afternoon. Parenthetically I should remark that the astronomer referred to was not myself, although dozens of my friends have made this tentative identification.

Although his car was in the sunshine, the area ahead was fairly well covered with cloud. Suddenly a brilliant yellowish oval disk appeared in the clouds before him. The astronomer, estimating the approximate distance of the object from the fact that it seemed to dart between the clouds, noted that it wobbled slowly along the horizon at an elevation of from 1 to 2 degrees. It moved without sound and left no exhaust or vapor trail to mark its path. It seemed to be self-luminous.

This object is one of a number featured by *Life* in the issue of 7 April 1952, to bolster up the author's contention that "There is a Case for Interplanetary Saucers." And, indeed, the object reported was certainly unusual, if not frightening.

From his observations, the astronomer estimated that the object may have been as much as 200 feet long and that its speed was perhaps 150 miles per hour, with a vertical rise about 750 miles per hour. He thought these figures were right to within 25 per cent, though the published observations imply an accuracy out of keeping with his crude observing technique.

The luminous source of this mysterious saucer is not immediately evident, though it appears to have been some sort of horizontal mirage, perhaps one of a very brilliant cloud shining like silver in the sunlight — a cloud that was itself invisible because of the darker clouds in the foreground. The motion, if real, could have resulted from a shifting of the mirage pattern itself, by a process that I shall describe in more detail later on.

A Colorado camper had a frightening experience in the summer of 1951. On a clear, midsummer afternoon he was stretched out before his campfire watching the thin smoke drift lazily upward and then spread out in a horizontal layer some 10 or 12 feet above the ground. Suddenly a ghostlike form, like a glowing balloon, drifted into his view. He could see it outlined against the trees on the other side of the fire. And curiously enough, the object seemed to be transparent, for he could see the forest dimly through its outline. Then a second ghost drifted into view. Thoroughly frightened by now, the camper leaped to his feet, but the saucers vanished at once. He ran quickly up a slope — but he never saw the saucers again.

Here again mirage of a bright cloud or of the sun is the answer, perhaps coupled with reflection from the layer of smoke above. The conditions described were ideal for mirages: an elevated layer of warm air, sometimes called a temperature inversion, with the stable film of haze contributing its part.

The Air Force has regarded one type of saucer as its own special property. A number of high-ranking Air Force officials were present at the testing of a new plane, whose secrets are not important for our story. The test was over and the plane swung in low for a landing. And then the startling thing happened.

A small, dark saucer seemed to detach itself from the belly of the large craft, drop, and then fly away at an enormous speed — presumably carrying with it the secrets that its occupants had collected while riding, like a lamprey, attached to the larger craft.

I gather that this strange spectacle, which has since had several repetitions, has been one of the major official excuses for secrecy. And yet this saucer phenomenon is easiest of all to explain. The mysterious traveler was a mirage of the plane. The Air Force will doubtless be glad to learn that its secrets are safe.

We note with some amusement that the Navy might not have been taken in by this mysterious occurrence, for the simple reason that naval officers are more or less accustomed to seeing mirages of ships or parts of ships stacked one on the other, some figures erect and some inverted. They might, therefore, have recognized the phenomenon as caused by mirage. For why should planes be any different from ships? Existence or nonexistence of a mirage depends on the character of the air, not upon the nature of the ship or other object whose image is formed.

Another hair-raising incident, specially featured by *Life* in the aforementioned article, occurred at 6:45 A.M. on 18 February 1952. A photographer, stopped for a traffic light, saw two bright objects in the sky, apparently "hovering above Tijeras Canyon." Their color was bluish white and one was "shaped like a bell pepper." Estimates placed the distance and diameter at 20 miles and 136 feet, from which data we derive the fact that their apparent diameters were small, about one-tenth that of the sun. Although *Life* states that the time was "just before sunup," as a matter of record, the event occurred almost exactly at sunrise, with a minute or two leeway at most. No astronomer can fail to note this coincidence. Although the mountains may have delayed the effective sunrise to some extent, no one can reasonably doubt that the mysterious bright objects derived their illumination from the sun or from clouds illuminated by the rising sun.

I have, myself, frequently seen sunsets long delayed by an unusual mirage effect. At the same time, I have often seen the sun's image itself twisted and distorted (Fig. 5) to form Chinese pagodas, towering mountains with plateaus, and not uncommonly, a "bell pepper," the very simile employed by the observer. In my opinion, these saucers were mirages or reflections from clouds. The pair of objects may have been due to the shining of sunlight through two distant valleys, with the rest of the canyon edge in shadow.

One other daytime object, also reported by *Life*, relates to observations of a mysterious occurrence on 24 April 1949. It is one of the best-authenticated of all saucer sightings. The phenomenon apparently had been observed under similar circumstances on several different occasions.

On the day in question, a group of technicians, during the preliminaries of launching a "skyhook" balloon, sent up a small weather balloon in order to check the wind drift and other meteorological factors. Charles B. Moore, Jr., was tracking the weather balloon with a theodolite, an instrument that the surveyor uses to measure angles around the horizon and elevations above the surface of the earth. As Moore leaned back to check the balloon with his eye, he suddenly noticed a white, oval object, distinct from the balloon and very much higher. Returning to his theodolite, he obtained a magnified view of this mysterious object. It looked like a long white sausage, and was rapidly changing its position. It dropped at an enormous speed for nearly a minute and then, without any warning, veered its course and sped upward, disappearing in a matter of seconds. Moore and his colleagues estimated that the object was 11 miles high, 100 feet long and traveling at 7 miles a second.

This and similar sightings in no way implied the presence of some mysterious saucer from interplanetary space, hovering "curiously" around our experiments and rushing off to report its findings to some interplanetary committee on astronautics. Rather, it was a mirage not unlike that observed to hover near the secret plane, though formed in somewhat different manner.

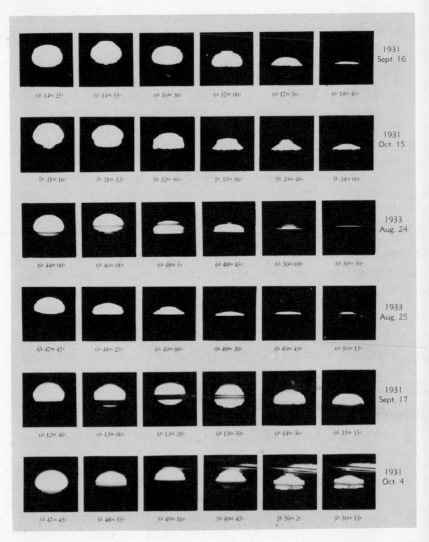

Fig. 5. Photographs of the setting sun, taken at Mount Hamilton, California.

This incident, kept in the classified files for more than two years, presents no serious difficulty to the person who understands the optics of the earth's atmosphere. The air can, under special conditions, produce formations similar to lenses. And, just as a burning glass can project the sun into a point of light, so can these lenses of air — imperfect though they are — form an image. What Moore saw was an out-of-focus and badly astigmatic image of the balloon above. If you happen to wear fairly strong lenses in your glasses, whether you are nearsighted or farsighted, take them off and hold them at arm's length and try to view a distant, luminous object like a candle, electric light, or streetlamp. You will see, far beyond the real object and at a considerable angle to it, an apparent image of the candle itself. As you move the lens, the image will appear to maneuver. As mentioned earlier, we here have to defer the discussion of how lenses of air play an important role in the formation of many varieties of flying saucers. We must remember that these lenses are crooked and bent, and often "dirty" as well. The dirt consists of layers of dust or fog between us and the object at which we are looking. No wonder that sometimes we get a distorted view, and imagine that the saucers we see are real!

So much for the saucers seen during the day. Let us turn briefly to consider the saucers of night, as seen from the ground.

All night saucers, of course, appear as lights in the sky. Their colors range over the entire spectrum, an amber glare being perhaps the most prevalent. Some of the daytime reports also refer to a reddish glow, seemingly from the blast of an exhaust. Others mention the "electric blue" edging, especially near the top of a saucer.

I see no reason for distinguishing between saucers that move singly and those that come in random groups or even in echelon formation. To my mind, they are all basically the same phenomenon. Although newspaper reports have given greater publicity to the saucers that skip at high speeds across the sky, there are also many reports that refer to an indeterminate, hovering motion. In fact, during one summer night in 1948, a group of saucers gamboled for nearly an hour over the town of Roswell, New Mexico. Many persons saw the display and I have talked with some of them. One of the descriptive comments pictured them as behaving like "shiny, yellow soap bubbles." Indeed, the action of many saucers suggests bubbles.

Although few of the reports give any detail of seeming internal structure to the saucer, occasionally one finds mention of an inequality of illumination over the surface, areas of shadow or areas of brightness. An active imagination might lead one to conclude that the saucer possessed a series of windows and that its interior brightness was dazzling.

Dr. Vincent Schaefer has explained to me how a person sufficiently interested to go beyond the apparent facts can solve a saucer mystery. He reported: "One evening after dark, while along the salt marshes in New Jersey opposite New York, I glanced at the sky and saw a white disk moving at high speed in a southeasterly direction. As I watched intently, another one appeared and then vanished. The air was unusually clear at the time, and it was not until I got into a position to see the city that I found the explanation.

"A layer of thin stratus cloud was momentarily illuminated by a high-powered searchlight which was being swung rapidly in a rather erratic manner from some theater or other advertising activity around Forty-Second Street. The clear air failed to show the blue scattering commonly associated with such lights, except in the region close to the source. The next morning the New York papers headlined: 'Flying Saucers Seen in Jersey'!"

Life has publicized the multiple-saucer groups, of which the prototype appeared on 25 August 1951, and on several successive nights thereafter, at Lubbock, Texas. This incident is also one of the best-authenticated records. Three professors of Texas Technological College, all standing together, simultaneously and independently saw an irregular pattern of lights flash quickly and noiselessly across the sky. Several nights later an 18-year old student photographed the objects, which took the form of a V, like flying geese or planes (Fig. 6). The professors who first saw the objects emphasized the fact that the lights they saw were spaced at random.

The photographs leave much to be desired and raise a number of questions. If the objects were moving as rapidly as reported by the three professors, no one could possibly have photographed them

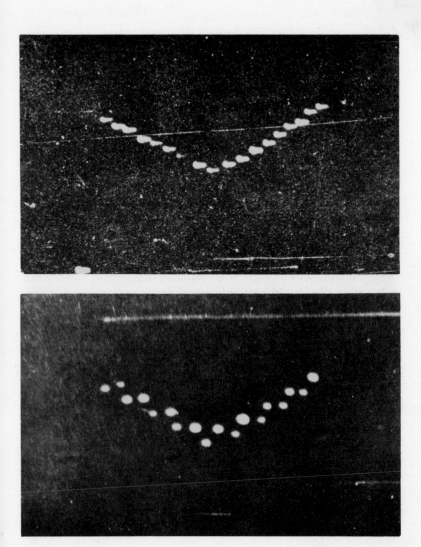

Fig. 6. The Lubbock lights, photographed 30 August 1951 at Lubbock, Texas, by Carl Hart, Jr.

with the techniques reportedly used. However, the speed of motion
may well have been different in the two cases, and there seems to be
no reason to doubt the reality of the phenomenon.

In a sense, the Lubbock lights are by no means exceptional or
unusual, although the number of objects seen at one time is perhaps
appreciably greater than the average. And the tendency that the
objects have of flying, occasionally, at least, in geometric formation,
is in itself a significant clue to their origin. I assume that the cause
is reflection in a rippling layer of fine haze, probably just over the
heads of the observers. The source of light may be a distant or even
nearby house or group of houses, a row of street lamps, or automobile headlights.

One of the incidents referred to by *Life* is an observation by a
distinguished colleague of mine, Clyde W. Tombaugh, of Las
Cruces, New Mexico, the astronomer who, in the year 1930, discovered the planet Pluto. He is accustomed to watching the sky and
at the same time is not easily deceived by something like ordinary
planes. Since the *Life* report contains minor inconsistencies, particularly related to the date, the direction of flight, and details of the
apparition, Tombaugh has kindly sent me both the necessary information and drawings from his original notes. The date was 20 August
1949, and the flight occurred about 10:45 P.M., M.S.T.

Mr. and Mrs. Tombaugh and his mother-in-law observed six or
eight rectangles, glowing with "a faint yellowish-green color." When
the flying rectangles appeared, they were already past the zenith
and moving toward a point on the horizon some 25 or 30 degrees
east of south. They were in rapid and uniform motion, requiring only
about 3 seconds to swing from a point near the zenith to a distance
of 50 degrees from the zenith, at which point they disappeared.
During their travel time, the rectangles seemed to contract along
the direction of motion, giving one the impression that they were
flat objects and that the diminution of size resulted from the increasing distance. The total span of the group was probably about
1 degree; in other words, they appeared twice as big as the full moon.

Of these objects Tombaugh says, "In all of my several thousand
hours of night-sky watching, I have never seen anything so strange
as this. I was so astonished that my impression of it was somewhat

confused. How I wish I could have had some binoculars in hand. No sound whatever."

Tombaugh reports having seen three other objects, but they were merely exceptionally brilliant points, and might well have been bright meteors or flashes of a light imaged by mirage. They can in no sense compete with the spectacular procession of rectangles, whose behavior seems to put them in the class of Lubbock lights, which they happen to have antedated by almost exactly two years.

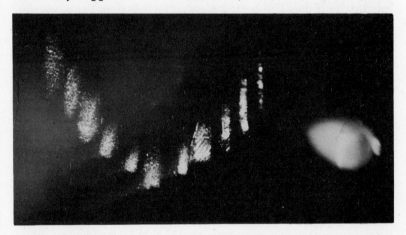

Fig. 7. Model saucers, photographed in the author's laboratory, in imitation of the Lubbock lights. Note the bright image to the right, like that of a "mother ship."

Tombaugh goes on to say that, in his opinion, the objects were not and could not have been space ships, or indeed any sort of solid craft, although the six rectangles referred to suggested "lighted windows" in a craft otherwise invisible except for a faint glow something like a wake, or ripples behind the thing.

I have given this account in some detail, because it represents the impressions of a highly skilled observer. If such a person can admit confusion, what about the average individual who has had no previous training in observational techniques? Small wonder that he gives conflicting and, at times, meaningless reports.

But what were these mysterious lights? I can only hazard here the same guess I made about the Lubbock lights — that a low, thin layer of haze or smoke reflected the lights of a distant house or some other multiple source. The haze must have been inconspicuous to the eye, because Tombaugh comments on the unusual clarity of the sky.

At this point I call attention again to the observations of my own, referred to in the first chapter. Had those blobs of light, standing mysteriously in the sky so near the moon, been just a little bit brighter, or if they had been somewhat farther from the moon so as to be completely detached, or if they had been in actual motion, I should have considered them spectacular. As it was, the actual events succeeded only in mystifying me. At no time did it enter my mind that these objects could possibly be ships from space. Rather, I felt that Nature was playing a trick on me, and I was disgusted with my own temporary inability to see the "magic" behind the trick. A layer of haze, perhaps disturbed and tilted by the moving car, probably caused the trick reflections of the moon.

This discussion leaves us with just one more ground-based night-time phenomenon: the green balls of fire said to flash over the hills of New Mexico, spreading a sickly hue over the landscape. I have not seen these objects myself, but — authoritative statements to the contrary — I have the firm belief that most of them are meteors. Bright green meteors are common and should be well known. In my opinion, any astronomer who avers that green meteors are new, or that the color must come from burning copper, cannot be much of an authority. Actually, the green color comes from burning magnesium. But more of these objects in a later chapter.

4

Hoaxers and jokers

The Arnold story was scarcely 24 hours old before the hoaxers, jokers, and publicity seekers of the nation moved in. The subject matter lent itself admirably to such activities. People had seen saucers in the sky. People wanted to see more. And so the jokers started tossing wheel-shaped objects of all sorts and descriptions from the tops of the tallest buildings. These activities produced the desired result. The women screamed, as they are supposed to on such occasions. The men — at least after they realized that the object would not explode — bravely picked it up and showed its true nature. Everyone had a good laugh. And the newspapers had a field day.

So did the Air Force! In those early days, the hoaxes far outnumbered the true sightings. In any event, chasing down a hoax and establishing its character involves an investigation that may take from 10 to 50 times longer than that required for the honest report.

Thus, the sky rained wheels. Wheels of cardboard and wheels of plywood. Wheels decorated with fragments from an old electric fan; wheels marked with hammer and sickle and labeled U.S.S.R. in big red letters. Spectacular wheels, with fireworks attached, showering glowing sparks as they sailed from rooftop to street. Wheels!

And even when no wheels or saucers were available, imagination supplied the rest. For example, a woman excitedly telephoned the F.B.I. and earnestly reported that representatives of a foreign nation were flying overhead and practicing code in the skies. In fact, she had plainly seen them spell out the word "PEPSI" right over her head!

In August of 1948, citizens of Columbus, Ohio, saw a round object, "20 to 30 feet in diameter, with a constant gray-black perimeter and transparent center," moving over the city at a slow and steady rate. Occasionally it shot out a thin trail of smoke. After considerable investigation, the Air Force established this object definitely as a "carnival balloon."

Letters and telegrams piled up. The majority of them proposed some idea or theory about the cause of the saucers and advised the Air Force on procedure. Some of the letters came from frightened people who regarded the saucers as a sign of divine displeasure — a proof that the Day of Judgment was drawing near. One person, tired of all this nonsense, advised the Commanding General, U.S.A.F., by wire, to "shoot down flying saucers, disks, skeets, and washtubs if of foreign origin and not American."

Another person had convinced himself that the saucer scourge was part of a "world-wide mapping survey expedition," under the auspices of a world government of "the empire of oppressed and subjugated peoples of the earth," led by "the Ancient Three — who were, who are, and who will be."

There are letters from people who have recipes to capture the flying saucers — recipes usually vague and hazy, but pointing out the importance of America's getting control of the secret of the saucers before Russia does — recipes about as effective as the familiar one: "To catch a bird, first put salt on its tail."

In reality, the jokers and the self-deluded caused no serious trouble. The jokers were at least honest, and readily, if somewhat shamefacedly, confessed to a desire to fool some of their friends. "Honestly! I had no idea that flying saucers were being taken seriously by the U. S. government!" And the joker departed somewhat mystified and also a little frightened by the saucers.

In the United States, practical jokery has had a long and honorable ancestry. And everybody relishes a good laugh. But sometimes a hoax or a joke can really backfire. The official Air Force memorandum of 27 April 1949 contains the following passage, quoted verbatim:

One of the biggest tempests was stirred up by two Tacoma, Washington, men, Fred Chrisman * and Harold A. Dahl. In July 1947, a few days after Kenneth Arnold's Mt. Ranier saucers hit the headlines, Dahl

* Or Crisman; Kenneth Arnold used the latter spelling.

reported sighting six disks from a boat in which he was patrolling off Maury Island, Washington.

Dahl said that one of the disks fluttered to earth and disintegrated, showering his boat with fragments which caused some damage and killed his pet dog. He and Chrisman then attempted to sell the story to a Chicago adventure magazine which in turn contacted Kenneth Arnold in Boise, and asked him to check its authenticity.

Arnold went to Tacoma with Captain Emile J. Smith, United Airlines pilot, who had also received "saucer" publicity when he reported seeing disks on the Fourth of July while on a routine flight out of Boise.

From Tacoma, Arnold summoned two officers of Army A-2 intelligence to aid in the investigation of Dahl's and Chrisman's claim. Thus began a story of secret hotel-room meetings and mysterious and anonymous telephone calls which ended in death for two of the participants and exposed the Tacoma disk story as a hoax.

At a meeting in the Winthrop Hotel, Dahl produced some fragments which he alleged came from the disk that damaged his boat. He related his entire story of the incident to Arnold, Smith, and the two Army Intelligence men. The next day the two officers left to return to Hamilton Field, California, to participate in an Air Force Day program, taking some of the fragments with them for technical analysis.

But tragedy struck enroute. The plane crashed, killing both officers, although the crew chief and a hitchhiker — the other two passengers — parachuted to safety.

Shortly after the crash, newspapers and wire services in Tacoma began receiving a series of anonymous telephone calls informing them that the fallen B-25 had been carrying "flying-disk fragments" and that the plane had been shot down from the air with a 20-mm cannon by saboteurs. While one Tacoma paper hinted that the plane had been sabotaged because of the disk fragments it carried, a thorough investigation of the crash revealed no indication of foul play. (The crash was caused by a burned exhaust stack which in turn caught the left wing afire. The blazing wing broke from the fuselage and tore off the plane's tail.)

The mysterious caller added that a U. S. Marine Corps plane found a few weeks before on Mt. Ranier had also been shot down by the unidentified "saucer saboteurs."

On the day of the crash, Chrisman and Dahl took Captain Smith to view the boat which allegedly had been damaged by the falling disk.

"I saw what may have been repairs to the windshield and lights, but I was not personally satisfied that they were made as a result of the claimed incident," Smith told investigators.

Later, under questioning, Chrisman and Dahl broke and admitted that the fragments they had produced were really unusual rock formations found on Maury Island and had no connection with "flying disks."

They admitted telling the Chicago magazine that the fragments "could have been remnants of the disks" in order to increase the sale value of their story.

During the investigation, Dahl's wife consistently urged him to admit that the entire affair was a hoax, and it is carried as such in Project "Saucer" files.

Here indeed was a pretty "how-do-you-do"! Deaths, crashes, caused by what the Air Force has insisted was a hoax. A hoax, moreover, conceived for personal gain! And yet, the government did not prosecute or even carry the investigation to conclusion. Or, if they did, they have since remained completely silent.

The exponents of interplanetary saucers have tried to read into this seeming vacillation of the Air Force a tacit admission on the part of the government that real saucers had attacked and destroyed the plane because of its mysterious cargo: the saucer fragments. According to these apologists, the disaster caught the Air Force "between the devil and the deep blue sky." Here is the common (and erroneous) reasoning. The government could not prosecute with good conscience, since it knew that the saucer was real. To hush the matter up was equally dangerous from the standpoint of security. So they branded the whole thing a hoax, buried the details of the story deep in classified files, and refused to say anything more.

Kenneth Arnold, who was present, and Ray Palmer, editor of *Fate*, the magazine to which Chrisman supposedly tried to sell his saucer story, have recently reviewed the story in detail.[1] The additional facts given are not particularly complimentary to Chrisman or to Dahl. Though both Arnold and Palmer tried to be objective in their analysis, the extraordinary experience that Arnold underwent would have tended to convince anyone that the saucers are real. They found it hard to attribute everything to sheer coincidence.

My own guess is that the Air Force felt that no useful purpose would be satisfied by pushing further a case that they believed to be a hoax. The question whether the men involved had or had not violated a law fell in some other department — and that department did not have the information on which to act. Indeed, although a plane crash and deaths did occur, the authors of the hoax were responsible only secondarily for this disaster. If the calamity had not occurred, the affair would scarcely have been worth special comment.

For example, the flying disk that "fell" in Black River Falls, Wisconsin, was much more spectacular. It looked like a disk and perhaps might have even been able to "fly," though hardly under its own power. Anyway, the "finder" went into business, charging fifty cents admission just to see the device. But the local police stepped in and preserved it in a bank vault until the Air Force could take over. This saucer, allegedly found in the grass near the fairgrounds where the finder exhibited it, proved on analysis to be "patently a hoax . . . It will be held for a reasonable length of time and then disposed of in the nearest ash receptacle." So said the official report from Mitchel Field, where the analysis was made.

This "saucer" was by no means the only one that went on exhibition as a primary attraction at this or that local fair. Usually, they met with a similar fate. One county fair in Colorado heralded "a recently fallen saucer" as one of its attractions. I was sufficiently intrigued by the report — not, I assure you, from any belief that the object on exhibition had ever been an interplanetary saucer — to investigate. Though I was among the early attendants at the fair, the saucer had vanished already. According to fair attendants, some government officials had refused to let it remain on exhibition, because they did not want the information about saucers to become public. I wonder whether it ever existed.

We have had a perfect epidemic of saucer photographs. Seeing is believing! Photographs don't lie! — unless they happen to be of yourself, of course. Then you say, "Do I really look like that?" and rush back to the studio for another sitting.

Many of the saucer photographs have had a most innocent beginning. Jim Smith is trying to get his children to hold still for a picture, but little John (age 3) insists on running around and is much more interested in throwing up his hat than getting his picture taken. "Look, dad! A flying saucer!" exclaims Mary (age 15), as John's hat sails unusually high.

The pictures get taken, but one negative is left. "What shall we do now, to finish off the roll?" asks Jim Smith, tired of the struggle to get John to pose. "Why not a flying saucer?" Mary suggests. She runs into the house, returns with a tin pieplate, and skims it high while Jim snaps the last picture.

A few days later Jim picks up the prints. The family group is only so-so. But the saucer picture is a wow! Enough motion to give the impression of tremendous speed! Jim shows it to the boys at the office, just for the laugh.

"What did it look like, Jim?" one of the force asks.

"Like a tin pieplate, spinning through the air," he replies with complete honesty. Just then Mr. Jones, the boss, asks if he can have the print to show to a friend. This turn was something Jim hadn't bargained for, but he hands the print over, intending to brief Mr. Jones later.

But Mr. Jones has other ideas. He leaves the office unexpectedly early. When Jim opens the paper the next morning he is startled to see the banner headlines, "Flying Saucer seen over Fleaville." And there is the picture, credited to Jim Smith, of the Jones Widgit Manufacturing Company. It turns out that Mr. Jones hoped that this indirect advertising would help the firm and that he knew Jim wouldn't object.

Now Jim Smith is committed. After all, he can't let the boss down. He runs into a flurry of interviews, and has a bout with newspaper photographers. He even gets a raise. But after a few days the excitement dies away, to Jim's great relief. He justifies his position first to himself and then explains it to the family — and tries to forget it all.

Then, a few weeks later, a government representative calls, asks for the original negative, and wants to know all about it. After a moment of indecision, Jim confesses, feeling like a criminal and wondering what the sentence is, and expecting at least to lose his job. The investigator quietly takes notes and keeps the picture. He then tells Jim not to worry, that the affair will be kept quiet. But Jim has the sensation that sentence has merely been suspended, and that flying saucers must be something highly important, if the government sends people around the country to check up like this.

Sometimes the Jims do not confess so readily. They brazen out the interview with denials. And other Jims may not be as innocent as Jim Smith was. Some persons have taken photographs with the hope of selling them at a huge price. *Look* recently asked me to report on the authenticity of some highly publicized saucer photographs taken in South America. The pictures, however, proved to be so amateurish that no special study was needed to establish their hoax character.

Anyone can toss up a dish or a pieplate and take a picture of it. It takes a really skilled photographer to set up an elaborate model of an imaginary space craft, photograph it in the laboratory, and then fit it realistically into some well-recognized background, like the New York skyline or the Capitol building in Washington. Official files contain such examples of photographic art. And indeed one enterprising Air Force photographer jokingly constructed a picture of a saucer over Dayton, Ohio, where Wright Field, center of the investigation, is located. The saucer was clearly a dish and its motive power was immediately evident: a pair of bird's wings (Fig. 8).

Another type of saucer photograph comes as the result of an accident. Someone unintentionally allows the sun to fall on the camera lens while he is taking a picture. When this happens, usually the picture is badly fogged, but occasionally freak internal reflections have produced cigar-shaped blotches in the sky. The photographer did not see the saucer when he was taking the picture, but it must have been there!

These freak images can occur in other ways, too, through a light leak in the camera, improper loading or unloading techniques, defects in the shutter or holes in the bellows, use of old film, dirt in the camera, improper development, and so on. The astronomer who sees a foggy patch on one of his photographs of the sky does not immediately decide that it represents either a flying saucer or a comet. He will need at least two independent photographs as a check, before he announces discovery of a new comet. I think it significant that, of all flying-saucer pictures made available, the Air Force cannot point to a single one as authentic or even as possibly authentic.

The greatest saucer story of all, greatest because of the number of people who believed it or greatest because of the top billing it still gets from saucer protagonists, was perpetrated on 8 March

1950, in Denver, Colorado. A guest speaker at a general science class at the University of Denver spoke glibly and convincingly of various saucer crashes that had occurred some 500 miles southwest of Denver. The midget operators of the vehicles were dead, scorched

Fig. 8. A "flying saucer" over Dayton, Ohio.

by the heat generated by rapid passage through the earth's atmosphere. And so on!

The event deserves special treatment, because of the wide circulation it has received, both in the newspapers and in Frank Scully's book, *Behind the Flying Saucers*. I shall therefore postpone discussion of it until Chapter 12.

With respect to hoaxes, conscious or otherwise, the Air Force is certainly not guiltless. The attitude of secrecy, however necessary it may be, has a peculiar kickback that serves to enhance the public jitters. Here is an authentic situation.

A man has seen a flying saucer, has honestly reported it to the press, and has talked about it to his friends. He has enjoyed *his* saucer. Suddenly an Air Force investigator phones and asks for a confidential interview. At the meeting a little leather-covered photograph establishes the investigator's authority. A detailed questioning follows, with questionnaires and diagrams. Finally the investigator shuts his book and thanks our saucer observer for the information. This is the moment the observer has been waiting for; he wants the official to tell him what the saucer really was. But here, the official is decidedly noncommittal; he says that the saucer was "nothing important," but then contradicts his statement by cautioning the observer not to mention the incident further to anybody.

Consider the poor observer, and ponder his dilemma. He may conscientiously try to obey the order. But his friends, noting his sudden silence regarding the saucer, question him about it. Finally in self-defense he tells a few of his closest friends — but the story spreads and the flying-saucer scare grows. Everybody scares each other.

If someone who knows this story happens to see a saucer, he may very well refuse to report it. He doesn't want to be frightened, and he doesn't want to have his private saucer taken away from him.

Anyone who really wants to believe that flying saucers are interplanetary — despite what I or anyone else may say about them — can find ample authority for his belief in the official Air Force release on flying saucers, dated 27 April 1949.

The possible existence of some sort of strange extraterrestrial animals has also been remotely considered, as many of the objects described acted more like animals than anything else. However, there are few reliable reports on extraterrestrial animals.

"Few reliable reports"? A single reliable report would be enough to justify all the interplanetary-saucer theories and more. This remark, certainly intended to be facetious, is out of place in a report like the Air Force release. To those who are not able to form inde-

pendent judgments, yet who know that extraterrestrial animals are
not known to astronomers or biologists, this statement seems to be a
hedge, an indirect admission that the Air Force has such evidence
in its possession. The fact of the matter is that no one, not even the
Air Force or the Atomic Energy Commission, has the slightest
evidence indicating that extraterrestrial animals or persons or beings
of any sort whatever exist.

5

The scientific detective

▀▀

How are we to interpret these mysterious objects? Despite the confusion of records, despite the hoaxes and the jokes, despite the hysteria and hallucinations, how can we completely ignore the vast accumulation of data related to saucer phenomena? The great bulk of the reports must be honest. Indeed, the large number of apparently reliable confirming witnesses proves that people have seen something.

Of all the interpretations, the possibility that these objects are craft from outer space is the one that has fired the public's imagination. The question, "Do you believe in flying saucers?" means not, "Do you think that strange lights are flying across the sky?" but, "Do you believe that interplanetary space craft really exist?"

A confused and somewhat frightened American public wonders what the saucer scare is all about. Whether people like to be confused is open to question. But they certainly like to be frightened in a shivery sort of way — like going to a double-feature horror movie with Boris Karloff on both bills. The average person seems to want to believe that the saucers are vehicles from "outside" and that flocks of manned saucers are skimming about the earth all the time. He who debunks the saucers and shows that they are truly natural phenomena will not be popular. We Americans want to preserve and cherish our illusions. We don't want to be told that Santa Claus is a myth.

But there is even more to the flying-saucer legend than a desire to make science fiction come true. I was surprised to find that there exists a sort of "Cult of the Flying Saucers." No one can tell you who the high priests of this organization are or whence came the tenets of its faith. But thousands of people, some wishful thinkers and others true believers, regard the flying saucers as real, manned space craft. And a number of reputable magazines have contributed to the gaining of converts.

The legend of the "little men" pops up again and again in mysterious ways. If it isn't true, it ought to be! The details of the saucer craft and how they allegedly derive their motive power from "magnetic rays" sounds convincing — to all but the scientist. These so-called explanations, full of high-sounding phrases, are meaningless jargon — pseudo-scientific double talk.

Certain well-meaning individuals ask, "Are not the scientists themselves trying to hide the existence of the flying saucers, merely to cover their own confusion and their failure to understand the mysterious sources of power? Or perhaps they are temporizing, in the hope of learning these super secrets of the universe, so that they can gain control of the world — for better or worse?"

The mad scientist, struggling for power, has always been good for a shiver, ever since "The Strange Island of Dr. Moreau" frightened our grandfathers.

Here are a few other wild rumors or surmises. Perhaps the villain is the Air Force, or maybe the Atomic Energy Commission. It is the scientists high in governmental circles who are hiding the true facts, because they want to learn the secret of saucer propulsion in order to use it against the Russians. We have imprisoned the few little men who survived a saucer crash in New Mexico because we want to force them to give us the scientific information that their super brains have evolved. The more you argue against this type of reasoning the more difficult the problem becomes. The mere fact of denial lends credence to the ideas.

I regard the true cultist as a hopeless case. No matter how much scientific evidence I drag out to convince him that flying saucers are other than interplanetary vehicles, he will not be convinced. He will misinterpret the motives behind my argument. He will defend his position with religious fervor. To him the flying saucers have become a religious symbol, perhaps a proof of the existence of a power beyond the skies.

But for those who are willing to examine the evidence calmly and quietly with me, let me urge that neither emotion nor preconception should influence us in any way. Let us try to draw as realistic a conclusion as possible.

In our attack on the problem we shall try to combine the skill of a detective with the logic of a scientist. Let us be guided by that most famous of detectives, Sherlock Holmes himself, who declared: "How often have I said to you that when you have eliminated the impossible, whatever remains, however improbable, must be the truth." [1]

As for our scientific outlook, we shall adopt the precepts laid down by the French scientist, Henri Poincaré, who, in his famous volume, *Science and Hypothesis*, pointed out that we can always find an infinite number of hypotheses that will explain a given set of observational data. The scientist must choose the simplest.

A layman, watching a group of scientists arguing about some technical question, may gain the impression that the disagreement between them is serious. If he could check the argument in detail, however, he would find that the scientists are usually in almost complete agreement about the basic facts and that the arguments usually concern matters on the fringes of human knowledge, where the definition of "simplest" is itself unclear. What appears simplest to one scientist may not be simplest to another.

Those who have either advocated or accepted the space-craft solution of the flying-saucer mystery presumably think that they have adopted the formula of Sherlock Holmes. They imply that there is no reasonable explanation for these phenomena and hence, since all other ideas seem to have failed, conclude that some superhuman intelligence must be responsible.

How simple science and life would be if, every time we encounter some seemingly inexplicable fact, we could blame it on an outside force over which we have no control. Indeed, such a mode of thought is as old as man himself. Our prehistoric ancestors personalized all the forces of nature. Gods blew the winds, threw lightning bolts, and stoked the fires that belch from volcanic craters. Goddesses brought the spring and poured the gentle rains. The echo was a mischievous nymph who pined away until only her voice remained. Supernatural beings guided the planets in their courses. The ancients, seeing the luminous lances of the aurora borealis shining in the northern sky, imagined a battle of the gods in progress, the warriors advancing and retreating with their weapons flashing green sparks across the sky. Brilliant showers of meteors have made men fear that the end of the world was imminent. The ancients interpreted a solar eclipse as a dragon devouring the sun and rejoiced when their beating drums frightened the dragon away.

How simple this type of science! No laboratory experiment to prove or test the hypothesis. No complicated mathematics to study the details of the process. Nothing to argue about here. For each new and unexplained fact, we invent a new god — or assume the existence of superintelligent beings from another world.

How simple — and how wrong!

Centuries of civilization have taught us the futility of inventing mysterious forces and superhuman beings. You could explain *anything* that way. Such explanations, however, are completely useless and nature falls into chaos, subject to the whim of a pagan deity instead of to the orderly process of natural laws.

Suppose that you walk down a street and see a man lying on his back, his eyes tightly shut. The first thought that passes through your mind is that he has been hit by a car — but perhaps the street is too narrow for a car. You consider other possibilities: he was hit by a bicycle; he is drunk; he tripped on the curb; he likes to sleep in the street. Perhaps you find out, in one way or another, what happened, or perhaps you walk away without having found out.

But you do not say to yourself: "I can't tell right now exactly how he got there, so for the time being I shall assume that he dropped from Mars."

Instead, you assume that some natural explanation must exist and if you are interested enough (if he is dead and you represent the company that insured him against accidents), you find out.

As a scientist, I am not bothered if I cannot give a complete, ironclad explanation for every phenomenon I meet. Unraveling the puzzles of science is my business — as well as my pleasure. I find the world still full of unsolved problems. I look for explanations, but I do not arbitrarily invent forces that make explanation unnecessary.

The astronomer can foretell to within a fraction of a second the circumstances of the next solar eclipse; the meteorologist is not absolutely certain of the details of tomorrow's weather, even if he can forecast it with reasonable accuracy. Do you, in consequence, postulate the existence of some superhuman agent whose peculiar sense of humor is particularly satisfied when he makes tomorrow's weather deviate from today's prediction?

There are many facts about thunder and lightning that we still do not understand in detail. The meteorologist cannot tell you exactly how many flashes of lightning will occur tomorrow or where they will strike. Shall we, then, reinstate our belief in the pagan god Thor and his thunderbolts? I think we should be uncivilized if we excused our ignorance by postulating either a devil or a superhuman force as a cause.

Why, then, have so many civilized people chosen to adopt an uncivilized attitude toward the flying saucers? I think there are three reasons.

First, flying saucers are unusual. All of us are used to regularity. We naturally attribute mystery to the unusual.

Second, we are all nervous. We live in a world that has suddenly become hostile. We have unleashed forces we cannot control; many persons fear we are heading toward a war that will destroy us.

Third, people are enjoying this fright to some extent. They seem to be a part of an exciting piece of science fiction.

Such analysis, however, is more the province of the psychologist than of the natural scientist. Let us, then, hasten back to our flying saucers. In our role of scientific detective we may examine the steps of reasoning that have led so many to accept the interplanetary concept. Is there any flaw in their argument? And if so, can we turn it to advantage and employ the arguments as an aid to further understanding of the saucers themselves?

Despite the enormous number of cases that we can write off immediately as hoaxes, balloons, clouds, birds, planes, kites, and the like, we must conclude that the flying saucers are real — real, that is, in the sense that people are actually seeing something. The stimulus for a view of a flying saucer comes from without, not from within one's mind. The saucers are not fancy or hallucination.

When I say that the saucers are real, however, I do not necessarily mean that they are solid objects or even that they are material.

For example, I think of the rainbow as "real," although no one has ever touched a rainbow or picked it up. Let us keep this distinction firmly in mind while we examine further evidence and arguments about the nature of flying saucers.

Dozens of persons have stated that the saucers are disks of metal. Stop right here and face this proposition squarely. For, if we accept it, we are almost forced, step by step, to the final conclusion that saucers are interplanetary space ships.

But when one questions the persons who swear that the saucers are metallic, one will find them hedging. How do they know that it is a metal? The best and, to my mind, the only sure test of a metal is the ease with which it carries electric current. Who has held a saucer long enough to give it such a test?

We now glimpse the real meaning of the statement that the saucers are metal. What the observer intended to say was that the saucer had a metallic glint — which is something altogether different. Everyone has seen a leaden sky, a silvery lake, a steely gleam in a man's eye, the coppery tresses of a redhead. There are plastics that look so metallic that you would almost swear they were a true metal. A piece of clear glass will reflect light, under certain circumstances, even better than a metallic surface.

These observations dispose of the "must-be-metal" argument. The saucers may be metal or nonmetal. They may be solid, liquid, or gas. They may be only light itself — as long as that light looks as if it had been reflected by a metal.

At this point you may object that this kind of argument is working backward. What have we gained by pursuing it? Aren't we merely back where we started? Well, we have to retrace our steps because our original conclusion that the objects must be metal is highly questionable. Therefore we had to undo the argument before we could make real progress. Let us continue.

Many witnesses have attested to the fact that the saucers sometimes move with "tremendous speed" and undergo very rapid "accelerations." If we are to believe the reports, the often-stated corollary that "no known terrestrial craft has ever attained such speeds or could withstand such accelerations" follows immediately. The observers further point out that "no human being could possibly live through the extremely rapid changes of pace that the saucers undergo."

These conclusions are completely justified on the face of the evidence. But here the enthusiasts for interplanetary saucers interpose a bit of magic and, before you know it, you are carried away by the argument. The trick is an old one and you have to watch your step not to be taken in by its subtlety.

"No known terrestrial vehicle can move or accelerate so rapidly." And then the "switch:" *therefore the saucer must be a craft of nonterrestrial origin!*

"No human being could withstand such tremendous acceleration." And again the switch: *therefore the craft must be piloted by superhuman beings from interplanetary space!*

I do not deny that these hypotheses explain the observations. Remember what Poincaré said: you can fit any set of facts if you make your hypotheses complicated enough. I cannot think of any hypothesis more complicated than that of a race of interplanetary beings. But if there are simpler possibilities we should at least consider them before turning to a concept that really explains nothing. We might just as well invoke the assistance of ghosts, witches, hobgoblins, or various pagan gods — except that they are not as romantic, as modern, or as "darling" as the little men of the saucers.

What sort of conclusion, then, are we justified in drawing from the foregoing evidence? Since we are agreed that no known craft or vehicle could move in such a fashion, should we not carefully explore the idea that the saucers are something other than a craft or vehicle? Since we are also agreed that no human being could withstand the enormous accelerations that these saucers exhibit on occasion, should we not further conclude that they are not manned craft? The evidence indicates that saucers are not even material.

The primary objection to any solution other than that of a manned craft rests in the reports of an apparent intelligence behind the saucers' movements. They seem to possess an uncanny ability to forecast each movement of the operator of a plane, and parry or dodge. Only a shadow, or an image in a mirror, can do as well. This gives us a clue. The saucers must in some way depend on reflection or bending of light rays in the earth's atmosphere — reflections from fog, mist, raindrops, or ice crystals, or bending by alternate cold and warm layers of air.

I shall show in later chapters exactly how such natural phenomena, either in combination or singly, can explain these mysterious objects. The saucers, then, are only patterns of light, no more substantial than the square of sunlight falling on the floor of my study. They are as real as the shadow that follows me on a sunny day — and no more solid. Small wonder that all attempts to capture a saucer have led to naught!

Of course, if we accept the idea that the saucers are not craft or vehicles, then the question of their being manned does not come up at all. And really our only justification for assuming that the saucers were a type of craft comes from the belief that the objects are solid and metallic and from their alleged ability to dodge. But a rainbow shows a similar ability to resist capture. Merely because it moves elusively if we try to capture it, should we endow it with motive power controlled by intelligence?

At this point, those who argue for the "visitors from space" usually raise the question of the distribution of saucers in space and time. Why were they not observed before? Why should we have such a concentration of them in the southwestern part of the United States? And why, especially, are there so many sightings in the neighborhood of White Sands, Los Alamos, and other laboratories doing secret work on rockets or atom bombs? Is this concentration not clear evidence of a directed intelligence? The saucers flying around our V-2 rockets or "skyhook" balloons suggest a curiosity that we associate only with human intelligence.

These questions are somewhat complicated and we shall have to answer them separately. Let us take the last problem first. Certainly, the behavior of the saucers snooping around our balloons was mysterious. But, then, the whole saucer business is itself mysterious and that is what we are trying to explain. We are not inevitably rejecting the interplanetary solution. We are merely asking for permission to consider other natural possibilities before accepting the interplanetary hypothesis. The introduction of such terms as "curiosity" and "suspicion" prejudices the answer. Let us just admit that the whole business is mysterious and leave it at that. If proximity always implies curiosity, then my shoes are curious about my socks, since they often appear together.

No! The mysterious interloper proves to be not material at all, but a distorted image of the original balloon — an image formed by a lens of air and focused far above the ground. Since the lens is imperfect and shifts with the breeze, the image flies erratically about — and finally disappears.

Those who ask why saucers are so commonly observed in the neighborhood of our defense plants forget that people working and living in these areas must be more sensitive to happenings around them than other people. During the height of the saucer scare, various night patrols were set up in these areas, to watch for and report the occurrence of saucers. To this increased sensitivity, add the enormous growth of population that has occurred in these areas during the last seven or eight years, and it will be clear that the concentration of reports in time and space presents no serious problems.

In addition, as I shall detail later on, sky and climate have much to do with the phenomena. The atmospheric conditions and high transparency of the desert air are important contributors to the production of saucers, so that their apparent concentration in the southwestern areas of the United States is not the least bit mysterious.

But why are we just getting the saucers now? If the phenomenon is a natural one, why did we not see them before 1947?

Public hysteria of course has a lot to do with the matter. We are all suffering from international jitters and have been conditioned to report anything the least bit unusual. People look at the sky more frequently and are more sensitive to any unusual occurrence (Fig. 9).

However, many of the apparitions we are now reporting as flying saucers have always been there. People have seen them and have reported them in the past. They are even mentioned in the Bible. And occasionally we have experienced a saucer scourge — never as great as the one today, but nonetheless significant. An outbreak of saucers in 1897 will comprise the principal topic of the next chapter. The claim that we are just now seeing them is complete nonsense.

The best reference to ancient saucers is a volume called *The Books of Charles Fort*, published for the Fortean Society by Henry Holt and Co. in 1941. Charles Fort, who died in 1932, must have been a remarkable man. He had an interest in collecting oddities:

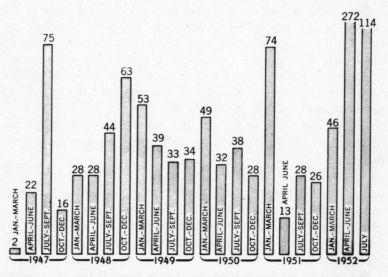

Fig. 9. This frequency chart of saucer sightings shows no marked pattern except the big maximum following Arnold's observation in June 1947 and the much larger one in 1952. The diagram charts only the unexplained saucer sightings.

oddities of life, oddities of the world, oddities of science – the oddities that seem not to fit with at least the simpler phenomena of science – oddities like flying saucers.

Here was a phenomenon, observed occasionally, reported most frequently in newspapers and then forgotten, but occasionally discussed in the serious literature of science where, as Fort noted, scientists either expressed their skepticism of the observation or tried to explain it in some wholly inadequate fashion. Thus flying saucers have generally been excluded from the literature of science.

"Damned by the scientists themselves," Fort would say. The first of his volumes, *The Book of the Damned*, summarizes in a very extensive way, with footnotes and detailed references, a wide variety of paradoxes of nature that seem to lie outside of the usual pattern of the universe, such as falls of stone, rains of fish, showers of ashes, inexplicable noises — *lights and flashes in the sky!*

Fort pokes fun at the scientist who excludes such data. He tries to interpret the lights (and noises) from the sky as evidence of men and vehicles from other planets. Hence the idea of interplanetary craft is not new. Fort's close associates affirm that he himself did not believe these hypotheses, but that he wrote in this fashion primarily to needle the scientists.

Whatever his motives, Charles Fort did a real service for the researcher into the past of the flying saucers. Even so, I have found checking and reading the originals a heavy task, because Fort was not particularly selective but included all references to lights in the sky that he could discover, no matter what their origin: peculiar cloud effects, meteors, and auroral displays, as well as genuine flying saucers.

And we discover that saucers, wheels, disks, and their prototypes have a long and honorable ancestry. I have traced saucers back into the Middle Ages. The trail grows dim, not because saucers were fewer, but because other more frequent natural phenomena — even lightning — were more terrifying, and equally mysterious. Comets and eclipses, omens of evil, appear frequently in the older chronicles. But they too are more spectacular than saucers.

While we are on the subject of detection, let us consider certain features that commonly appear in the saucer reports. After describing the time, location, color, and a few other miscellaneous things related to the saucer's appearance, the observer usually gives his impression of the size, distance, and speed of motion.

Here is a typical example, which refers to a daytime sighting. "The saucer was about 100 feet in diameter and it flew at an altitude of 10,000 feet . . . It suddenly veered and shot straight up with a speed of 5 miles a minute."

Now this report contains more information than it has any right to do. The saucer might equally well be either 10 feet in diameter at a height of 1,000 feet or only 1 foot in diameter at a height of 100 feet. The estimated speeds would be correspondingly lower. And, without additional information, there is absolutely no way that we can tell which, if any, of these distances is correct.

An observer can tell only the *angle* that an object spans, *not* the distance and size. A saucer whose diameter and distance are such that their proportion is 1 to 100, as in the above example, appears just slightly larger than the sun or moon!

If you see a saucer, hold out your hand at arm's length, and see how big (or small) the saucer appears relative to a thumbnail or the length of a finger. Such measures will help you remember and interpret what you actually saw.

One personal experience may be significant as an illustration. One day while I was walking along a country road, I chanced to look upward. I saw a distant plane, traveling soundlessly and at an enormous speed. My first and natural reaction was, "So we have a new type of plane." In a matter of seconds the plane was nearly overhead, and then to my consternation I saw it falter and approach me. I tried running away because the plane seemed about to crash —and indeed it did, almost in my face. I stooped and picked it up — a tiny, powered model. I could then see its owner running across the field and waving at me to indicate that I was not to walk off with his property. As for my reactions, they were entirely natural. I had unconsciously judged speed and size from the mere fact that I am familiar with the general size of planes. In a similar way, those persons who may have a preconceived idea of the size of a flying saucer will very likely get exaggerated ideas of the height or speed at which they fly.

Edgar Allen Poe, in his story, "The Sphinx," uses this inability of the human eye to judge both size and distance as a basic theme for a horror story. The plot is a bit far-fetched, but certainly relevant.

The story is laid against a background of death during an epidemic of cholera. Taking refuge in the home of a friend, a man looks up from his reading to regard the naked face of a hill, whereupon he sees a living monster of tremendous proportions. He describes the apparition in vivid terms.

Estimating the size of the creature by comparison with the diameter of the large trees near which it passed — the few giants of the forest which had escaped the fury of the land-slide — I concluded it to be far larger than any ship of the line in existence. I say ship of the line, because the shape of the monster suggested the idea — the hull of one of our seventy-fours might convey a very tolerable conception of the general outline. The mouth of the animal was situated at the extremity of a proboscis some sixty or seventy feet in length, and about as thick as the body of an ordinary elephant. Near the root of this trunk was an immense quantity of black shaggy hair — more than could have been supplied by the coats of a score of buffaloes; and projecting from this hair downwardly and laterally, sprang two gleaming tusks not unlike those of the wild boar, but of infinitely greater dimension. Extending forward, parallel with the proboscis, and on each side of it, was a gigantic staff, thirty or forty feet in length, formed seemingly of pure crystal, and in shape a perfect prism: — it reflected in the most gorgeous manner the rays of the declining sun. The trunk was fashioned like a wedge with the apex to the earth. From it there were outspread two pairs of wings — each wing nearly one hundred yards in length — one pair being placed above the other, and all thickly covered with metal scales; each scale apparently some ten or twelve feet in diameter. I observed that the upper and lower tiers of wings were connected by a strong chain. But the chief peculiarity of this horrible thing, was the representation of a *Death's Head*, which covered nearly the whole surface of its breast, and which was as accurately traced in glaring white, upon the dark ground of the body, as if it had been there carefully designed by an artist. While I regarded this terrific animal, and more especially the appearance on its breast, with a feeling of horror and awe — with a sentiment of forthcoming evil, which I found it impossible to quell by any effort of the reason, I perceived the huge jaws at the extremity of the proboscis, suddenly expand themselves and from them there proceeded a sound so loud and so expressive of woe, that it struck upon my nerves like a knell, and as the monster disappeared at the foot of the hill, I fell at once, fainting, to the floor.

For some time he keeps the matter from his host, but eventually decides to describe the apparition in minute detail. The host recognizes what it actually is: the "Death's Head Sphinx moth." He leans forward and places himself in the exact position where his friend had just seen a reappearance of the creature.

"Ah, here it is!" he presently exclaimed; "it is reascending the face of the hill, and a very remarkable looking creature, I admit it to be. Still, it is by no means so large or so distant as you imagined it; for the fact is that, as it wriggles its way up this thread, which some spider has wrought along the window-sash, I find it to be about the sixteenth of an inch in its extreme length, and also about the sixteenth of an inch distant from the pupil of my eye."

This story is not really scientific, because no one could possibly see the details as described in an object only one-sixteenth of an inch away from the eye. It would be completely out of focus.

However, I have been able to produce the effect of a flying saucer in a manner not too different from that described by Poe. Although this source is new, I believe that it will account for a fair number of saucer sightings.

A single thread from a spider web hanging in a graceful horizontal loop between two branches or across a window is almost invisible except when the full sunlight falls upon it. Its surface is almost mirrorlike, so that we see a brilliant reflection from only the small portion of the loop lying in the direction of the sun. If the strand of web is close to the eye, the out-of-focus effect will make it look like a brilliant saucer against the sky or distant scene. If a slight breeze disturbs it, the image will dance around and seem to veer, as the saucers have been reported to do.

To study the effect on a slightly larger scale, look at the bright reflection of the sun in a shiny, round lead pencil or fountain pen, preferably of dark color. Fine silk or nylon thread, or a fisherman's leader, reproduces the effect even better. Note that each eye sees a different image. If one tries to focus on the reflection, so as to see a single object, the pencil will be out of focus. Thus the saucer seems to be far away. Windborne cobwebs may thus be one of the major causes of unexplained saucer phenomena.

6

The flying-saucer scare of 1897

▰▰▰▰▰▰▰▰▰▰▰▰▰▰▰▰▰▰▰▰▰▰▰▰▰▰▰▰▰▰▰▰▰▰▰▰▰▰▰

The flying-saucer epidemic of 1947 was by no means the first time that strange apparitions in the sky had frightened the American public. Fifty years earlier, on 22 November 1896, inhabitants of Oakland, California, sighted an unfamiliar object in the sky. Passengers on an Alameda streetcar saw something flying above them, a sort of winged cigar, projecting a stream of brilliant light from its head.

To understand the reactions of these Californians, we must try to recapture the mental attitude that existed at that time. The wizard, Thomas Edison, had made electric lighting practical, and the arc light was well known to all. A couple of daring manufacturers had just started to build "horseless carriages" a few months before. Such things as airplanes or airships simply did not exist. Some individuals had practiced "ballooning" for years, but the gas bags of that date were either spherical or pear-shaped. People talked about "steerable" or — to use the more elegant French equivalent — "dirigible" balloons. Contemporary patents were already picturing the cigar-shaped bags that later came into practical use as the famous "Zeppelin" of World War I.

No wonder, then, that the people of Oakland were excited! The cigar-shaped body and the appearance of the searchlight clearly suggested that the object was an airship of some sort.

The *Oakland Tribune* reported that "when first seen, the object seemed to be floating over San Leandro. It moved rapidly, going at least 20 miles an hour. It shot across the sky in the Northwest, then turned quickly and disappeared in the direction of Haywards." The early story places considerable emphasis on the number and reliability of independent witnesses.

The excitement that gripped Oakland strongly resembled the one that swept the world after the saucer stories of 1947 first appeared.

There were hundreds of people who reported that they knew someone who had talked with somebody else who could point out the
person who had built the airship. To make matters more complicated,
the *Tribune* stated several days later that a certain reliable person
named Carlson would vouch for the fact that the inventor had
actually flown such a craft over the city. The *Tribune*, still not
supporting the story beyond all question, warned: "This unknown
Darius Green is wrapped in mystery and when he alights from his
aerial flight evidently folds up his invention, tucks it under his
vest and quietly goes up the back stairs so as not to have to answer
embarrassing questions from his family . . . as to where he was at."

As the story spread to neighboring towns, residents of Red Bluff,
Chico, and Leesville also reported the object during the early
evening. Although some persons maintained that the mysterious
thing was a star, others rejected the theory, because of "its distinctly
rocking motion, which was like the motion made by a kite." (The
description strongly resembles that given by observers of modern
saucers.)

The *Tribune* reported: "The uncertainty of the thing has been
causing much speculation and now the streets are lined with an
inquisitive throng, all gazing heavenward." Professor Charles
Burckhalter, of the Chabot Observatory, maintained that the
people were seeing only Mars and Venus in the evening sky. "Venus
is as brilliant as an arc light and does move slowly through the
heavens," said Burckhalter. "The theories in regard to the airship
are pure imagination, and if there were any such object in the
heavens we would certainly know of it."

But the "airship" continued to fly here and there on the night of
30 November. Many people saw it between the hours of 8:00 and
8:30. They described it as "moving in the teeth of the wind," a point
of some importance because the balloons of that day were freely
drifting and not steerable. Reported one of the observers, "No light
was visible, merely the weirdly peculiar body silhouetted against the
clear sky." He further stated that the object seemed to be at least
100 feet long and that it was floating at an altitude of 1500 feet.
It possessed a triangular tail. Suddenly the object rapidly accelerated
and moved at tremendous speed toward Lorin, where it turned

again toward San Francisco and passed over Oakland a second time.

The man who made this report was Case Gilson, a well-known amateur astronomer of that region. He ruled out planets and meteors and was quite sure that the object he saw was not a kite.

Fifty years later, the *Oakland Tribune*, commenting on the event in its issue of 11 May 1952, states: "No one seems to have seen the mysterious craft after that.

"Balloon, airplane — or flying saucer?

"You pays your money and you takes your choice."

But the *Tribune* was wrong. Others had seen the "aircraft" and, although the incident may have died down in Oakland, a wave of airship hysteria gradually spread over the entire United States. In some places it caused a religious sensation, many of the superstitious believing that the end of the world was at hand. The ship, so it seemed, was gradually moving East. Salt Lake City saw it, and then Denver, Omaha, and Kansas City.

New York Herald, Sunday, 11 April 1897

THAT AIRSHIP NOW AT CHICAGO

CITY EXCITED BY THE APPEARANCE OF
.RAPIDLY MOVING LIGHTS IN THE SKY

ASTRONOMERS INCREDULOUS
THEY BELIEVE THAT THE LIGHTS PROCEED
FROM A STAR IN THE CONSTELLATION OF ORION

IS A DIRIGIBLE BALLOON.
SO SAYS SECRETARY MAX HARMAR, OF THE
CHICAGO AERONAUTICAL ASSOCIATION

(By telegraph to the *Herald*.) Chicago, Ill., April 10, 1897. — For weeks despatches have been coming in from various points between here and California regarding an airship. At first no attention was paid to them, but they became so frequent that the public began to be interested. Then the airship was seen at Omaha, and proceeding eastward, was seen last night in Chicago. The general public believes in the airship theory, while the astronomers say it must be a star.

Late last night Professor Hough, of the Northwestern University, turned the great Dearborn telescope toward the west, and took a look at the strange visitor. The citizens who saw it said the ship displayed red and green lights, just as a vessel on the ocean would do, but the professor, after a long look, said, "Why, it must be Alpha Orionis."

"Can you read that name on the airship?" he was eagerly asked.

"Why, no," replied the Professor with a laugh, "Alpha Orionis is a star of the first magnitude, and is in the constellation Orion."

"But what about the red and green lights so many people have seen?" he was asked.

"That," said the veteran astronomer "must be the effect of the atmosphere, which apparently causes the star to change colour." Then he added, "I think Alpha Orionis is the only airship the people have seen, but if there be another it has disappeared long ere this."

Until two o'clock this morning thousands of amazed spectators declared that the lights seen to the northwest were those of an airship or some other floating object miles above the earth, and viewed the apparent phenomenon with the deepest interest, tinged with a certain degree of awe, wonder and uneasiness.

Men of unquestioned veracity declared the moving body was an airship. Some declare they saw two cigar-shaped objects and great wings. All agree with regard to the lights. The first was white, and wonderfully resembled a searchlight. It switched from side to side, as though attempting to light up the darkness on all sides. After this came a green light, then a smaller white light, and finally a red light. Professor S. W. Burnham, a well-known astronomer, agrees with the explanation given by Professor Hough. He said: "Alpha Orionis is a star of the first magnitude. Its position in the northern sky, its parti-coloured lights, make a striking object. Shining through misty clouds and aided by refraction it would give the appearance of a rapidly moving body. One's imagination could easily give strange form to it. This star, too, looks to be but a comparatively short distance above the earth."

CHICAGO IS EXCITED

STAR OR AIRSHIP, CHICAGO AND HER SUBURBS ARE INTENSELY INTERESTED, AND THE SUBJECT IS ALMOST THE SOLE TOPIC OF CONVERSATION

That there was "something" in the northern sky there is no doubt, and it was a very curious "something." The "something" seemed to come from the mists of the lake, and, moving westward, was in plain sight of Chicago and Evanston.

The airship or star seems to be most irregular in its movements. At Kankakee, where the State Insane Asylum is located, it was observed, going in a northeasterly direction at 9 o'clock last night. It was apparently one thousand feet above the earth, and moving very rapidly. The headlight appeared as large as an ordinary electric arc light. At one time the vessel rose very rapidly, and afterwards seemed to drop a long distance.

In addition to the headlight, spectators claimed to have noticed smaller lights behind, indicating that the object was of considerable size. It was apparently headed toward Chicago, and traveled very rapidly.

SAYS IT IS A REAL AIRSHIP

There is a general disposition to laugh at the theory that the object seen by so many thousands of people is really an airship, but attorney Max L. Harmar, secretary of the Chicago Aeronautical Association, does not smile at it. To him the fact of a real airship moving across the country was not a surprise.

"There is only one thing that surprises me in the presence of the airship," said Mr. Harmar. "We expected it on Sunday, and it is hard for me to believe the vessel arrived here so soon, unless the conditions were exceptionally favorable. Yes, I have a good idea concerning all this mystery. I know one of the men who is in the airship. The car contains three persons, but the exaggerated stories concerning the ship are laughable.

"Spectators have announced it as their belief that the ship was composed of steel. This was a mistake. It is paper. There is the customary inflated gas reservoir, but the inventors have discovered the secret of practical propulsion. They can steer the vessel in any direction they desire. Word was received here several weeks ago that the party had started from San Francisco, and that the ship would stop here for the purpose of registration. The end of the trip is to be at Washington City, where the ship will be brought to earth and given up to inspection. President Octave Chanute, of the Chicago Society, has full information concerning the ship. He, with a number of other wealthy men interested in the problem, has furnished the money for the venture. Mr. Chanute is in California at the present time. I would not care to furnish details as to the experiment, as it would be unfair to the inventor and would take off the edge of public interest."

I should like to believe that the remarks of Mr. Max L. Harmar were intended irony. He says that the ship is not steel, but of "paper" and that it possesses "the customary inflated gas reservoir." Perhaps, like many of his contemporaries, he agreed that the ship was largely created from imagination — imagination inflated by the newspaper stories. As in the 1947 saucer scare, hoaxers and jokers, ready to capitalize on the event, quickly entered the picture.

New York Herald, Monday, 12 April 1897

SNAPSHOTS OF THE AIRSHIP

TWO EXCELLENT PHOTOGRAPHS MADE WHILE THE
CRAFT WAS FLYING THROUGH SPACE

PRODUCED AS EVIDENCE

OBTAINED BY A NEWS DEALER IN ROGERS PARK, NEAR CHICAGO,

IN THE EARLY MORNING

ITS INVENTOR HEARD FROM

WRITES TO OFFICERS OF THE TRANS-MISSISSIPPI
EXPOSITION FOR SPACE TO EXHIBIT IT

(By telegraph to the *Herald*.) Chicago, Ill., April 11, 1897. — The fact
that the much talked of airship is a reality, and not a phantom, is apparently attested by two remarkable photographs, now in this city, which
it is alleged were taken while the machine was in motion. Walter McCann,
of Rogers Park, a town 28 miles north of here, took two snapshots with
his camera at what he believed to be the airship, and secured two excellent negatives. It was early in the morning, and the vessel was scudding
along at a rapid rate, but the pictures he secured are very good ones.

The work of Mr. McCann dispels any thought of an optical illusion.
Three witnesses assert that they saw him take the photographs, which
were obtained this morning about half-past five o'clock.

Mr. McCann is a news dealer in Rogers Park. It is his custom to get
up very early in the morning, particularly on Sunday, to deliver the
Chicago papers. In his store he has a small camera, the property of his
young son. When McCann sighted the strange object in the sky, early
this morning, he at once came to the conclusion it was the airship of
which there had been so much talk and which had set so many people
to thinking. He rushed into his store, seized the camera and secured a
good picture of it. G. A. Oversocker, who was also looking at the ship,
suggested a second snapshot, and the result was a much better negative.

PICTURES ARE GENUINE

The pictures developed from these plates were tested by acids tonight,
and were pronounced genuine productions of an object in the air, and
not the creations of a studio. William Hoodlees and E. L. Osborne, the
latter an operator in the telegraph office of the Chicago and Northwestern
Railway Co., in Rogers Park, saw McCann and Oversocker at the hour
named, and asserted they not only witnessed the photographing of the
object in the air, but saw the vessel.

The craft, according to the statement of all these witnesses, is an invention without wings or sails. All agree that the outlines of a man could
also be seen. Through a glass they were of the opinion that they could

see the man in motion, as though he were engaged in steering the vessel. The upper part of the ship apparently consisted of a cigar-shaped silken bag, attached to which was a lightly constructed framework. In the center of the framework the man was located. A propeller or rudder was attached to the framework, the rudder being shaped like the hull of a ship, except that it was sharp at both ends. Apparently the framework was composed of white metal.

Mr. McCann told his story tonight at his store on Greenleaf Ave. "I had read for some days about the airship," said he, "but thought it must be a fake. This morning about half-past five o'clock I was attending to my usual duties when I saw a strange looking object in the sky coming from the south. It looked like a big cigar. It came nearer, and then I saw it was certainly not a balloon. Then I thought of the airship and ran for the camera. At the corner of Greenleaf Avenue and Market Street I took the first shot, while a few minutes later I took another further up from the railroad tracks. It was 500 or 600 feet from me when I photographed it, and I saw it plainly. It went north a distance and then gradually turned east."

ITS INVENTOR HEARD FROM

A despatch from Omaha tonight says that the mystery surrounding the much talked about airship promises to be cleared within a few days, through the medium of the Capitol Trans-Mississippi Exposition or a hoax is to be perpetrated on the exposition authorities.

Secretary Wakefield received a letter yesterday from Omaha and signed "A. C. Clinton." It was as follows. "To the Exposition Authorities: — My identity up to date has been unknown, but I will come to the front now, i.e., if you guarantee me 87,000 square feet of space. I am the famous airship constructor, and I will guarantee you positively of this fact within a week.

The airship is my own invention, and as I am an Omaha man, I wish it to be heralded as an Omaha invention. It will carry safely 20 people to a height of from 10 to 20 thousand feet. I truly believe I have the greatest invention and discovery ever made. Will see you April 17 at the headquarters."

The exposition authorities will await his appearance with interest.

The first airship seen — one that seemed actually to fly and appeared to be under control of its pilot — within the last six months was near Sacramento, California. About 1 o'clock, on the morning of Monday November 16, several persons said that they saw the object passing rapidly over that city. Several asserted they saw a cigar-shaped flying machine, and heard voices from it. According to George D. Collins, a lawyer of San Francisco, the object was a real airship. In an interview Mr. Collins said: —

"The reports about the airship are perfectly true. It was my client's airship. During the past 5 years he has spent at least $100,000 on his work. He has not secured his patent, but the application is now on file in Washington. I saw the machine at the inventor's invitation. It is made of metal, is about 150 ft. in length and is built to carry 15 persons. There was no motive power, so far as I could see; certainly no steam.

"The machine was built on the meroplane system and has two canvas wings 8 ft. wide and a rudder shaped like a bird's tail. The inventor climbed into the machine, and after he had moved the mechanism for a moment I saw the thing rise from the earth very gently. The wings flapped slowly as it arose and then a little faster as it began to move against the wind. The machine was under his full control all the time. When it reached a height of 90 ft. the inventor shouted to me that he was going to make a series of circles and then descend. He immediately did so, beginning by making a circle of about 100 yds. in diameter and then gradually narrowing until the machine got within 30 ft. of the ground. It then fell straight down and touched the ground as lightly as a falling leaf.

WENT ON LONG TRIPS

"In this recent trip the ship started from Oroville, in Butte County, and flew 60 miles in a straight line, directly over Sacramento. After running up and down over the capitol, my friend came right on a distance of 70 miles or more, and landed on a spot on the Oakland side of the Bay, where the machine now is. It is constructed on an absolutely new theory of flight."

Then came John A. Hernon, an electrician of San Jose, Cal., who in an interview on December 1, said he had been to Honolulu and back in an airship, but refused to say anything as to the inventor or the model of his machine. Hernon is the patentee of a platinum speaking apparatus. He said that six days previously he went to San Francisco to see the inventor, and went on horseback to a point on Sandy Beach, where he found the airship.

"We got on board," said he, "and rose very high, the height being measured by a meter on board ship. We traveled westward, and before daybreak we saw the lights, which the inventor said were Honolulu lights. We then turned toward the eastward again, and at dusk on Saturday evening we finished our two days' cruise and landed near our starting point. The airship rose by means of two propellers. The movement was noiseless and swift. The motive power is neither steam nor electricity."

Following this, on January 2 a despatch came from San Francisco saying that an airship on a large scale would soon be sent up from there. An order was placed with a Pittsburgh production company for a large amount of aluminum to be used in the construction of the ship, and work had been commenced. This statement was made by authority of Dr. C. A.

Smith, president of the Atlantic and Pacific Aerial Navigation Co. A company was formed and 86,400 shares were authorized by the incorporators at a par value of $1.00 per share.

MYSTERIOUS CRAFT IN OMAHA

The identity of the South Omaha "thing," as it is generally called, remained a mystery, and after many attempts to gather some information regarding it, these efforts were abandoned. Then, on the night of March 29 the object was again observed, this time by the majority of the residents of Omaha. It was in the shape of a big bright light, too big for a balloon, and glowed steadily. It sailed over the city to the northwest and there disappeared. It moved very slowly and seemed to be quite near the earth. A despatch from Denver the following night said the strange visitor had been seen there, but only for a few moments.

Once more the stranger disappeared and remained out of sight until the present month, when a telephone message was received from Evanston, 11 miles north of Chicago, saying that about 20 minutes to 9 o'clock that night a mysterious light, evidently that of an airship, was seen passing rapidly over the city, going west-northwest. The light was more like an electric light than anything else. It seemed to be about a quarter of a mile above the earth.

Despatches began pouring in to Chicago from various points in Indiana, Illinois, Missouri, Iowa and Wisconsin on the night of April 9. For the first time, also, the object was seen in Chicago, and thousands stood along the lake shore and gathered at various points to view it. The moving object was first observed by Robert Lowen, of No. 1926 Sherman Ave., a jeweler. He was standing in the store door when his attention was attracted by a moving light in the heavens. The light appeared to be over the lake, a short way out and was moving in a westerly direction. Mr. Lowen took a strong field glass and looked at the object. He was able to discern four lights close together and moving in unison.

The first was a bright white light, and appeared to be a searchlight; directly back of this was a smaller green light further to the rear. Lowen called several passers-by to look at the light through the glasses, and all pronounced them of the colours green and white.

A later dispatch cleared up the mystery of the craft's apparent return to Omaha, which it had visited nearly two weeks earlier.

New York Sun, Sunday, 11 April 1897.

AIRSHIP WAS A BALLOON

SENT UP BY TWO PRACTICAL JOKERS OF OMAHA TO FOOL THE PEOPLE

Omaha, Neb., April 10. — The "airship" which has caused such a sensation in Omaha, is now declared to be a balloon, and the men who sent it up are said to be Roy Arnold and Jack Rogers. They are practical jokers, and they bought an enormous balloon to send up on April 1, but it rained that night, so they held it off for a later day.

On last Monday night they took the balloon and went over to the hollow back of the State Institute for the Deaf, where they inflated it and sent it up.

Suspended from the balloon was a wicker basket filled with a composition resembling shavings, which they touched off just as it ascended and this was the light. The balloon struck a current of air and it carried directly over the central part of the city, and Arnold says that when they came back on the car everybody was talking of the "airship" and all were excited. He accounts for its strange course on the theory of striking different currents of air.

New York Herald, Tuesday, 13 April 1897.

SURE IT'S AN AIRSHIP

OSCAR D. BOOTH THINKS HE KNOWS THE MAN WHOSE MACHINE HAS ASTONISHED THE WEST

(By telegraph to the *Herald*.) Chicago, Ill., April 12, 1897. — Oscar D. Booth, of No. 158 South Peoria St., has constructed an airship, and he firmly believes the strange object seen by Chicago is another airship. He thinks the mysterious craft was made and is being operated by an inventor named Charles Clinton residing near Dodd City, Ford County, Kan.

The airship theory set forth in Clinton's patent papers, on file in Washington, is a true though bungling solution of the problem, according to Booth. The fact that the curious object was first seen in Kansas strengthens Booth's belief. "That a machine has already been launched and is even now soaring through the air I have little doubt," he said. "Why, various persons have seen the wings and the cigar-shaped car. They are not all fools, and the reports come from so many places, too."

Referring to the Kansas ship, Booth spoke good words for his rival. "His machine is practical, I am sure," he said. "When I first read of the airship being seen over Kansas I ran through the papers in my possession to see what Inventor resided in Kansas. I found the plans which this Ford County man had filed. He has wings, or large propellers, placed at both ends of the cigar-shaped car, and has two engines. Above is a balloon. The general shape of the machine corresponds with the description given of the one flying over Chicago. It is likely the same one."

The hoaxers continued to multiply. Two old soldiers reported that the airship, illuminated at both ends and moving through space with wonderful rapidity, suddenly appeared over Kalamazoo, Michigan.

The men had scarcely time for a glimpse at the flying machine when they heard a dull explosion and the craft disappeared. The report, they said, was like that from a heavy cannon and they heard many projectiles flying through the air. Though these two men were the only ones to see the explosion, others reported that they had heard a sound like "thunder" and two miles from the spot searchers found a large coil of heavy wire and some fused metal. How like some of the saucer reports of today! Doubtless the exhibition of these fragments amply repaid the searchers for their trouble.

A man in Waterloo, Iowa, built a structure of canvas and lumber, secretly placed it in an outlying lot during the night, and put it on exhibition the following day. His audience, according to the report, numbered 5,000 persons.

The mysteries multiplied when a fisherman from Detroit reported that he had seen the airship rise from the surface of Lake Erie. He described its occupants fully and minutely. A man 25 years old was dressed in a checked hunting suit and wore a long peaked cap. A handsome woman sat beside him, with a boy of 10 at her feet. The man was fishing in the water, but as the boat approached, the airship rose until it stood directly above the vessel, about 500 feet from the surface, where it circled for several minutes.

Suddenly the fisherman observed a tremendous splash in the water. A large swordfish had been dropped from the ship. The stunned fish was captured and placed on exhibition. The mysterious people were then carried away by the high wind. Presumably, the physical presence of the swordfish established beyond question the authenticity of the story.

A "respectable citizen" of Birmingham, Iowa, reported that he and others saw a ship alight in a meadow a mile from town. Before they could reach it, the ship rose and disappeared. The ship possessed a car with two men as travelers who waved their hands as the ship departed.

In Washington, Iowa, "a half dozen reliable citizens" saw something queer in the sky, a light that changed color — with a shadow above the light.

The Reverend Mr. Gray, a Baptist minister, was properly cautious. "I do not believe it was a star," he said. "I do not pretend to say that it was an airship, but I know it was something unusual. I believe something more will be heard from it. I do not believe it could have been a burned-out star. It disappeared in the Southwest."

Citizens of Greenberg, Indiana, also reported the airship. A newspaper correspondent in a nearby city had warned people to be on the lookout. And, as predicted, the object appeared about 3 hours later, approaching from the west at a speed of 10 miles an hour. No light was burning, but the ship was plainly outlined against the clear sky.

The ship reversed its course and swung back from the east, this time "with three lights — a green, red, and a large white one in the center." The rest of the story follows:

New York Herald, 15 April 1897.

Professor George Keelty, who obtained a good view of it from his observatory, says the searchlight is of medium power. He probably got the best view of anyone although he did not get in his tower until it was passing away the first time. For the last two days and nights Professor Keelty has been on constant watch for the machine, thinking it would pass over this way, but he temporarily left his post tonight when it appeared. The second time he could not see it so clearly, owing to the darkness.

He says the machine is about 60 feet long, the balloon being about 50 feet long, it is cigar-shaped, the car hanging about 20 feet under the balloon. The car was entirely enclosed, it being impossible to see in it, but two men were visible in the lookout. One was apparently 50 years old, with a beard, and the other young. The oldest one wore a stiff hat and the younger a cuban crushed hat. The lights would occasionally be changed from one color to another, and would sometimes be extinguished.

HAS GREAT SPEED

The ship would make usually about 10 miles an hour, but on disappearing the last time it dashed off at the tremendous speed of fully 150 miles an hour. It went in a southwesterly direction. Newton Kennedy saw it out at the edge of the city and described it as did Prof. Keelty.

Note that two of the following stories indicate the tendency of the "ship" to move ahead as it is approached. This characteristic is shared by the 1947 model.

New York Herald, 15 April 1897.

AIRSHIP SEEN BY DAYLIGHT
SEVERAL PERSONS AT DIFFERENT PLACES ASSERT
THAT THEY SAW THIS STRANGE CRAFT ALIGHT

(By telegraph to the *Herald.*) Carlinville, Ill., April 13, 1897. — The mysterious airship has been seen in the northern part of this (Macoupin) county, about half-past two o'clock Sunday afternoon alighted on the farm of Z. Thacker, 1 mile north of Nilwood. It was seen by William Street, Edward Teeples, and Frank Metcalf. It remained about 15 minutes, and continued north. The craft was seen again at 6 o'clock alighting in a grove two miles south of Gerard and a mile north of the mining camp in Green Ridge. A large crowd of miners from that place and a storekeeper, who locked his door to accompany them, started to inspect the strange apparition. As they approached within a half a mile, it arose and sped north.

The Chicago and Alton operators telegraphed ahead to be on the watch, and at 8 o'clock it passed over Sherman, 32 miles north of Gerard, at the apparent rate of 30 miles an hour. It was last sighted over Williamsville, about 15 minutes to 9 o'clock, headed for Peoria. Those who saw the airship say it was cigar-shaped, with wings and a canopy on top. One man avers that he saw a man working about the craft, apparently fixing the machinery. The fact of its alighting twice and remaining such a long time in the same locality leads to the conclusion that the machine was injured in some manner.

New York Herald, 16 April 1897.

TWO BAGS OF BALLAST LEFT BY THE VISITOR IN LYNN GROVE, IOWA

(By telegraph to the *Herald.*) Lynn Grove, Iowa, April 15, 1897. — The citizens of Lynn Grove are certain there is no longer any doubt of the existence of an airship. A large object was seen soon after 10 o'clock this morning slowly moving in the heavens in a northerly direction, and it seemed to be preparing to alight. James Evans, a livery man; F. G. Ellis, a harness dealer; Benjamin Buland, stock dealer and David Evans and Joseph Crosby jumped in to a wagon and started in pursuit. They saw what seemed to be an airship alight on the Jones farm, four miles north of town, but when they were within 700 yards of it, it arose and started toward the north. Two bags of ballast were thrown out, and these are now at Robertson Campbell's drug store.

The men who chased the ship are certain there were two men on board. They say the object had four wings. Every citizen of Lynn Grove saw the object as it sailed over the town, and there has been great excitement all day.

APPLETON, WIS., CITIZENS TOO SOBER MINDED FOR SUCH THINGS

(By telegraph to the *Herald*.) Appleton, Wis., April 15, 1897. — No reputable citizens here have seen any airship. This is a university town, and we are too sober minded for such things.

Since yesterday several iron arrows, with letters attached have been brought to town from the surrounding country. They purport to have been dropped from the airship, and recount its voyages from Tennessee and Colorado to Wisconsin. Boys, bicycles, and mischief are responsible for many pranks, and we who are in the secret find it difficult to enthuse properly over the heavenly visitor.

TRUTHFUL CITIZENS OF GRAND RAPIDS, MICH., HAVE NOT SEEN IT

(By telegraph to the editor.) Grand Rapids, Mich., April 15, 1897. — Grand Rapids' citizens are sober, law abiding and truthful. The airship has not yet been seen here.

AFFIDAVITS MADE BY ELEVEN RESIDENTS OF ANDERSON, IND., WHO SAW IT

(By telegraph to the *Herald*.) Cincinnati, Ohio, April 15, 1897. — A local newspaper publishes this afternoon 11 affidavits of residents of Anderson, Ind. in reference to the supposed airship said to have been seen travelling over Indiana during the last week. All the affidavits are by well-known citizens, and all refer to April 11 as the time when the object was seen.

All say they saw it at night, and that it was a strange looking object, from which at times, a bright light flashed, which was larger than a star. It was moving north, at an altitude of probably 5000 feet, and at a speed of probably 20 miles an hour. None says that it was an airship, but all agree that they cannot account for it on any other theory. This is a sample of the affidavits: —

"This certifies that I, J. O. Morrison, viewed a strange body in the heavens on the evening of April 11, which I am at a loss to account. It moved in a northerly direction, and at times a strange light was flashed from it."

The fame of the airship spread abroad, where the incident found supporters and scoffers. The affair probably caused greatest concern in Paris. French aviation authorities, arguing pro and con, generally were more "con" than "pro."

New York Herald, Thursday, 15 April 1897. (Editorial.)

PARIS INTERESTED IN THE AIRSHIP

Even Paris has caught the airship contagion. The *Figaro*, according to a commercial cable despatch, publishes a special article based on the report sent from New York to the European edition of the *Herald*, which will undoubtedly furnish interest to Parisian readers for some time to come. Paris is evidently quite as anxious to get the truth about the high flier as we are, but unfortunately our western chroniclers are not inclined to take the matter as seriously as could be desired.

That the problem of aerial navigation will eventually be solved is, of course, sure, but whether this Omaha phenomenon has made the solution remains to be seen. In Europe there are at least a dozen well-known scientists working on the problem, and many half-successful efforts of flight have been made, not taking into account Hiram Maxim's idea of spending energy uselessly in the endeavor to lift a machine into space by main force.

Poets, romanticists and dreamers have pictured the airship of the future. Flammarion has filled his book on the "Fin du Monde" with attractive pictures of airships floating genially through space, and he followed the Hungarian Maurus Jokii, who 30 years ago made the airship the great means of communication between the various cities of the magnetic world.

Military authorities everywhere are anxious to get their balloon observatories free from the tether holding them to the earth, while custom house authorities are trembling for fear of the smugglers utilizing the new contrivance for evading European Bingley bills. Let us hope the Omaha airship may be tracked to its lair and another grand discovery be credited to this fin de siecle age.

And in the news columns of the same day, we get the French viewpoint.

The *Figaro* publishes a special article, based on the *Herald*'s cables, respecting the airship. It says: —

"The news seems to be more than a canard, seeing the details and preciseness in which are related in the *Herald* the exploits of this airship. It has traveled over the new world at an average height of from 5 to 600 meters, and is stated to have been seen by thousands, and, what is more, photographed.

"About 6 months ago it was announced that the inventor, a native of Omaha, had solved the problem of aerial navigation, but no notice was taken of the assertion. It would appear that this was a mistake, as this airship has neither sails nor wings, and resembles the traditional spindle.

"With a telescope a human being was observed in the machine. In Chicago during the night, a searchlight flooded the city, with rays, which caused in some quarters such terror that many people believed the end of the world had come.

"These statements are so astounding that one doubts their reality, notwithstanding the full details given by the *Herald*. No machine exists in

France that can lift its weight by screws or any other system by 1-third, without counting engineers and passengers or provisions or fuel.

"Americans are no further advanced in the science of aerostatics than the French, and to accept the statement of an airship travelling at a 100 kilometers an hour we must admit the discovery of a new force or a new application of a force hither unknown to the extent of 3 or 4 times greater than any existing."

And in the same issue appeared a story so patently a hoax that one wonders how anyone could have been deceived. But, after all, the airship was great news!

LETTER FROM THE AIRSHIP?
SAYS THE CRAFT IS CALLED THE PEGASUS AND CAN FLY 150 MILES AN HOUR.

(By telegraph to the *Herald.*) Chicago, Ill., April 14, 1897. — All sorts of telegrams come in here in regard to the alleged airship seen in this section of the country but it seems to be impossible to get anything reliable in regard to it. It has been several weeks since the agitation started but the reports did not begin to arrive in close order until the 5th of this month. Since then they have come in every night. Some of the newspapers here declare it is a nonsensical story, yet the reports in most cases have come from reliable persons. Of course, the practical joker has come to the front, and in some cases small balloons with lights attached have been sent up in various towns, but in the majority of cases the persons who saw or thought they saw an object in the sky have treated the matter in the most serious manner.

A despatch received tonight from Appleton, Wis., says that on Sunday night many persons saw an airship pass over that city. Last night, on the farm of N. B. Clark, near there a letter was picked up attached to an iron rod 18 inches long, sticking in the ground. The letter, which was not signed, was as follows:

Letter from the Airship.

"Aboard the airship Pegasus, April 9, 1897.

"Problem of aerial navigation has been solved. The writers have spent the past month cruising about in the airship Pegasus, and have demonstrated to their entire satisfaction that the ship is a thorough success. We have been able to attain a speed of 150 miles an hour, and have risen to a height of 2,500 feet above the sea level.

"The Pegasus was erected at a secluded point ten miles from Lafayette, Tenn., and the various parts of the machine were carried overland from Glasgow, Ky., to that point being shipped from Chicago, Pittsburgh and

St. Louis. We have made regular trips of three days each from Lafayette to Yankton, and no harm has come to the Pegasus thus far.

"Within a month our application for the patents for a parallel plane airship will be filed simultaneously at Washington and the European capitals. It is propelled by steam and is lighted by electricity, and has a carrying power of 1,000 lbs."

From Grand Rapids, Wis., the report comes that the airship passed over there at 9 o'clock last evening, and was seen by a hundred reputable citizens. Similar reports come from Elkhart, Ind., Ripon, Wis., and Lake Forest.

R. J. Thompson, secretary of the Illinois Commission to the Tennessee Centennial, says the commission will pay $25,000 for an actual airship, to exhibit at the exposition.

Oscar D. Booth, of 158 South Peoria street, an inventor of airships, was asked tonight if he thought it likely a man could build and launch a flying machine and keep it secret.

"I judge that the flying machine seen over Chicago is one made only for a trial trip, probably a small one," he replied. "It would be very easy to take a medium sized ship to a secluded place, put together the parts and start it off. Now, with my invention I could leave Chicago without a soul knowing it. My car is only 9 feet long, and could easily be drawn to some quiet spot. I have everything ready but the balloon."

Two days later came the great sensation and a climax to the story. The airship dropped a message, which was found on a farm near Astoria, Illinois. A reed 3 feet long, sticking in the ground and marked with a red, white, and blue streamer, carried a packet and a dirty envelope with the words: "From the airship — notice to the finder: — Please mail letter inside. Passed over here about half past two P.M. April 16, 1897, about 2300 feet high, going East and North. Excuse dirt, have just done oiling. Harris." The letter itself was addressed to Thomas A. Edison, written in cipher, and signed "C. L. Harris, electrician, airship number 3."

The final story appeared in the *New York Herald* on Tuesday, 20 April 1897.

THAT LETTER TO EDISON
"THE WIZARD" DESCRIBES THE "AIRSHIP" EPISTLE AS A FAKE
AND EXPRESSES AN OPINION ON AERIAL INVENTION

That letter from the "airship" to Thomas A. Edison, a copy of which was printed in a despatch from Astoria, Illinois in the *Herald* yesterday, has not reached the distinguished inventor. The missive was dated April

16 and signed "C. L. Harris, electrician, Airship N. 3," and was found tied to a reed near Astoria. I showed Mr. Edison yesterday afternoon the letter published in the Herald.

"This is the latest, isn't it?" inquired he, leaning back in his chair and glancing over the letter a second time. "You can take it from me that this is a pure fake. I have had several men in my employ, but I know nothing of C. L. Harris."

Mr. Edison then grew more thoughtful and stated that he had no doubt that airships will be successfully constructed in the near future. In reference to the western "airship" he added: —

"It is absolutely absurd to imagine that a man would construct a successful airship and keep the matter secret. When I was young we used to construct big coloured paper balloons, inflate them with gas and they would float for days.

"Whenever an airship is made it will not be in the form of a balloon. It will be a mechanical contrivance, which will be raised by means of a very powerful motor of little weight. At present no one has discovered such a motor, but we never know what will happen. We may wake up some morning and hear of some invention which sets us all eagerly to work within a few hours, as was the case with the Roentgen rays.

"I am not, however, figuring on inventing an airship. I prefer to devote my time to objects which have some commercial value. At best airships would be only toys."

Significantly, this story of Edison's broke the airship bubble. Although the great scientist had in no way explained what it was people had been seeing in the sky, the mere fact that he correctly pointed out that there was no airship killed the sensation. People were interested in *airships*, not in the natural phenomena, however mysterious, that may have been producing the illusion.

About a week later there was a short message from someone in Cripple Creek, Colorado, who thought he had seen an airship. But clearly the news of Edison's pronouncement had not yet penetrated to him.

It is perhaps even more significant, as a sign of the era, that the *New York Herald* for 25 April 1897 carried a long story with illustrations about the serious plans made by Salomon Andrée for a balloon flight over the North Pole. On 11 July 1897, he left on this daring adventure with two companions.

Nothing further was heard of their expedition from that day on, except for several messages by carrier pigeons, until in 1930 a chance landing on an out-of-the-way area of Spitzbergen led to discovery of the remains of the ill-fated expedition. Thirty-three years had elapsed, but the records of the expedition were still intact. Photographs and diaries recorded how the polar balloon, encrusted with a layer of ice, gradually lost buoyancy and descended. The men landed safely but were unable to take off again.

The 1947 scare, except for its size and duration, closely followed that of 1897. There were the original rumors, the self-hallucinations, the hoaxes, and the interest in sky-watching. A few of the reported incidents probably referred to true flying saucers. But the famous searchlight that flashed red, white, and blue must have been a star in the majority of cases. A star that twinkles — especially one low on the horizon — does not twinkle uniformly in all colors. Hence the seeming effect of the flashing shades. The dark, cigar-shaped gas bag in many cases was only a lenticular cloud or a mirage, which would have escaped notice except for the special significance momentarily attached to an object of this shape.

The similarity of the two patterns of reports also shows in the repeated statements about the reliability of independent witnesses. We have the scoffing experts and the counter scoffing (so-called) "authorities" who profess to know the real truth behind these stories and who cite names, dates, and places to substantiate their claims. I have checked and can find no document that indicates that the inventors referred to ever got a patent on an airship.

I strongly believe that the duration of the 1947 scare has resulted from the insistence upon the reality of interplanetary saucers. When one can show that the saucers are not associated with some living beings, they will cease to be news. And as they disappear from public notice, sightings will be fewer and fewer — not because flying saucers will be any scarcer but because people will cease to be interested in watching the skies.

The airship of 1897 may seem tame compared with the saucers of 1947. But we must remember that space flight to us, in the light of today's scientific knowledge, seems less spectacular and more reasonable than airship flight did fifty years ago. Man eventually built a successful dirigible and went on to conquer the air completely. The unmanned rocket of today is a forecast of the manned space craft of tomorrow.

The following excerpt is from a letter I received from William E. Marsh, of Oklahoma City.

Permit me to add a little personal note to the "flying saucers" of 1896–97, which evidently you are not old enough to have witnessed. I saw them!

I was 14 years old on January 25, 1897. My father, who owned a small-town morning paper in Indiana, promised me a paper route when I was fourteen and I actually had to take a route two weeks earlier. As you correctly recount, the "airship," as it was called then, rather than the flying saucer, had appeared the previous November and by the spring of 1897 it had been seen everywhere, particularly on days when news was dull and an energetic reporter had to produce something. I myself saw it about five o'clock one morning on my route and watched it proceed over perhaps 15 degrees of sky. Being somewhat sleepy and not a complete amateur as a liar I discerned it plainly as thousands of other neurotics and ordinary liars did all over the country.

I would point out that this began seven years before Kittyhawk, but for several years we had had liberal doses of science-fiction planes crowding the air.

It was not long after this yarn got too stale to report, that the kissing bug invaded the country. Some industrious reporter (I am not untrue to what was my profession, I just know reporters) told a story of an enormous beetle, three or four inches long, which landed on a young lady's lips and bit her severely. The story caught on quickly, and in a week the kissing bugs were biting all the girls from Maine to California. It soon went the way of the airship of 1896–7.

7

The great saucer of 1882

▸▸

On the night of 17 November 1882, one of the greatest flying saucers of modern times sped swiftly and silently across the heavens, exhibiting the characteristic cigar-shaped form when it attained maximum altitude.

The object was remarkable in other ways. By all odds, it was the best-observed flying saucer in history, and it is one of the most difficult to explain. The observers included a number of distinguished scientists skilled in the art of observation. E. Walter Maunder, Greenwich astronomer and one of the foremost students of the sun, and J. Rand Capron, a well-known spectroscopist, saw the event from England. Observers on the Continent included the Dutch scientists Professors Audemans and Zeeman, of whom the latter eventually received a Nobel prize for his researches on magnetism.

For a description of this phenomenon, let us turn to the account given by Maunder, not the original report that he gave at the time of the event, but one that he wrote almost 34 years later. I have checked the two versions and find that they are consistent with one another.

Professor Maunder entitled his paper "A Strange Celestial Visitor." [1]

In response to the invitation of the Editors of the *Observatory* to furnish some reminiscences to the 500th number of this Magazine, I tried to recall my most striking experiences during the past 43 years, and my memory has gone back to one that stands out from its unlikeness to any other.

It was a quiet and fairly clear evening in the late autumn, and the time was nearly two hours after sunset. The Moon was near her first quarter, and had crossed the meridian a little more than half an hour before. There was, therefore, a fair amount of light in the sky, and the principal stars were clearly seen.

I was at the Royal Observatory, Greenwich, and, as a violent magnetic storm had broken out at about 10ʰ 15ᵐ in the forenoon, was expecting an auroral display. I had therefore taken up my position close to the "Sheep-shanks Dome," on the "Library Leads," as the flat roof over the smaller library was then called, whence I had a view uninterrupted in all direc-tions except for the great dome towards the S.E. Nor was my expectation disappointed, for as the sunset tints faded away in the W.S.W. quarter, a rosy glow, at first hardly to be distinguished from them, spread itself all over the N.W. and gradually strengthened, until about 5.30 P.M. a brilliant ray, mainly of the same red or rosy colour, but with a greenish vein in it, shot up from the horizon in the north and reached the zenith. Other less conspicuous glows and rays showed themselves, but presented no features of special interest.

Then, when the display seemed to be quieting down, a great circular disc of greenish light suddenly appeared low down in the E.N.E., as though it had just risen, and moved across the sky, as smoothly and steadily as the Sun, Moon, stars, and planets move, but nearly a thousand times as quickly. The circularity of its shape when first seen was evidently merely the effect of foreshortening, for as it moved it lengthened out, and when it crossed the meridian and passed just above the Moon its form was that almost of a very elongated ellipse, and various observers spoke of it as "cigar-shaped," "like a torpedo," or "a spindle" or "shuttle." Had the incident occurred in the next century, beyond doubt everyone would have selected the same simile — it would have been "just like a Zeppelin." After crossing the meridian its length seemed to contract, and it disap-peared somewhat to the south of the west point. Its entire passage from rising to setting took less than two minutes to complete, and it disappeared at 6ʰ 5ᵐ 59ˢ G.M.T.

I watched for several hours longer, but no repetition of the phenomenon occurred. A pale greenish glow fringing the upper edge of the great London-smoke cloud in the north was observed, but it showed little, if any, structure or movement.

The "torpedo," on the other hand, was many times brighter than this northern glow, much brighter even than the Great Comet (of 1882) then visible in the early morning sky, and it had a clearly defined outline, but a plain and uniform surface. The greatest length which it presented was about 30°; its breadth was from 2° to 3°. But in colour the light of the "torpedo" was evidently the same as that of the auroral glow in the north, and this showed me in the spectroscope the familiar auroral line in the "citron-green," to which, indeed, its colour was plainly due, a line now considered to be coincident with a prominent line in the spectrum of krypton.*

This "torpedo-shaped" beam of light was unlike any other celestial object that I have ever seen. The quality of its light, and its occurrence

* We now know that the green auroral line comes from oxygen.

while a great magnetic storm and a bright aurora were in progress, seem to establish its auroral origin. But it differed very widely in appearance from any other aurora that I have ever seen. It was unlike auroral shafts and rays, with their glancing, flickering movements so generally radiating from the magnetic north, since its motion was a steady uniform progress from (magnetic) east to west. It was equally unlike auroral "arches" or the auroral "crown," and its clearly defined outline and restricted size differentiated it as distinctly from ordinary diffused auroral glows.

It appeared to be a definite body, and the inference which some observers drew from this was that it was a "meteor," not in the old vague sense of some object high in the Earth's atmosphere, but in the sense of a solid cosmical substance the orbit of which has brought it within the terrestrial atmosphere. But nothing could well be more unlike the rush of a great meteor or fire-ball, with its intense radiance and fiery train, than the steady — though fairly swift — advance of the "torpedo." There was no sign of the compression of the atmosphere before it, no hint that the matter composing its front part was in any way more strongly heated than the rest of its substance — if substance, indeed, it possessed. The gleam of a search-light, focused on a cloud and steadily swept along it, is a more accurate simile for the impression which the appearance produced upon my own mind.

The late Mr. Rand Capron, of Guildford, who made the study of aurorae one of his chief specialties, communicated an interesting discussion [2] of the observations of this singular phenomenon to the *Philosophical Magazine* for 1883 May, pp. 318–339, a paper which I briefly summarized in the *Observatory* for 1883 June (vol. vi, pp. 192, 193). For myself, the "torpedo beam" stands out in my memory, not only as a celestial object unique in my experience, but as associated with the great magnetic storm of 1882 Nov. 17–21, and as synchronizing with the great sunspot group, No. 885 of the Greenwich Photoheliographic Results, the largest I had then observed. From that date onward I had no doubt that in some way or other magnetic disturbances on the Earth were connected with disturbances in the Sun, though it was not until more than twenty years later that the nature of the connection became clear.

J. Rand Capron, F.R.A.S., F.N.S., gave a detailed analysis of all available observations.[3] Capron points out many interesting features of "the auroral beam," as he terms the phenomenon. And indeed several independent arguments suggest that the apparition was of the character of or at least associated with the auroral display that Maunder reported.

First, the month of November 1882 was remarkable for its high degree of magnetic activity (disturbances of the magnetic compass) and for the associated series of auroral storms that appeared over a wide geographic area.

The sun, which we now know to be the source of both auroral and magnetic activity on the earth, was intensely spotted. In fact, one of the largest spots ever recorded up to that time was visible on the surface of the sun.

As Maunder reported, the expectation of seeing a brilliant auroral display had brought out many distinguished observers, who were certainly well repaid for their effort by the sight of the remarkable beam.

Another fortunate circumstance resulted from the expected auroral display. Five students of auroral spectra, including Capron, quickly and independently swung their spectrographs around to get some idea of the colors of light radiated by this object. All seemed to agree that the light was auroral, and showed the characteristic green line — "citron," as some of the observers graphically described the precise tint. In addition, Capron reported a "faint greenish-white continuous spectrum." By that expression he meant that some radiation seemed to be present other than that from a glowing gas. And indeed the range of colors reported by many observers placed as much emphasis on the white as they did on the green shade.

Of course, everyone finds difficult the precise estimation of the color of faint illumination. At night we are all more or less color-blind. Even in brightest moonlight it is difficult to separate flowers according to their shade. A bright aurora, however, will usually appear distinctly green, sometimes with red fringes. Hence the fact that many observers emphasized the "brilliant white" hue of the beam suggests, from the color estimates alone, that we are perhaps overemphasizing the auroral association.

But there is another reason for associating the 1882 beam with auroral activity. A number of observers independently noted that the beam did not swing exactly from east to west along a path parallel to the rising and setting of the stars. The motion was somewhat askew with respect to the geographic north and south and corresponded much more closely to magnetic coördinates. Since the aurora is a magnetic phenomenon, with the positions of the auroral rays, curtains, and arcs dictated by magnetic rather than geographic directions, this triple coincidence of a beam associated with an auroral display, apparently also containing auroral radiation, and conforming to the geometry of the aurora is indeed suggestive.

As for the shape of the beam, the descriptions and similes varied, though they have left little doubt as to the general outline. Near the horizon, the object appeared to be nearly circular, but as it rose higher in the sky it lengthened as previously described (Fig. 10). Then, on setting, the object reverted to the original circular form. It gave the impression of being a roughly cylindrical object some-

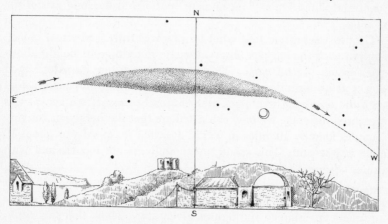

Fig. 10. Sketch of the great saucer of 1882.

thing like an enormous baseball bat hurled directly toward one, parallel to the ground, and overhead. While still at some distance away, the bat looks to be nearly circular. Then it lengthens out as it swings over head and contracts again as it sails away.

The actual words used to describe the shape of the beam varied: "spindle-shaped," "like a torpedo, or weaver's shuttle," "cigar-ship," "lenticular," "like a 'comet's tail,'" or "like a discus seen on edge." – Yes, almost the very words we have sometimes used today: "a flying disk."

The suggested colors were "white," "pearly white," "greenish white," and "yellow white." Various observers described the texture as "glowing." The reports of the detailed structure of the object varied, perhaps, more than any other reported feature. Some of the observers noted no structure at all. Others regarded the outline as clear-cut, with well-defined boundaries. One of the observers from Holland used the adjective "feathery" to indicate that the outline was not quite sharp.

Descriptions of the internal structure also varied, from structure-less uniformity to an actual internal "boiling." One notice called attention to an apparent "rough splintered appearance" of the ends. Many observers, however, saw an internal shadow ranging from "central dullness" to a "dark nucleus" parallel to the long axis of the spindle.

On the assumption that what he saw was truly a physical object, Capron used the various observations to determine its height above the surface of the earth. This study placed the torpedo-shaped object at an altitude of about 130 miles — a value not inconsistent with the observed heights of other auroral forms. If we accept this measured distance, we now can calculate that the body was roughly 70 miles long by 10 miles in width, and that its speed was about 10 miles per second. This speed, incidentally, is not inconsistent with values observed for various meteors.

Although some of the persons watching this phenomenon thought they were seeing a material body, perhaps the 1882 equivalent of the interplanetary saucer, the figures given above show that this could not have been either a single large body or a swarm of small ones. It could not even have consisted of a cloud of "cosmic dust," as a few persons suggested.

A solid body of this size, moving at this speed through the upper air, would have produced a very different type of phenomenon. Its leading edge would have seemed to be on fire and sparks would have showered behind to form a long, luminous trail that would probably have persisted for hours.

The swift, silent motion, performed without any changes of shape ascribable to the motion itself, makes it imperative for us to discard the hypothesis that the body was solid. Similar arguments apply perhaps even more forcefully to liquid objects, which could scarcely persist for any time in interstellar space, without either solidifying or evaporating. Hence we are left with just one possibility: namely, that the luminous region was gaseous — that is, if we are to consider it as being material at all.

We generally accept the idea that great clouds or filaments of gas, shot from the sun, cause the aurora borealis. We have occasionally seen the sun spewing intense clouds of gas into space, and many scientists believe that the aurora occurs when one of these clouds strikes the earth, causing the upper air to glow. For the moment, I see no better alternative than to describe the great saucer of 1882 as some unusual form of auroral activity.

I have studied what happens when a cloud of hot hydrogen gas encounters the earth. The earth's magnetic field tends to concentrate the gas and focus it, by a sort of funnel action, along a parallel of magnetic latitude. The more common form of the aurora consists of a curtain hanging nearly vertically over such a parallel rather than a cigar-shaped beam tunneling its way through. But the beam of 1882 certainly followed a parallel, and the new science of "magneto-hydrodynamics" indicates that such tunneling can occur. The studies further show that the magnetic fields themselves would probably serve to bind together a cloud of gas and temporarily keep it from dispersing or diffusing away, as gas would ordinarily do if no magnetic field were present. Some of the modern ideas will appear in a later chapter.

There is no doubt that the 1882 saucer was very different from the average modern variety, but nonetheless a flying saucer, which term includes a multitude of odd atmospheric apparitions. Condensations and bright auroral beams have appeared with sufficient frequency to cause special comment. I have checked a number of such references and find that what they describe might be luminous auroral fragments, swinging through space as independent units.

One of the earliest phenomena of this type occurred on 12 October 1859, as reported by Charles P. Knight,[4] who observed from Solva, Pembrokeshire, England. Although Mr. Knight uses the word "meteor," we assume that he was using that word in its more general sense, to indicate some phenomenon of the upper air.

I send you an account of the most extraordinary appearance in the sky this evening, which has quite frightened the superstitious here. We had a fine day except two short showers in the afternoon, the wind had been

southeast until this evening when it changed to south; the moon rose in a
nearly cloudless sky; there were scattered rain clouds in the eastern
horizon, and rather a dense bank in the western horizon; a few very light
filmy rain clouds were moving rapidly from southeast to northeast. At
6:30 there was a slight shower, after which the sky was almost cloudless,
the only kind of clouds being a very few rain clouds at a low elevation.
The moon was unusually bright. At 7:20 a brilliant red light appeared to
the south by east, about half-way between the zenith and the horizon, it
looked very much like the red smoke from a port fire, and faded away all
round from a focus of light in the center (its shape was oblong); in
about fifteen minutes it rose to the zenith, and as it rose the red shot up
from it in long streaks on all sides, except to the northeast, but particularly one broad mast that stretched right away to the western horizon, of
a beautiful rose colour all the way; some clouds near the horizon in its
track were coloured purple by it. This may have been either by seeing it
through them, or its being beneath them. The center of the meteor was
now dark crimson, blood red, darker than the clear sky, but the stars
shone brightly through it. The reddest rays were those to the west and
south; those to the south gradually faded to pale green; those to the northwest and north were in more marked and finer lines, and only red near
the center; and a few, after appearing for a short distance pale green,
shot out to the northeast, growing wider apart as they approached the
moon, and passed it, clearly showing that the dark spaces between the
rays could not be shadows caused by the moon. Only one ray to the northeast was red; they were all fainter as they approached the moon, and
much fewer in number than on the western side of the heavens. It lasted
until 8:15; all the red colour gradually faded away, and only left the
focus from which it had sprung still in the zenith; it became pale green,
and then disappeared. The last rays to fade were those to the northeast.
No rain fell during the time it lasted. The air was calm. A good deal of
ground sea coming into the bay from the westward.

A somewhat similar phenomenon was described by Erasmus
Ommanney,[5] 26 August, 1894, from Llanberis, North Wales. He
reports:

I was outside the hotel in Llanberis at 10.30 P.M. admiring the lustre
of the stars — for it was a cloudless night — when, gazing upwards into
the region of Cassiopeia, I was startled by a sudden flash from a brilliant
effulgence of white light situated proximately to the two stars of greatest
magnitude in that constellation, which immediately resolved itself into a
clearly defined disc, about three times the diameter of Jupiter. After a brief
interval I observed a body of brilliant orange colour discharged from the
disc, which was projected directly towards Perseus. This body assumed a
form resembling an elongated flatfish, but terminating in a point, the disc

forming a nucleus to the apparition, which was marvellous to behold; but its visibility proved to be only of short duration, for the white disc, or nucleus, suddenly disappeared, leaving the orange coloured mass quiescent for about half a minute, and then I saw it fade away gradually, and it vanished out of my sight.

The appearance of this strange body did not occupy more than five minutes of time; its dimension in length I estimated was about fifteen degrees of arc. I likewise noticed an important fact — that it evidenced no motion in space.

During my professional career, including Arctic and Equatorial services, a great part was spent in nightly watchings, in which all sorts of meteoric phenomena came under my notice, yet I never beheld one which manifested such marked singularity and distinctiveness combined. I could only regret that no one was at hand to affirm what I saw.

D. E. Packer [6] reported a slightly different though possibly related phenomenon, a connection between an aurora and a meteor. On 14 September, 1908, at 8:40 P.M. on a clear, moonlit night, he was watching an auroral display, which possessed one very spectacular feature,

a bright, horizontal cloud observed stretching across the fore part of Ursa Major, and superposed upon a dark cloud or darkness, so intense as to appear almost black in the general twilight. The bright cloud was in a constant state of fluctuation, flashing up and fading with almost the same rapidity as the well-known scintillation effect observed in bright stars. The colour was a pale white, and, as far as could be judged, the cloud was stationary over the magnetic meridian during the whole period of observation. At 8:45 a meteor from Perseus approached it, and on entering the cloud at its eastern extremity burst out with extraordinary splendour, far surpassing Venus in lustre, and exhibiting a string of many smaller nuclei on each side of the main nucleus. At 8:50 the cloud at this point had thrown out a streamer, which was traceable between Auriga and Perseus into Aries. At 9 P.M. the streamer had faded, and the cloud showed signs of disruption into two separate masses, united by a narrow neck; also there now appeared evidences of other clouds forming in the neighbourhood, less luminous than the main cloud, and more difficult of observation, owing to the increasing moonlight. Subsequently the main cloud became more compact as at first, the fluctuations became less pronounced, and by 9:30 no traces of the phenomenon were visible.

Here are three separate events. Although the accounts of 1859 and 1894 do not mention the aurora specifically, it is significant that intense sunspot activity marked both of these years.

The association with the passage of a meteor suggests one additional way that the great 1882 saucer may have occurred. When a meteor, even a small sand grain, passes through a layer of the upper air it may act like a match, to "ignite" or intensify any faint auroral glow already present. The actual process is complicated, and certainly not one of combustion. But it may very well be related to magnetohydrodynamics as previously described.

Fig. 11. A display of northern lights at Rothenburg, Germany. The oval form at the left suggests that this picture may refer to a saucer similar to that of 1882. The Biblical inscription says "Watch and pray" (Matthew 26:41).

We do not know exactly what happened back in 1882. There are many gaps and uncertainties in our knowledge, but even so I contend that any natural explanation, however incomplete and tentative it may be, is highly preferable to one that invokes the aid of fairies, ghosts — or interplanetary saucers. Saucers, mind you, 100 miles long!

I have sometimes wondered whether the reported "great green fireballs" of New Mexico might be auroral phenomena related to the 1882 beam. I conclude, however, that they are not. Most of the green fireballs are probably meteors and the rest will be a type of mirage or reflection saucer. On some occasions the green glow of a faint aurora borealis seen on the northern horizon may be turned downward and focused by air lenses or by ice crystals to produce an elevated saucer. And indeed, if this were done, the resulting saucer would certainly display the characteristic auroral green. But the aurora borealis is a rare phenomenon in New Mexico, since this state is so far from the magnetic pole. Hence intense auroral displays with saucers resulting from that kind of activity will be extremely rare. As for the green fireball variety, we shall consider them in more detail in Chapter 18.

8

The unknown lights of Japan

My search of the literature has uncovered a most startling and descriptive article in one of the standard scientific magazines,[1] which contains data important to the understanding of the saucer problem.

The article tells of lights that followed a ship throughout the night. Since the lights were multiple, one might say that they vaguely resembled the previously mentioned "Lubbock Lights," although in my opinion they bore even closer relation to the "foo fighters." A ship cannot dodge or parry like an airplane. It docilely accepts almost any circumstance that it encounters. The story, "An Atmospheric Phenomenon in the North China Sea," written by Charles J. Norcock, is interesting enough to reprint in its entirety. Note especially the location, near Korea. Also note that the phenomenon occurred on the 24th of February, when the oceans were still extremely cold, although somewhat warmer breezes might have been blowing from the land.

During a recent wintry cruise in H.M.S. *Caroline* in the North China Sea, a curious phenomenon was seen which may be of interest to your readers. The ship was on passage between Shanghai and the western entrance of the famous inland sea of Japan. On 24th February, at 10 P.M., when in latitude 32° 58′ N., longitude 126° 33′ E., which, on reference to the map, will be seen to be sixteen to seventeen miles south of Quelpart island (south of the Korean peninsula), some unusual lights were reported by the officer of the watch between the ship and Mount Auckland, a mountain 6,000 feet high. It was a windy, cold, moonlight night. My first impression was that they were either some fires on shore, apparently higher from the horizon than a ship's masthead, or some junk's "flare up" lights raised by mirage. To the naked eye they appeared sometimes as a mass; at others spread out in an irregular line, and, being globular in form, they resembled Chinese lanterns festooned between the masts of a lofty vessel. They bore north (magnetic) and remained on that bearing until lost sight of about midnight. As the ship was passing the land to the eastward at the rate of seven knots an hour, it soon became obvious that the lights were not on the land, though observed with the mountain behind them.

On the following night, February 25th, about the same time, 10 P.M., the ship, having cleared Port Hamilton, was steering east, on the parallel of 34°, when these curious lights were again observed on the same bearing, at an altitude of 3° or 4° above the horizon. It was a clear, still, moonlight night, and cold. On this occasion there was no land in sight on a north bearing when the lights were first observed, but soon afterwards a small islet was passed, which for the time eclipsed the lights. As the ship steamed on at a rate of seven knots an hour, the lights maintained a constant bearing (magnetic) of N. 2° W., as if carried by some vessel travelling in the same direction and at the same speed. The globes of fire altered in their formation as on the previous night, now in a massed group, with an outlying light away to the right, then the isolated one would disappear, and the others would take the form of crescent or diamond, or hang festoon-fashion in a curved line. A clear reflection or glare could be seen on the horizon beneath the lights. Through a telescope the globes appeared to be of a reddish colour, and to emit a thin smoke.

I watched them for several hours, and could distinguish no perceptible alteration in their bearing or altitude, the changes occurring only in their relative formation, but each light maintained its oval, globular form.

They remained in sight from 10 P.M. until daylight (about 5.30 A.M.). When lost sight of, the bearing was one or two points to the westward of north. At daylight, land 1,300 feet high was seen to the north and north-north-west, distant fifty miles, the mirage being extraordinary.

Thus, these lights were seen first on longitude 126° 33′ E., and last on longitude 128° 29′ E. At first the land was behind them, but during the greater part of the distance run it was forty-five or fifty miles away to the north; and the bearing of the lights for at least three-fourths of the distance did not change.

On arrival at Kobe I read in a daily paper that the "Unknown lights of Japan" had, as was customary at this season of the year when the weather is very cold, stormy, and clear, been observed by fishermen in the Shimbara Gulf and Japanese waters. The article went on to say that these lights were referred to in native school-books, and attributed to electrical phenomena. On mentioning the matter, however, to the leading Europeans in Yokohama and Tokio, they appeared to have no knowledge of the matter.

Captain Castle of H.M.S. *Leander*, informed me that, not long ago, the officers of his ship saw lights in the same locality which they thought at first were caused by a ship on fire. The course of the vessel was altered at once with a view of rendering assistance, but finding that the lights increased their altitude as he approached, he attributed them to some volcanic disturbance, and being pressed for time, resumed his course.

The background of high land seen on the first night dispels all idea of these extraordinary lights being due to a distant volcano. The uniformity of the bearing renders the theory of their being fires on the shore most improbable. I am inclined to the belief that they were something in the nature of St. Elmo's fires. It is probable that there are travellers among the readers of your interesting journal who have seen or heard of this phenomenon and will be able to describe its origin and the atmospheric conditions necessary for its appearance.

I should perhaps mention that I discovered the above reference only after I had developed my own theories about the nature of flying saucers. In view of the emphasis that I have set on "looming mirages," I call special attention to the fact that an exceptional mirage seemed to accompany the mysterious "Lights of Japan."

The recorded behavior of many of the saucers, but especially the foo balls — which term I use to designate the docile variety of lights that tend to accompany a plane on its travels — suggests very strongly the behavior of the lights that followed H.M.S. *Caroline*.

This behavior, in turn, suggests something that many people have noticed and perhaps have even commented on at some time during their lives. While riding on a train or in an automobile at night, looking out at the moon, have you not sometimes had the impression that the moon is following you? Indeed, the landscape lying between you and the distant horizon, whatever its character may be, seems to be swishing past at a rate that blurs your sense of perception. The fields, the nearby shrubbery, the telephone poles flash by before you have a chance to see what they actually are. But if there is a moon, it too seems to follow along, pacing you while forests, rivers, and bridges rush madly past.

I suppose that children are more sensitive to this phenomenon than grown-ups, because the average person has become used to it, even though he does not fully understand it. If you put a toy balloon out the window of the car and hold the string, the moon and the balloon will have much in common. They keep pace with one another while the intermediate country flashes past. In fact, if the balloon is small enough, you can scarcely distinguish it from the moon. Your sense of perspective may help if the balloon is near enough. But if the balloon is, say, 20 or 30 feet away, you will not be able to tell, at least from a single point of observation, which of the two objects is the nearer, unless you are able to identify one or the other from surface markings or other characteristics.

What I am saying is simply this. The moon seems to dash after you at the same mad rate that a balloon or any other object would, if attached to your moving vehicle, be it automobile, train, plane, or even yourself.

Suppose, for example, that, instead of putting a balloon out of the window, you merely set a mirror there — a mirror that catches and reflects the moonlight. You can reach out and touch the mirror. You have a sense as to the position of the image. As I shall show later, this sensation of distance where mirrors are concerned is entirely illusory. But in any case, let us say that you can see both the moon and its image. Unless you know that the mirror is there, you will not be able to tell which is the moon and which is the image; they both behave so similarly. Indeed, if you are driving a car, and the image of the moon comes from a window, a mirror, or a fender, the image will possess many characteristics that the moon itself does. You could readily convince yourself that the moon is "riding along on one of the fenders of your car."

Some people would say that this phenomenon is an optical illusion. I would not class it as such, because there is really no simple way of telling which object is real and which the mirror image. I have, of course, assumed that the two are essentially imaged perfectly. If you can get an illusion that the image is near, you can certainly get the impression that the moon itself is close — if you do not immediately recognize it as the moon, for example.

One of the top advisers to the Air Force told me the following story. Our pilots in Korea have occasionally seen, riding along on the wings of their planes, the same sort of foo balls or foo fighters that our pilots observed over Germany and Japan during the last stages of World War II. A scientific mission sent specially to study these foo balls, to find out if possible what they were, spent many hours in the air, waiting in vain for one of the mysterious lights to put in its appearance. After many nights of fruitless search, one of the crew members suddenly called out, "Foo ball at three o'clock low!" The science mission dashed to the window and looked out.

Sure enough! There was a yellow-orange ball, hanging just below the wing tip. They called for a turn to get a better look and suddenly realized that the foo ball was — only the rising moon. This expedition completed its mission and returned to the United States without even having seen a single foo fighter. Was this seeming avoidance of the investigating mission something deliberate on the part of the foo fighters? Were these mysterious objects apprised of the expedition's arrival so that they could adopt the tactic of nonappearance as the best defense, in order to retain their secrets?

I do not want to imply that any appreciable number of the foo fighters are only mistaken apparitions of the moon. Some of them, no doubt, can be attributed to reflections of the moon in the wings.

I think that the time of occurrence of these objects carries its own implication. Note that, over Germany and Japan, they appeared only during the *last stages* of World War II. Many of the planes participating in bomber missions were, by this time, partially damaged and considerably patched. Some of these battle scars were by no means as aerodynamically perfect as the original wings had been. Little eddies formed around them, whirlpools that were ready to partially reflect some of the light falling upon them, whether from the moon in the sky or from the plane's own illumination.

When air is cold and supersaturated, a sudden increase of pressure can cause fog or ice crystals to form. The tiny suspended particles will reflect enough light to make the globule seem to be luminous.

In many cases where fine ice crystals or tiny snowflakes are already present, each individual particle is ready to act as a mirror — if we look at it from the right direction. These tiny flakes are often invisible unless viewed by special means, because they all tend to fall horizontally. Thus, if the moon were halfway between horizon and zenith, we should see its reflection only if we were to face the moon and look at a point 45° below the horizon, as if we were looking in a sheet of water.

But if a plane, a ship, a car, or any other moving object were to disturb the tiny mirrors, the effect would be something like breaking a true mirror into thousands of little pieces. The true reflection would be tremendously reduced in brilliance, but in any other direction a fraction of the original luminosity would appear. And so the foo ball originates — reflections in myriads of tiny mirrors of ice crystals or water droplets!

As long as one moves along steadily forward, the reflected light from a foo ball follows automatically. However, as Fig. 12 will show, for every turn of, say, 10°, the reflected image appears at twice this angle, or 20°. An angle of 45° produces a deflection of 90°, and so on. Hence, if a man sees a foo fighter and tries to run away from it, the reflection will veer at exactly twice the rate that he turns his plane. This turning rate will reflect his own skill at controlling the plane.

Here is a fairly simple demonstration of what I am saying. Hold a hand mirror or the mirror from a compact firmly against your forehead. Stand in front of a source of bright light, bright enough that its reflection appears clearly on the wall in front of you. Face the source so that the reflected light goes directly back toward that source. Now, continuing to hold the mirror in place against

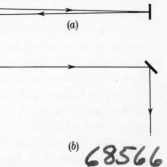

(a)

(b)

68566

Fig. 12. (a) A mirror set at right angles to the beam sends light rays backward in the direction they came from. (b) A mirror set at 45° reflects the beam at 90°, or twice the angle that the mirror has turned through.

your forehead, slowly turn your head to one side or the other and you will find that the reflection moves on twice as fast as you turn your head. It is this property of an image as compared with the source of light that confuses the operator of a plane with respect to a foo ball.

On some occasions the foo fighters may well be a mirage. In Chapter 1, I told of an experience of my own, one in which several ghostly images seemed to fly close to the moon. At no time during the actual experience did I have the illusion that these objects were close at hand, perhaps near enough for me to touch. And yet, as I recall what happened as I rode along in the car, looking at the moon rising over Sacramento Peak and seeing these two ghostly objects, why should I have been spared the illusion that they were close rather than extremely far away? As I have thought over the

proposition, I have decided that the primary reason was their nearness to the moon, and their tendency to chase along after the moon.
Although I thought of them as being very distant, they might just
as well have been attached to the car, because they followed it
just as well as they did the moon. They might have been a reflection
in the window, except for the fact that I had already opened the
window; a reflection in my spectacles, except for the fact that I
considered that possibility and swung my head back and forth to
check.

But the apparition might very well have been a foo ball, or rather
two foo balls, attached to the car. I suspect that our car was moving
under some thin layer of haze, perhaps tilting or deforming the
layer so that the moon would be imaged in the bumps. This theory
would also explain why the pair of ghostly attendants faded at the
moment we stopped the car; the reflecting bumps would then disappear. The situation is not unlike that of a person riding in a fast
motorboat. He might see the moon reflected in the bow wave thrown
up by the boat. But the reflection would vanish when the boat
stopped.

On another occasion, I should try such tactics as driving the car
back, stopping it several times, climbing out and getting back in
again, and even waving my own hand to see whether I could induce
a tilting of the haze layer to give the effect of a mirror surface close
to me. I do not know whether any of these processes would work
or not. That would depend upon how far away the reflecting layer
was. But I am now completely convinced that what I saw was merely
a reflection of the moon, a sort of a mirage, but one in which the
reflecting layer was close at hand, despite the fact that the source
of light and, therefore, the effective image, were very distant. If
the intervening terrain had been wooded, to give the illusion of
rapid motion, rather than the empty desert, I might very well have
had the impression that the foo fighters were indeed speeding
along after the car, like the foo balls of the planes.

After this interim argument, turn again to the log of H.M.S.
Caroline and note several specific points. Although the almanac
shows that moonlight did not persist through the night, the appearance of these lights in the direction of magnetic north again

suggests the aurora borealis. The source of light was probably just the aurora, probably a fairly distant aurora whose full brilliance was not visible from the ship, even though "a clear reflection or glare could be seen on the horizon beneath the lights." This light, reflected in a thin layer of frost crystals, could have produced the effect.

The persistence of the marked mirage into the morning strongly suggests that the low-lying illumination of the bright horizon had been raised in the sky. Indeed the reported altitude of 3° or 4° is large but by no means exceptional. The disappearance of the lights when the island intervened is quite understandable. The nearby land would have temporarily interrupted the mirage, through production of convection currents as well as by occultation of the distant source of illumination.

The description seems to rule out the suggestion made by the observer himself, namely, that the lights represented some sort of electrical disturbance, such as St. Elmo's fire.

In addition to these foo balls associated with planes and ships, I have found references to similar occurrences seen from trains. For example, a railroad postal clerk reported [2] that he and an associate had seen a light, dull rose in color, which followed after the train. The speed was variable, but nevertheless the light moved along behind the train, sometimes losing and sometimes gaining distance.

The night was dark and a heavy rain was falling. Such atmospheric conditions are, of course, not conducive to the formation of an ordinary mirage. However, raindrops — like the eyes of animals — seem to be self-luminous in the dark and send back a considerable amount of light in the direction from which the light originally came.

This experience suggests another source of foo-ball origin. In fact, given either rain or fog, the light reflected directly backward will give a surprising imitation — if one changes course — of seeming to follow after. Thus anyone seeing the illumination might well gain the impression that someone out there in the dark was trying to parry the motion. More of this phenomenon will appear in Chapter 14.

I have found one reference to a Canadian incident,[3] where an old woman, walking along a country lane at night, reported that a ball of fire followed her, stopping whenever she stopped, and moving on as she moved. Although the data for complete evaluation of this event are not given, it clearly belongs in the foo-ball category.

Both newspapers and scientific literature of the past contain what seem to be countless references to mysterious lights in the sky — lights of all different sorts and origins, each of which produced its own sensation as it occurred.

About the time of our Civil War "The False Lights of Durham" caused considerable concern over a period that lasted nearly two years. Mysterious lights occasionally appeared off the coast of Durham, England, where treacherous shoals abounded. Many of these lights, according to the records, enticed ships to destruction and, as wreck after wreck occurred, authorities finally conducted a full-scale investigation.

They accused some fishermen of setting the false lights but the fishermen pointed out that many of the ships reported to be wrecked were in bad shape and that their value for insurance was far greater than for transport. Feelings ran high as one investigation succeeded another. But finally the matter was dropped. Everyone agreed that the affair was "mysterious," but no one understood exactly what had taken place. We know now that mirage was probably responsible.

"The Luminous Owls of Norfolk," seen about the same time, were probably another instance of mirage. And yet the populace lined up to see these mysterious luminous birds flying in the vicinity of Norfolk.

Throughout the 19th century many objects were seen in France and reported in the scientific literature. Here are translations of a few of the more significant ones.

Saturday, October 28, near Luzarches about 4:30 in the afternoon, the setting sun shone through the tops of tall trees. Although the sky was clear at the zenith, a band of heavy gray clouds stretched almost to the horizon. This cloud band, which appeared to be moving rapidly from southwest to northeast, carried the rose tints of the sunset at its edges. On the uniform gray background near the horizon, a globe of the same rose color as the cloud's edges detached itself and began to move with the same speed and direction as the large cloud. It seemed closer to the ground than to the cloud's lighted edge and it had about the same angular spread as the moon.

The globe grazed — or rather seemed to graze — the tops of trees near the horizon. I followed its motion for nearly 15 minutes, during which time its color remained essentially constant. As it reapproached the horizon toward the west, its size diminished slowly until nothing but a point remained. The weather was hot, humid, and somewhat stormy." [4]

On November 1, 1886, some observers in Constantinople were astounded to see an oval, highly luminous body five or six times the size of the moon, seemingly floating in the air. It was bright enough to "light the camp near the station."

The following morning, about dawn, they saw a "luminous flame, shining first with a blue radiation and later changing to green, moving around the dock near a ferry boat. It lighted houses and streets for a full minute and a half. Then it fell into the sea, soundlessly." Estimates of the height of the light varied from 15 to 20 feet. [5]

M. Callandreau, observing from Vannes at 8:40 P.M., 3 January 1898, saw a very interesting object which he reported, from want of a better description, as a "double meteor, of a very low speed." He had time to examine it in the telescope; because of its slowness, it took 5 to 6 minutes to cross the small angle of 45° from northeast to north.

The telescope showed that the two bodies were of unequal size or brightness, the larger proceeding with a wobbling motion, the smaller more steadily. According to Callandreau's description, it appeared to be "two balloons of light tied to one another." He reported having seen a somewhat similar phenomenon back in 1863. [6]

In addition to the foregoing, the French literature contains numerous references to what was popularly called a "flying gas-jet." The descriptions of some of these bodies clearly suggest that we have here to deal with a phenomenon analogous to that of the flying saucer of today. A saucer by any other name is still a saucer.

Richard S. Lambert recently reviewed Canadian legends relative to flying saucers, [7] the "feux follets" or "fi-follets" — fire spirits — names attached to lights seen wavering in unexpected places. The superstitious and often illiterate natives thought that the objects were souls of men, themselves actually living but spending the hours of night in the service of the devil. He who chanced to encounter one

would surely die. The French word *feu*, or fire, is probably responsible for the American word "foo."

Another story of considerable interest appears in *Fur Hunters of
the Far West*, a book by Alexander Ross published in 1855. It is a
tale of daring adventure in a ship along the shores of Lake Superior.
Three "foo fighters," balls of pale red fire, hung on the masts of the
vessel and in the rigging for fully half an hour during a storm. Some
persons have attributed this observation to a sort of brush discharge
of lightning called "St. Elmo's fire," but we do not have enough data
for a decision. In many cases, the effect is undoubtedly electrical,
but mirages are probably responsible for others.

Lambert also reports the weird case of the "Marsh Point Ghosts,"
which appeared near Cornwall, Ontario, in 1845, Marsh Point was an
island separated from the mainland by a canal. One night in
September, a farmer passing by on the mainland noticed some
peculiar lights flitting around a house on the Point, one inhabited by
two elderly women. Thinking that the unseasonable lights perhaps
indicated serious illness, he went down to the Point the following
morning, to inquire after the health of the inhabitants. He was surprised to find not only that both were well, but that they had not
seen anything of the lights.

For quite a time the lights were a sensation in the Marsh Point
district. The local people would band together to watch and check
the appearance of the luminous objects. Sometimes they occurred in
considerable numbers, and seemed to be playing a sort of game,
chasing after one another on the ground and then rapidly running
up to the top of a tree and later descending.

A most frightening occurrence happened when one of the lights
left its associates, crossed the canal, and ascended to the top of a tall
tree. Then, after a time, the light descended again, went back
across the canal, and rejoined its comrades, "which gathered about
it like a lot of gossips to hear the news; or like friends gathering
about a returned traveller to offer congratulation for safe arrival."
No one ever solved the mystery of the Marsh Point ghosts, probably
because the investigators were themselves so afraid that they would
not dare venturing into the zone where the spirits were disporting
themselves. But, had they done so, I suspect that they would have

seen the lights moving on ahead, as lights from mirages usually do,
and that the Point would have been deserted as they arrived.

As for somewhat older reports, we have the following:

From time to time the west coast of Wales seems to be the scene of
mysterious lights. In the fifteenth century, and again on a larger scale in
the sixteenth, considerable alarm was created by fire that rose "out of the
sea." Writing in January, 1694, the Rector of Dolgelley stated that 16
ricks of hay and two barns had been burned by "a kindle exhalation which
was often seen to come from the sea." Passing over other alleged appearances in March, 1875, a letter by the late Mr. Picton Jones appeared in
"Bygones," page 198, giving an account of curious lights which he had
witnessed at Pwllheli, and now we have a statement from Towyn that
within the last few weeks, "lights of various colours have frequently been
seen moving over the estuary of the Dysynni river and out at sea. They
are generally in a northern direction, but sometimes they hug the shore,
and move at a high velocity for miles towards Aberdovey, and suddenly
disappear." Can any authorities upon natural phenomena furnish further
information on this subject? [8]

9

"Strange signes from Heaven"

▀▀▀

The farther back one tries to trace saucers, the more confused the record becomes. Part of the difficulty, of course, arises because original records are difficult to find. But the most important reason is that early observers of meteorological phenomena lump together anything seen in the atmosphere as "a meteor." The fact that we still call anything having to do with the atmosphere "meteorology" recalls this early usage. Nowadays we rarely apply the term meteor to other than a "shooting star." But if the early observers made any distinction at all, it was between "aerial meteors," which included objects like whirlwinds; "aqueous meteors," which covered fog, rain, hail, snow, and clouds; and "luminous meteors," which included, in addition to shooting stars, lightning bolts, flying saucers, the aurora borealis, and even comets.

With such spectacular phenomena as comets, bright fireballs, lightning, solar halos, and even eclipses to compete with, the flying saucers had little chance — unless they proved to be exceptional. Thus, whenever we do find an apparition whose description identifies it clearly as a flying saucer, the details are sometimes more useful than those of more modern ones because of their vividness.

However, the imagination of the observer was often a hindrance to accurate presentation. We have to remember that these early observers were ignorant, and generally illiterate. Even the most intelligent people of the times, say in the early 17th century, had no idea what a comet really was. Their textbooks described it as an "exhalation of the earth." Superstitious people believed that any celestial apparition was a sign from Heaven, presaging some unusual event on the earth — death, war, pestilence, or even the end of the world. Thus fortunetellers, oracles, and soothsayers flourished, preying upon the superstitious ignorance of their fellow men.

Increase Mather, in the early 1680's, gave a series of sermons to his Puritan flock in Massachusetts, in which he tried to prove that strange heavenly apparitions did presage terrible events. He took special issue with the scriptural passage from Jeremiah,[1] "Thus saith the Lord, Learn not the way of the heathen, and be not dismayed at the signs of heaven; for the heathen are dismayed at them." Instead, Mather expounded "Heaven's Alarm to the World," calling comets "God's sharp razors on mankind, whereby he doth poll, and his scythe whereby he doth shear down multitudes of sinful creatures. . . Doth God threaten our very heavens? O pray unto him, that he would not take away stars and send comets to succeed them."

And as Isaac Newton, in England, began to establish order in the universe through his law of gravitation, Increase Mather tried to counter the suggestion that "signs" were natural phenomena. As proof of his contention,[2] he refers to the total solar eclipse of 1682, when Harvard College "was eclipsed by the death of the learned president there, Mr. Chauncey; and two colonies — namely, Massachusetts and Plymouth — by the death of two governors, who died within a twelvemonth after. . . Shall, then, such mighty works of God as comets are be insignificant things?"

But signs of the times prevailed over signs in the heavens. And by 1726 we find Increase Mather's famous son, Cotton, taking issue with the father. "Perhaps there may be some need for me to caution you against being dismayed at the signs of the heavens, or having any superstitious fancies upon eclipses and the like . . . I am willing that you be apprehensive of nothing portentous in blazing stars. For my part, I know not whether all our worlds, and even the sun itself, may not fare the better for them."

Thus, by degrees, comets, eclipses, halos, and other "meteors" came under natural law, as part of an ordered universe. We shall find that flying saucers will follow the same pattern.

In my search for literature about saucers, I found one small book that throws a great deal of light upon the reactions of our ancestors to mysterious apparitions. The full title of this book, which I have used in abbreviated form as a title for this chapter, is "STRANGE SIGNES FROM HEAVEN; Seene and Heard in *Cambridge*, *Suffolke*, and *Norfolke*, in and upon the 21 day of May last past in the afternoone, 1646. *MIRACULOUS WONDERS* seene at *Barn-*

stable, Kirkham, Cornwall, and *Little Britain,* in *London.* Where-
unto is annexed *SEVERALL APPARITIONS,* seene in the aire, at
the *Hague* in *Holland,* upon the 21/31 day of May last past, about
one of the clocke in the afternoone." These signs, so the introduction
states, are specifically "to warne and awaken the Eastern Association, with the Southerne Parts of the Kingdom."

The text begins: *

Incredulity hath always been the forerunner of misery ever since the
Creation; the old World would not be warned by Noah's building the
Ark until the flood came. Pharaoh would not be warned by God's Judgments till he was swallowed up of the Red Sea . . . The Lord, who is
slow to wrath and of much mercy, gave Signs from Heaven unto the
Jews, to forewarn them of their approaching destruction, but they regarded it not. The *Blazing Star* seen in our Horizon so many years ago,
which began towards *Germany,* fetched its compass to *Ireland,* and whose
blazing bush tail hung over *England,* was but a nine days wonder, although those countries hath since found the effects thereof, the Almighty
divert his Judgments from us if it be his will, which we may justly fear
hangeth over our heads, by reason of our continual crying sins, notwithstanding the many tokens of his anger showed unto us by strange and
fearful apparitions seen in the air (the 21 of May last past) in many parts.

About *New-Market,* in the county of *Cambridge,* there were seen by
diverse honest, sober, and civil persons, and men of good credit, three
men in the air, striving, struggling, and tugging together, one of them
having a drawn sword in his hand, from which Judgment God in his
mercy preserve these three Kingdoms of *England, Scotland,* and *Ireland,*
from further conflicts and effusion of blood.

Betwixt *New-Market* and *Thetford* in the County of *Norfolk,* there was
observed a pillar or cloud to ascend from the earth, with the bright hilts
of a sword toward the bottom of it, which pillar did ascend in a pyramidal
form, and fashioned itself into the form of a spire or broach steeple, and
there descended also out of the sky the form of a pike or lance, with a
very sharp head or point to encounter with it.

Also at a distance, there appeared another Spear or Lance, with a very
acute point out of the Sky . . . The first Spear which came down from
Heaven point blank, was after a while clean elevated higher, and that
spire or spear which went up from the earth, ascended after it, to encounter with it the second time.

This continued about an hour and a half.

At *Sopham,* in the County of *Cambridge* aforesaid, a ball of wild-fire

---

* I use modern spelling to simplify reference.

fell upon the earth, which burnt up and spoiled about an Acre of Grain, and when it had rolled and run up and down to the terror of many people and some townsmen that see it, it dissolved and left a most sulphurous stink behind it. . .

Also at *Brandon* in the County aforesaid, was seen at the same time, a Navy or Fleet of Ships in the Air, swiftly passing under sail, with Flags and Streamers hanged out, as if they were ready to give an encounter. . .

In all these places there was very great thunder, with rain and hail stones of extraordinary bigness and round, and some hollow within like rings.

The Lord grant that all the people of this Kingdom may take heed to every warning Trumpet of his, that we may speedily awaken out of our sins, and truly turn to the Lord, fight his battles against our spiritual enemies, and get those inward riches of which we cannot be Plundered of, and so seek an inward Kingdom of Righteousness and Peace.

The book tells the punishment brought down upon a Mrs. Haughton, who swore, "I pray God that rather than I shall be a Round-head, or bear a Round-head, I may bring forth a child without a head." The term "Round-head," as she used it, applied to the Separists, a political religious movement in the government.

The book goes on to state that her child did not live, but rumors about its physical appearance attained such proportions that the minister of the parish finally "caused the grave to be opened, and the child to be taken up and laid to view, and found there a body without an head . . . only the child had a face upon the breast of it, two eyes near unto the place where the paps usually are, and a nose upon the chest, and a mouth a little above the navel, and two ears, upon each shoulder one." The book concludes with a description of strange sights seen in Holland on the same day.

First, came a little round thing about the bigness of a table or board, like unto grey paper: and without it was seen the likeness of a Lion and a Dragon which furiously fought together, which Dragon after a while did spit fire furiously, but was overcome by the Lion; and yet the Lion appeared in sight.

2. Appeared by the Lion a multitude of soldiers, with another Dragon likewise, and with a multitude of soldiers both foot and horse . . . and the lion and the dragon continued still in sight.

3. There appeared also a King with three Crowns on his head, . . . but the Lion and Dragon abode still in sight.

4. There appeared also a number of peoples heads, and one great

head amongst them: and a multitude of bodies without heads which vanished away, yet the Lion and Dragon abode as before continuing in sight.

5. There appeared yet likewise one man sitting upon a horse, which shot himself through (as with a pistol) and fell backward, and so vanished away.

Lastly, there appeared a mighty fleet of ships in the Southeast, by the Lion and the Dragon, where the fight was, with a multitude of men aboard the ships, with half their bodies to be seen above board, which we saw perfectly hoisting up their sails, and driving to and fro, and as it were continued all standing still, till the Lion and the Dragon embraced one another and so fell backward, and disappeared; whereupon there appeared a great cloud which was not there before, and so drove away with the wind.

This curious collection of natural and entirely fictitious phenomena — for the incident of a child without a head appears to be highly questionable — illustrates the reaction of people to strange events.

Remember that these objects reported as visible in the sky must have been unusual. They occurred in the daytime and hence do not refer to the aurora borealis. The widespread apparition of the spears, lances, or steeples, clearly suggests an atmospheric condition rather than a peculiar cloud formation. The phenomenon was probably a solar halo, accompanied by mock suns, produced by ice crystals in high-level cirrus clouds in the air.

The "ball of wild-fire" was probably a lightning bolt or one of the sun dogs, an image brought to earth by optical illusion characteristic of some types of reflection. The "little round thing" was the first appearance of a mock sun, a single flying saucer. The apparition grew to a full-scale display of circles and crowns, as will be discussed further in Chapters 10 and 15.

Fully as important as the nature of the apparitions is the apparent fright of the people at seeing something unknown: "Strange Signes in the Skye," forecasting dire events. Sometimes the predicted retribution was long delayed, but eventually it came, even after three years, so say some of the records.

Among the ancient volumes that I have consulted to find references about flying saucers, the most outstanding was one by a Jesuit,

Franz Reinzer, *Meteorologia Philosophico-Politica* (Philosophical and Political Meteorology), published in Augsburg in 1709.

This remarkable book discusses all kinds of "meteors," and gives directions to the "Politicus," in other words, a high-ranking statesman, how to act under the various circumstances and turn these strange apparitions to his own advantage. The basic theme of this meteorological philosophy seems to be that when someone loses a battle, someone else must win. Hence, if a sign appears in the sky, regard it as a bad omen for your enemies but a good omen for yourself, and hold yourself in readiness to take advantage of the developing situation. Thus, in the meteorological sense, Reinzer is preaching the doctrine that "it's an ill wind that blows nobody good."

Apparently this book enjoyed wide popularity, for the original Latin was soon translated into medieval German. It is, moreover, beautifully illustrated with wood engravings, a number of which I reproduce here. From the fact that Reinzer rarely makes statements of scientific import, or even gives detailed descriptions of the observed phenomena, one judges that his concern was much more with philosophy than with nature. To each phenomenon he gives a moral as well as a natural interpretation. Consequently, the book has no great scientific significance, other than indicating the trend of the times. He quotes many authorities, including one D. Menzelius — flying saucer authority — perhaps an ancestor of mine.

Reinzer himself poses the question, "Do meteors come from natural causes or do they forbode something?" And then he neatly sidesteps giving any well-reasoned answer. He describes some natural phenomena:

A statesman sees how the sky darkens and how cloudbursts descend 'midst great thunder and lightning. He sees how the moon and stars become eclipsed. He learns how dragons fly and how fountains of fire spurt their glowing sparks. Lightning shines terribly. Comets appear. Swords and lances flash in the clouds. The sky opens and pours forth a deluge.

When the statesman sees such strange happenings should he not be afraid? No! These apparitions and events are only 'love-kisses' of the sky. No matter what appears, everything is for the best, all to some useful purpose. Fear of thunderstorms or meteors denotes weakness.

Even though Reinzer adopts this attitude for the statesman, he nevertheless points out that history itself bears witness to the fact that strange sights in the sky forbode terrible happenings on the earth.

Apparently the year 1462 was outstanding for its strange celestial warnings. Someone saw "a monk who fought with a king and after

Fig. 13. Fiery meteors in great abundance. A comet, a halo around the moon, a flying dragon over the house, shooting stars, and other lights in the sky.

Fig. 14. A pillar of fire, flaming arrows, and all kinds of fearful lights. Some of these apparitions are undoubtedly comets and shooting stars.

a while was vanquished and fell down from the sky. This strange apparition occurred in the vicinity of the moon. And in the selfsame year, in small Poland, a crucifix and shifting sword, which caused great consternation among the people, whereupon terrible robberies and lootings and other evil things occurred in Poland."

Here we might add, parenthetically, that the crucifix and sword commonly accompany an exhibition of mock suns.

"But," asks Reinzer, "if one sees in the air such sights which forebode the spilling of blood, how can the statesman avoid this bad luck that seems to beset the entire country?" Reinzer has a simple answer:

Arrows seen in advance can do little harm. Take heed of the warning in the sky. Terrifying and frightening as it seems, it really is not so terrible after all.

As an instance, he cites the fact that

in 1478 in Switzerland, the populace saw a fight in the air, followed, two months later, with all sorts of crosses and fiery balls striking the earth and leaving behind them invisible signs to baffle the curious, as Lycosthenes tells in the Basle Chronicles. In the very same year the Swiss had a great victory over the Prince of Milan, vanquishing 1,400 of their enemies and finding rich loot.

Bad as this omen was for the Prince, it was a good omen for the Swiss, primarily because it appeared in Switzerland. The author fails to point out the apparent conflict in his logic concerning the lootings in Poland. But, after all, one should not expect individuals to show greater logic in 1600 than we do ourselves today, as in the matter of flying saucers.

Reinzer describes many interesting phenomena, but mostly in political terms. He mentions the double sun and interprets it as a reflection, illustrating the phenomenon by the analogy of a mirror. He states that a battle under such a sun takes greater courage than even Hercules possessed, since he never fought against odds.

Reinzer talks about flying and falling stars and says that a real meteor is not something moving after all but something burning like a flame consuming a thread, moving uniformly along the thread as it burns. He further compares the formation of a shooting star to the progress of a flame along a trail of gunpowder. And then he addresses the statesman: "The more it rains, the greater the threats and menaces, the greater should be the love sparks which you yourself irradiate." It seems that he tried to transfer the natural characteristics of any atmospheric phenomenon to man and at the same time to endow the "meteor" with human or moral characteristics. His reasoning is hard for us to follow, but a few more references will explain its meaning.

He says, "Fire observed on the head and clothing of people, on their hair, or on the fur of animals, is not a true fire but imitation. Such an appearance is regarded by the ancient philosophers as a sign of great happiness, a sort of exhalation from the free spirit of animals."

Reinzer recognized that these mock fires might come from within as well as from without. "They may be due," he says, "not only to

natural emotion, or anger, or excessive drinking of wine, but also to
fever and illness. Thus a person, seeing 'spots before his eyes,' may
view them as luminous spots against the sky." But he did not explain
how to distinguish between these mock fires from within and the
lights that come from without, except to identify the latter as
"flying dragons."

Fig. 15. Ships with ancient foo
fighters attached. The one in the foreground has two lights, and thus is under the protection of Castor and Pollux, the twins shown in the star. The
distant ship has but one light, and
thus falls under the evil influence of
Helena, sister of Castor and Pollux.
This ship is clearly in distress.

Fig. 16. A real dragon on the
ground, with luminous dragons flying
overhead. The man with the club is
trying to fend off danger, disease, or
infection caused by the dragon under
the tree. The fiery dragons may be exhalations of the beast.

These luminous dragons that fly mysteriously through the night
arise from

condensations of sulphur emanation from the sky, because there are, of
course, real dragons existing on the surface of the earth . . . Dragons
are visible only when they are awake because when they are asleep the
luminosity is withdrawn into themselves. The fiery dragon is a hot but
not thick nebulosity. It shines either because of the dragon's motion or by
the vomiting of its internal fires. These lights are more abundant in
summer because their emanations rise more readily to the upper atmosphere.

He refers to the mist seen in winter around the noses of animals. The summer gives rise to more emanations, the winter to more condensations.

Reinzer notes that flying dragons signify pestilence, disease, and an air saturated with infection.

But the political figure should recognize that he stands too high to be infected. These infections are like darts, which the rabble tend to shoot at those in elevated stations. But neither dart nor poison can be effective. If you ignore the arrows they will be no more harmful that a will-o'-the-wisp or a mirage. Nevertheless, the statesman should beware and take a lesson from this effect. It demonstrates that the honor you pursue can lead you astray.

These flying dragons probably comprise a number of overlapping phenomena, as, indeed, the flying saucers do today. However, the flying saucer, if observed at all, would undoubtedly have been classified as a flying dragon back in the 15th to 17th centuries.

When I found that I could make flying saucers in my laboratory, I thought I was being ultra modern. But Reinzer antici-pated me long ago. "Can one make a flying dragon by artificial

Fig. 17. Will-o'-the-wisp, an ancient form of flying saucer; actually burning jets of gas, the so-called "foolish fire."

means? My answer is definitely 'Yes.' The recipe is simple. Take a long, thin strip of leather, steep it in brandy wherein camphor * is dissolved, and then dust it with finely pulverized gunpowder. Now carry it to the top of a high cliff, ignite it, and throw it into the air. And there you have the flying dragon!"

Reinzer has chapters and illustrations of many other natural phenomena, including ordinary lightning, comets, various cloud formations, mock suns and mock moons, the halo, colored clouds, the

* Spirits of camphor.

rainbow. Of these he quotes Seneca as an authority that these "upper meteors are mere phantoms, without substance." The volume, for all of its weird philosophy, is a remarkable book, and the pictures are outstanding. I wish that space permitted me to reproduce all of them here.

The occasional meteorological references that appear in notes between A.D. 1300 and 1600 refer to catastrophes associated with natural spectacles. Lightning becomes identical with hell-fire. Satanic spirits control the vagaries of weather. And this type of superstition reaches back into pre-Christian eras.

A remarkable book, called *Flowers of History*, by Roger of Wendover, chronicles the history of England from A.D. 447 up to 1235. Its pages abound with dragons, miracles, heavenly signs, evil spirits, and visions. One man, "restored to life from the pains of purgatory" in 699, described his descent into the abyss.

As we went on through the gloom, on a sudden there appeared before us great globes of murky flames, rising, as it were, out of a great pit, and falling back into the same . . . As these globes of fire continued, now to rise on high and then to sink to the bottom of the abyss, I observed that the wreaths of flame, as they ascended, were full of human spirits . . . glaring on me with their eyes of flame, and distressing me much with the stinking fire which they breathed from their mouth and nostrils.

And then the comets:

In the year 729, there appeared about the sun two terrible stars; one of which went before the rising sun, the other followed him when he set, as it were presaging destruction to the east and west; or at least, since one of them was the forerunner of the day, and the other of the night, signifying that mortals were threatened with calamities at both seasons. They extended their fiery tails to northwest, and, appearing in the month of January, continued nearly fifteen days. At this time, a terrible visitation of pagans ravaged the Gauls and Spain with miserable slaughter; but they not long after received in that country the reward due to their wickedness.

In the year of our Lord 747, stars were seen to fall from heaven, insomuch that all who saw them thought the end of the world was at hand.

In . . . 776, fiery and fearful signs were seen in the heavens after sunset; and serpents appeared in Sussex, as if they had sprung out of the ground, to the great astonishment of all.

In 794 . . . dreadful prodigies terrified the miserable English nation;

for fearful thunderbolts and horrible fiery dragons were seen passing through the air, foreboding a mighty famine and dreadful slaughter of the people.

If the reasoning of early observers seems obscure, unduly superstitious, and highly influenced by the imagination, we should not feel too superior because of our modern viewpoint. Here are some reactions, somewhat more modern, which speak for themselves. The second probably describes a cloud, the first perhaps also a cloud, but more likely a mirage-type flying saucer. Neither has much significance except to show that many people still attach religious significance to "Strange Signes in the Heavens," even to peculiar cloud forms.

Columbia, South Carolina. — Last Sunday evening, just before sunset, Miss Ida Davis and her two younger sisters were strolling through the woods, when they were suddenly startled by the appearance of a huge serpent moving through the air above them. The serpent was distant only two or three rods when they first beheld it, and was sailing through the air with a speed equal to that of a hawk or buzzard, but without any visible means of propulsion. Its movements in its flight resembled those of a snake, and it looked a formidable object as it wound its way along, being apparently about 15 feet in length. The girls stood amazed and followed it with their eyes until it was lost to view in the distance. The flying serpent was also seen by a number of people in other parts of the country early in the afternoon of the same day, and by those it is represented as emitting a hissing noise which could be distinctly heard. . . . Religious revival meetings have been inaugurated . . . and many declare that the day of judgment is near at hand.[3]

To the editor of the *New York Sun.* — Sir: On Tuesday afternoon of this week, a few minutes after 6 o'clock, I noticed from my window a very peculiar, solitary, vapory object in the heavens. Its position was about where the constellation of the dipper would be at that hour. Viz, due north, and 35 degrees above the horizon. In magnitude and contour it in a marked degree resembled a human form, head, body, and nether limbs, the body and limbs robed in shadowy drapery. The head, which was of brighter luminosity on the crown and forehead, had thick flowing hair, and the whole figure was extended horizontally with the head eastward and the front downward. But there was another feature quite as marked, and that was in appearances of wings projecting upward and backward from the shoulders. . .This last named feature gave the entirety the appearance of an angel.

Flying in mid-heaven, considered as a cloud, it was remarkable that it kept the same outline continuously (which is uncommon in those vapory objects). While I had it in view for a considerable time, it progressed swiftly toward the east. The luminosity of the shadowy angel was of a golden white, and presented a very beautiful appearance against the blue background of the sky. In addition to the startling outline of the object, the interest in it was greatly increased by its being at the time the only one visible in the whole northern heavens, except some low-lying black clouds on the horizon. I called the attention of several persons to it, one of whom discovered himself the resemblance I did.

Query — Was this a presage of a coming event? It reminded me of the words recorded in Mark 13:27: "Then shall he send his angels and gather his elect from the four winds"; and those in Daniel 9:21: "Gabriel . . . being caused to fly swiftly, touched me about the time of the evening oblation." — William H. Smith, Brooklyn, September 19.[4]

One of the earliest and most complete discussions of natural phenomena occurs in Pliny's *Natural History*, which was written about A.D. 75. I refer to a translation by Bostock and Riley, published in 1855. It is of some interest to note that Pliny divides comets, or "shaggy stars with bloody locks," into a number of classes, according to their appearance. One variety he calls *discei*, or simply a disk, which is of amber color and emits but few rays. He also describes "a white comet, with silver hair, so brilliant it can scarcely be looked at, exhibiting, as it were, the aspect of a Deity in human form." Pliny, as well as Seneca and Aristotle, mentions that "an opening sometimes takes place in the firmament, which is called the *chasm*." Perhaps some form of lighting is meant.

Pliny also mentions a

celestial flame . . . of a bloody appearance (and nothing is more dreaded by mortals) which falls down upon the earth, such as was seen in the third year of the 103rd Olympiad, when King Philip was disturbing Greece. But my opinion is, that these, like everything else, occur at stated, natural periods, and are not produced, as some persons imagine, from a variety of causes, such as their fine genius may suggest. They have indeed been the precursors of great evils, but I conceive that the evils occurred, not because the prodigies took place, but that these took place because the evils were appointed to occur at that period. Their cause is obscure in consequence of their rarity, and therefore we are not as well acquainted with them as we are with the rising of the stars, which I have mentioned, and with eclipses and many other things.

Pliny mentions halos, rainbows, and mock suns and moons:

Our ancestors have frequently seen three suns at the same time, as was the case in [various] consulship[s] . . . And we have ourselves seen one during the reign of the late Emperor Claudius, when he was consul along with Corn. Orfitus. We have no account transmitted to us of more than three having been seen at the same time.

He reports other mysterious happenings, such as the following account, which may refer to the aurora borealis: "A bright light has been seen proceeding from the heavens in the night time, as was the case in the consulship of C. Caecilius and Cn. Papirius, and at many other times, so that there has been a kind of daylight in the night."

He refers to stars that "move about in various directions, but never without some cause, nor without violent winds proceeding from the same quarter."

Of special significance is his reference to "Castor and Pollux," though he is referring not to the two stars we now call by these names but to a meteorological phenomenon that calls to mind "The Unknown Lights of Japan." Pliny says:

These stars occur both at sea and at land. I have seen, during the night-watches of the soldiers, a luminous appearance, like a star, attached to the javelins on the ramparts. They also settle on the yard-arms and other parts of ships while sailing, producing a kind of vocal sound, like that of birds flitting about. When they occur singly [a phenomenon called Helena] they are mischievous, so as even to sink the vessels, and if they strike on the lower part of the keel, setting them on fire. When there are two of them they are considered auspicious, and are thought to predict a prosperous voyage, as it is said that they drive away that dreadful and terrific meteor named Helena. On this account their efficacy is ascribed to Castor and Pollux, and they are invoked as gods. They also occasionally shine round the heads of men in the evening, which is considered as predicting something very important. But there is great uncertainty respecting the cause of all these things, and they are concealed in the majesty of nature.

Some of the references clearly are to the phenomenon called St. Elmo's fire, a sort of electric sparking or discharge similar to the sparks that jump from one's finger when one touches metal in cold weather. But some of the images, especially in the rigging of vessels, may be a flying saucer.

One of the earliest meteorological references that I have found, a book written by W. Fulk and printed in 1640, is surprisingly scientific in its outlook and refreshingly modern in its skeptical treatment of the more superstitious items. The book appears under the modest title *A Most Pleasant Prospect Into The Garden of Natural Contemplation To Behold the Natural Causes of all Kinds of Meteors, as well Fiery and Aerie as Watery and Earthy — of which sort are the blazing stars, shooting stars, flames in the air and thunder and lightning, earthquakes etc., rain, dew, snow, clouds, springs etc., stones, metals and earths: to the glory of God, and the profit of his creatures.*

A few quotations are useful in showing the beliefs of those times, with special reference to the fiery meteors and lights in the sky.

Vapor, as the philosopher saith, is a certain watery thing and yet is not water, so exhalation hath a certain earthly nature, yet it is not earth.

The author talks about vapors being drawn up by the sun, there to be released in the sky and fall as rain.

Exhalations are as smokes that be hot and dry, which because they be thin and lighter than vapors, pass the lowest and middle region of the air and are carried up even to the highest region, where for the excessive heat by a nearness of the fire, they are kindled and cause many kinds of impressions. They are also sometimes viscous, that is to say clammy, by reason whereof they cleaving together and not being dispersed, are set on fire and appear sometimes like dragons, sometimes like goats, sometimes like candles and sometimes like spears.

Fiery meteors . . . are therefore divided into flames and apparitions. Flames are they, which burn indeed, and are kindled with fire. According to their diverse fashions, they have diverse names: For they are called burning bubble, torches dancing or leaping goats, shooting or falling stars, or candles, burning beams, round pillars, spears, shields, globes or bowls, firebrands, lamps, flying dragons, or fire drakes, painted pillars or broached steeples, or blazing stars called comets.

Although the foregoing list contains much more than what we would call flying saucers today, the highly descriptive names by which they are known are of great interest. The author continues:

The time when these impressions do most appear is the night season for if they were caused in the daytime they could not be seen no more than the stars be seen, because the light of the Sun, which is much greater, dimmeth the brightness of them being lesser.

He describes the nature of "flying dragons or, as Englishmen call them, Fire Drakes," as vapors ignited between two clouds. He continues:

This dragon . . . flieth along in the air. Sometimes it turneth to and fro if it meet with a cold cloud to beat it back, to the great terror of them that behold it. Some call it a Fire Drake; others say it is the devil himself, and so make report.

More than 47 years ago on May Day, when many young folk went abroad early in the morning, I remember by five of the clock in the forenoon, there was news come to London that the Devil, the same morning, was seen flying over the Thames: afterward came word that he lighted at Stratford, and there was taken and set in the Stocks, and that though he would fain have dissembled the matter by turning himself into the likeness of a man, yet was he known well enough by his cloven foot. I knew some then living that went to see him and returning affirmed that he was indeed seen flying in the air, but was not taken prisoner. I remember also that some wished he had been shot at with guns or shafts as he flew over the Thames. Thus do ignorant men judge of these things that they know not. As for the Devil, I suppose it was a flying Dragon where of we speak, very fearful to look upon as though he had life, because he moveth, where as he is nothing else but clouds of smoke. So mighty is God that he can fear his enemies with these and with such like operations, whereof some examples may be found in Holy Scriptures.

This is really an astonishing record of a flying saucer seen prior to 1600. The report clearly illustrates the tendency of men throughout the ages to endow such an apparition with life of some sort, be it visitors from interplanetary space or the Devil himself.

The author discusses other kinds of lights. He describes one "seen in the night season," which appears to be the will-o'-the-wisp.

It seemeth to go before men, or to follow them, leading them out of their way unto waters and other dangerous places. It is also very often seen in the night of them that sail the sea. Sometimes it will cleave to the mast of the ship or other high part till it go out or else be quenched in the water . . . On land [this] is called ignis fatuus, "foolish fire" that hurteth not but only feareth fools. That which is seen on the sea, if it be but one, is named Helena, if it be two, it is called Castor and Pollux.

The author then distinguishes between the truly fiery meteors and "apparitions."

An apparition is an exhalation in the lowest or highest region of the air, not thoroughly burning, but by refraction of light either of the Sun or the Moon, seemeth as though it burned.

Here, indeed, is an outstandingly clear and altogether modern description of many kinds of saucer phenomena, as we have learned in other chapters.

The author goes on to talk about unusual apparitions, which appear as luminous holes in the sky, and then continues to discuss "fired whirlwinds." Sometimes

a whirlwind is set on fire within the cloud, then breaking forth flyeth round like a great cart-wheel terrible to behold, burning and overthrowing all dry things that it cometh near as houses, woods, corn, grass.

After describing rainbows, the author proceeds to discuss the mock suns or sundogs.

It is strange and marvellous to behold the likelyhood that, which Alexander the Great, sending word to Darius, said to be impossible, that two suns should rule the world. But often times, men have seen, as they thought in the firmament, not only two suns but oftener three suns, and many more in number though not so often appearing. These, how wonderful so ever they appear, proceed of a natural cause, which we will endeavor to express. They are nothing else but idols or images of the Sun, represented in a equal, smooth and watery cloud placed on the side of the Sun and sometimes on both sides, into which the beams are being received, as in a glass [mirror]. They express the likeness of fashion and light that is in the sun, appearing as though there were many suns, whereas indeed there is but one, and all the rest are images.

They are most often seen in the morning and evening, about the rising or going down of the sun. Seldom at noontime, or about the midst of the day, because the heat will soon dissolve them. Yet have there been some seen, which began in the morning and continued all day long, into the evening. Sometimes there appear many little suns, like unto little stars, which are caused after the same sort as we do see a man's face to be expelled in the pieces of a broken glass.

For a supernatural significance, they have oftentimes been noted to have portended the contention of princes for kingdoms: as not long before the contention of Galba, Otho, and Vitellius, for the empire of Rome, there appeared three suns.

The author points out that the moon also displays mock moons, and raises the significant question whether stars might also have similar images about them. He concludes that indeed it is possible, although he decides that usually the light will be too much weakened by reflection. Finally, he states his own philosophy about apparitions and signs in the sky:

We will close this book with a brief declaration of the natural causes of many things that are seen in the air very wonderful and strange to behold, to the great admiration of all men, not without the singular providence of God, to forewarn us of many dangers that hang over us, in these most perilous times.

The apparitions of which, as it is most wonderful, so the searching of the cause to us is most hard and difficult, a great deal the rather because no man hath hitherto enterprised (to my knowledge) to take out any cause of them; but all men have taken them as immediate miracles, without any natural means or cause to procure them.

And I truly do acknowledge, that they are sent of God as wonderful Signs to declare his power, and move us to amendment of life, indeed miraculous, but not yet so, that they want a natural cause. For if they be well weighed and considered . . . they differ little from such miracles as are recorded in the Scripture and admitted of divines. So that, as I abhor the opinion of epicures, to think that such things could come by chance, but rather by the determined purpose of God's providence; so I consent not with them that suppose when anything is derived from any natural cause, God the best cause of all things is excluded.

Some of these wonderful apparitions consist of circles and rainbows, of diverse fashions and placings, as one within another, the edge of one touching another, some with the ends upward, some downward, some aside, and some across, but all for the most part in uniform order — pleasant to behold. Such a like apparition is made with the sun or sun's images formed into these circles.

Another sort no less often beheld within these few years — but a great deal more strange and wonderful to look upon — are the sights of armies fighting in the air, of castles, cities, and towns, with whole countries, having in them hills, valleys, rivers, woods, and also beasts, men, and fowls, wonders of which there are no such kind on earth and finally all manner of things and actions that are on the Earth, as burials, processions, combats, men, women, children, horses, armies of certain noblemen, weapons . . . sometimes stars. Angels as they are painted with the image of Christ crucified, the beseiging of castles and towns . . . etc.

All these wonderful apparitions may be caused in two manner of ways: the ones artificially and the others naturally. Artificially, by certain glasses and instruments made according to a secret part of that knowledge which is called Catoptric [the science of mirrors and reflections] . . . but for the most part naturally when the disposition of the air hath been such that it had received the image of many things placed and done on the Earth.

10

Flying saucers of the Bible

▄▄

My search for saucers flying down the long corridors of history has found the path confused and dim. I have already said that superstitious imaginings have made difficult the task of distinguishing between such objects as mock suns, mirage, or the aurora borealis. Since our investigation has turned up examples of flying saucers in each of these categories, we cannot be too critical of the ancients. We cannot accuse them of lack of perception, even if we sometimes feel they were overimaginative — that is, of course, if their colorful pictures of swords and armies in the sky, of dripping blood, of severed heads, or of angels' wings are any more imaginative or more fanciful than the concept of a saucer as an interplanetary craft.

I have mentioned a few odd references to unusual sights seen in the 16th and 15th centuries, and even earlier. Legends and folklore abound with tales of luminous ghosts, some of which may have a realistic basis in saucer phenomena. We may derive some consolation from the fact that saucers have frightened other generations than our own.

Prior to the invention of printing in 1440, the only recorded chronicles were those passed down by word of mouth or by laboriously handwritten manuscript. Many documents were lost or crumbled away. Other manuscripts are inaccessible because of the difficulties of translating early medieval language. Without a dictionary or a guide, even the English of Chaucer is curiously obscure. Some of the earliest books, such as Pliny's *Natural History* and other similar works, survived. Here we find ample abundance of Pliny's faith in tall tales brought back from distant lands. Thus his natural history is a curious mixture of fact and fiction, in which animals that never lived, like the dragon and the unicorn, appear in company with familiar beasts of field and forest.

We have seen that Pliny's description of the meteors is very incomplete, but it leads us to suspect that not too much advance had occurred in the whole science of meteorology from his time until the 16th or 17th centuries, at the very least.

As I searched for early examples of the flying saucers, the story of the wheels of Ezekiel flashed into my mind. Could these wheels, by any chance, be a flying saucer? The Bible records in vivid form many meteorological phenomena — storms, thunder, lightning, and rainbows. What about Ezekiel's wheels? Are they solely symbolic or was the imagery derived from some natural phenomenon?

Many of the events that Ezekiel records are consistent with known facts of history, so that we can say definitely that he lived about 600 B.C. While he was still young and a priest in Jerusalem, he was captured and carried away to some site near Babylon or Nippur on the river Chebar. His writings show a longing for the city of his youth, while he was forced to live in country that was largely desert. He was a man of visions, some of them awesome sights like the valley full of bones (37:1–14).

If Ezekiel, in some of his visions, described familiar objects, or at least objects that he had seen and whose significance we can grasp, is there reason why his first vision should not also represent something that he had seen, a "signe in the Heavens" — a flying saucer?

There are certain passages in Ezekiel that suggest some sort of meteorological apparition: the appearance of a rainbow, the color of fire, of amber, of beryl (an irridescent glow ranging from orange to white), and finally of sapphire (blue).

My first thought involved trying to explain the vision as a simple nighttime mirage, but the vividness of the color seemed to suggest a daytime occurrence.

The agreement between Ezekiel's vision and a modern description of a deluxe-model exhibition of mock suns with attendant glories is, to my mind, completely convincing. The correspondence is so unique that it seems to me someone cannot have failed to note it and point it out. But, so far, I have not been able to find a reference.

Ezekiel's vision of the wheels appears twice, first in chapter 1 and again in chapter 10. Although there is considerable duplication, I give both; the minor differences and added facts all tend to corroborate this identification.

Chapter 1:

And I looked, and, behold, a whirlwind came out of the north, a great cloud, and a fire infolding itself, and a brightness was about it, and out of the midst thereof as the colour of amber out of the midst of the fire.

Also out of the midst thereof came the likeness of four living creatures. And this was their appearance; they had the likeness of a man.

And every one had four faces, and every one had four wings.

And their feet were straight feet; and the sole of their feet was like the sole of a calf's foot; and they sparkled like the colour of burnished brass.

And they had the hands of a man under their wings on their four sides; and they four had their faces and their wings.

Their wings were joined one to another; they turned not when they went; they went every one straight forward.

As for the likeness of their faces, they four had the face of a man, and the face of a lion, on the right side: and they four had the face of an ox on the left side; they four also had the face of an eagle. Thus were their faces: and their wings were stretched upward; two wings of every one were joined one to another, and two covered their bodies.

And they went every one straight forward: whither the spirit was to go, they went; and they turned not when they went.

As for the likeness of the living creatures, their appearance was like burning coals of fire, and like the appearance of lamps; it went up and down among the living creatures; and the fire was bright, and out of the fire went forth lightning.

And the living creatures ran and returned as the appearance of a flash of lightning.

Now as I beheld the living creatures, behold one wheel upon the earth by the living creatures, with his four faces.

The appearance of the wheels and their work was like unto the colour of a beryl: and they four had one likeness: and their appearance and their work was as it were a wheel in the middle of a wheel.

When they went, they went upon their four sides: and they turned not when they went.

As for their rings, they were so high that they were dreadful; and their rings were full of eyes round about them four.

And when the living creatures went, the wheels went by them; and when the living creatures were lifted up from the earth, the wheels were lifted up.

Whithersoever the spirit was to go, they went, thither was their spirit to go; and the wheels were lifted up over against them: for the spirit of the living creature was in the wheels. When those went, these went;

and when those stood, *these* stood; and when those were lifted up from the earth, the wheels were lifted up over against them: for the spirit of the living creature *was* in the wheels.

And the likeness of the firmament upon the heads of the living creature was as the colour of the terrible crystal, stretched forth over their heads above.

And under the firmament were their wings straight, the one toward the other; every one had two, which covered on this side, and every one had two, which covered on that side, their bodies.

And when they went, I heard the noise of their wings, like the noise of great waters, as the voice of the Almighty, the voice of speech, as the noise of an host: when they stood, they let down their wings.

And there was a voice from the firmament that was over their heads, when they stood, and had let down their wings.

And above the firmament that was over their heads was the likeness of a throne, as the appearance of a sapphire stone; and upon the likeness of the throne was the likeness as the appearance of a man above upon it.

And I saw as the colour of amber, as the appearance of fire round about within it, from the appearance of his loins even upward, and from the appearance of his loins even downward, I saw as it were the appearance of fire, and it had brightness round about.

As the appearance of the bow that is in the cloud in the day of rain, so was the appearance of the brightness round about. This was the appearance of the likeness of the glory of the Lord. And when I saw it, I fell upon my face.

Chapter 10:

Then I looked, and, behold, in the firmament that was above the head of the cherubims there appeared over them as it were a sapphire stone, as the appearance of the likeness of a throne.

And he spake unto the man clothed with linen, and said, Go in between the wheels, even under the cherub, and fill thine hand with coals of fire from between the cherubims, and scatter them over the city. And he went in in my sight.

Now the cherubims stood on the right side of the house, when the man went in; and the cloud filled the inner court.

Then the glory of the Lord went up from the cherub, and stood over the threshold of the house; and the house was filled with the cloud, and the court was full of the brightness of the Lord's glory.

And the sound of the cherubims' wings was heard even to the outer court, as the voice of the Almighty God when he speaketh.

And it came to pass, that when he had commanded the man clothed with linen, saying, Take fire from between the wheels, from between the cherubims; then he went in, and stood beside the wheels.

And one cherub stretched forth his hand from between the cherubims unto the fire that was between the cherubims, and took thereof, and put it into the hands of him that was clothed with linen: who took it, and went out.

And there appeared in the cherubims the form of a man's hand under their wings.

And when I looked, behold the four wheels by the cherubims, one wheel by one cherub, and another wheel by another cherub: and the appearance of the wheels was as the colour of a beryl stone.

And as for their appearances, they four had one likeness, as if a wheel had been in the midst of a wheel.

When they went, they went upon their four sides; they turned not as they went, but to the place whither the head looked they followed it; they turned not as they went.

And their whole body, and their backs, and their hands, and their wings, and the wheels, were full of eyes round about, even the wheels that they four had.

As for the wheels, it was cried unto them in my hearing, O wheel.

And every one had four faces: the first face was the face of a cherub, and the second face was the face of a man, and the third the face of a lion, and the fourth the face of an eagle.

And the cherubims were lifted up. This is the living creature that I saw by the river of Chebar.

And when the cherubims went, the wheels went by them: and when the cherubims lifted up their wings to mount up from the earth, the same wheels also turned not from beside them.

When they stood, these stood; and when they were lifted up, these lifted up themselves also; for the spirit of the living creature was in them.

Then the glory of the Lord departed from off the threshold of the house, and stood over the cherubims.

And the cherubims lifted up their wings, and mounted up from the earth in my sight: when they went out, the wheels also were beside them, and every one stood at the door of the east gate of the Lord's house; and the glory of the God of Israel was over them above.

This is the living creature that I saw under the God of Israel by the river of Chebar; and I knew that they were the cherubims.

Every one had four faces apiece, and every one four wings; and the likeness of the hands of a man was under their wings.

And the likeness of their faces was the same faces which I saw by the river of Chebar, their appearances and themselves; they went every one straight forward.

As a key to the scriptural interpretation, compare Figs. 18 and 19. The first is a schematic drawing combining observed features of

Fig. 18. Schematic diagram of sundogs and associated halos, the prototype of Ezekiel's wheels.

Fig. 19. Ezekiel's visualization of the apparition: four winged angels.

well-known solar halos complete with mock suns and "glories," a
phenomenon produced by ice crystals in the sky. The second is an
imaginative sketch, trying to interpret the Biblical account.

The similarity of the described apparitions to the solar halo is
remarkable. True, the phenomenon of mock suns varies according to
the type and size of the ice crystals, their density and distribution
in space, the relative quiescence of the different air layers containing
these crystals, and finally the altitude of the sun. The character of the
display can range all the way from a simple unadorned halo or a
single mock sun to the super-deluxe model known as the Petersburg
phenomenon, because the Petersburg (now Leningrad) astronomer
Lowitz was the first to observe and describe it, in 1794. We have
compromised on a somewhat simpler form, a minor modification of
the so-called "Roman phenomenon," one of the earlier records of the
mock suns and attendant glories, accurately observed and described
by the Jesuit priest, P. Scheiner, at Rome in the year 1630.

The two separate visions, according to the text of Ezekiel, refer
to independent apparitions. This accounts for some of the observed
differences.

One of the main features of the apparition, "a wheel in the middle
of a wheel," requires no imagination whatever.

The "four living creatures" would have to be the mock suns themselves, whose "appearance was like burning coals of fire, and like
the appearance of lamps." The reported flickering appearance is
common to such sundogs. Many of them seem to be composed of
myriads of twinkling sparks. These are the "faces."

From the description we clearly see that the figure contained a
cross, centered on the sun. The arms of the cross looked like the
spokes of a wheel; each formed the body of a figure, the mock sun
itself presenting the head. The description leads us to suppose that
the apparition occurred somewhat after sunrise, and presumably
these columns carried some of the dawn-pink glow. They seem to
have a feathery appearance, and very little exercise of the imagination would be necessary to see them as "wings" covering the body
of the figure. And the foot of each figure where it stands on the sun,
broadened by its brightness, could readily suggest the "straight"
image like "a calf's foot," sparkling with "the color of burnished

brass." The sun itself, perhaps even dimmer than its mock companions, contributed the brassy glow.

The Biblical text describes a whirlwind coming from the north, which doubtless was a storm that filled the sky with the crystals of ice and flakes of snow necessary for the formation of the apparition.

The two halos have some of the characteristics of a rainbow, with the red clearly showing on the inner side. The remaining colors are confused and we get at best a tint of amber. The outer iridescent arcs gave the appearance of curved wings outstretched and joined together to make the full circle, like children playing "ring around the rosy." And the warm glow of the red band of the rainbow seemed like outstretched human arms, also clasped together to form the circle.

We read, also, that the outer ring possessed "eyes," which we interpret to mean that the apparition contained some of the secondary mock suns that appear only rarely.

Commentaries point out that the same Hebrew word, in chapter 1, verse 24, is rendered as either voice or noise. And indeed the rushing noises may belong to the storm itself. The Scriptures frequently refer to thunder as "the voice of the Almighty." Thunder is uncommon in a snowstorm, but we are by no means sure that the apparition occurred in winter. If the cold region is highly elevated, we can see the phenomena at almost any time of the year.

As part of the apparition there is described a throne of "sapphire," that is, "clear heavenly blue." This throne would seem to be the curved arc above the outer wheel, and the description of its color fits almost uniquely; of all the bows and arcs associated with a fully developed apparition of mock suns, this upper arc is the only one that tends to show blue to any great extent.

The wheels did not turn but were "lifted up." And the living creatures went with them. In other words, as the sun rose the great wheels and the entire apparition moved with it.

The only obscure passage in the whole description relates to the faces. Commentaries point out that the comma after "lion" does not appear in the original. Apparently, therefore, imagination supplied four faces, the face of a man (in front), the face of a lion to the right, the face of an ox to the left, with the face of an eagle invisibly turned away. I shall not attempt to interpret the image further, except to say that many authorities have called attention to the similarity between this wheeled throne and the chariot — perhaps the "chariot of fire" that carried up Elijah "by a whirlwind into Heaven." [1]

There are other visions referred to here and there in the Scriptures that suggest the mock suns for their inspiration. Some of the imagery appears in Isaiah 6: the seraphims, six wings instead of four (which presents no problem because the cross extending outside of the circular halo could give the appearance of an upper wing), and also the "live coals."

The book of Daniel, chapter 7, tells of four great beasts coming up from the sea, being lifted up from the earth and standing upon their feet. The vision goes on to mention the throne and wheels as burning fire. The reference to night may imply that the apparition was one of mock moons rather than of suns.

Here also we find references to "horns," which is a characteristic feature of many phenomena, especially when well developed.

Most of the commentaries, referring to the construction of a "wheel in the middle of a wheel," have supposed that these two wheels were like hoops set at right angles to one another, say like the earth's equator and a similar circle perpendicular to it running through both poles. The confusion so resulting has led to what I consider a significant fact. Despite the vividness of Ezekiel's wheels, out of a number of the more famous illustrated Bibles, including the one by Doré, I have not been able to find a single artist who has shown the wheels. Raphael depicts the vision but without wheel or chariot.

Without some guidance from meteorology, the artists were unable to interpret the confused images. But with meteorology as a guide the whole description falls into place and — whatever religious significance one may wish to assign to it — the origin of the vision becomes clear. In fact, Ezekiel proves to take top rank as an observing scientist and recorder of important meteorological phenomena.

Much of the imagery of Revelation seems to follow the same pattern. Chapter 12 seems to refer to a lunar phenomenon, a fully developed apparition with horns. Chapters 4, 13, 14, and 15 of

Fig. 20. Ezekiel's vision, by William Blake.

Revelation contain similar imagery, though by no means as clearly outlined or delineated as in Ezekiel.

Here is Milton's adaptation of Ezekiel's chariot:

> Forth rush'd with whirlwind sound
> The chariot of Paternal Deity,
> Flashing thick flames, wheel within wheel, undrawn,
> Itself instinct with spirit, but convoy'd
> By four Cherubic shapes. Four faces each
> Had wondrous; as with stars, their bodies all
> And wings were set with eyes; with eyes the wheels
> Of beryl, and careering fires between;
> Over their heads a crystal firmament,
> Whereon a sapphire throne, inlaid with pure
> Amber, and colors of the showery arch.
> He, in celestial panoply all arm'd
> Of radiant Urim, work divinely wrought,
> Ascended; at his right hand victory
> Sat eagle-wing'd; beside him hung his bow
> And quiver with three-bolted thunder stored;
> And from about him fierce effusion roll'd
> Of smoke, and bickering flame, and sparkles dire.
> Attended with ten thousand thousand Saints,
> He onward came; far off his coming shone;
> And twenty thousand (I their number heard)
> Chariots of God, half on each hand, were seen.
> He on the wings of Cherub rode sublime
> On the crystalline sky, in sapphire thron'd,
> Illustrious far and wide.[2]

11

The invasion from Mars

▸▸

We who live in the age of science know that we should observe the world through rational, scientific eyes. Science has taught us not to fear the shooting star, not to bother searching for the pot of gold at the end of the rainbow, not to hold an eclipse or a comet responsible for disaster. Of course, science has its limitations. Medical science has advanced rapidly during the past decades; yet some forms of cancer remain incurable. Atomic power is still an untamed giant, apparently more capable of destroying than of enriching man's culture. Nevertheless, the development of the airplane, the electronic brain, and the atomic bomb confirms the authority of science. This authority we accept as the criterion of our everyday attitudes and reactions. The more we adopt the scientific faith the more do we question our superstitions. We no longer expect good luck merely because we find a four-leaf clover. We do not understand all the problems of space travel, but we confidently and somewhat impatiently await the day when men will visit the moon.

Although men may claim to reason scientifically, few realize to what extent outmoded prejudices still distort our understanding. Many people stuff their children with spinach, in true Pop-Eye fashion, when in fact spinach is less nutritious than most other vegetables! Are we any more scientific when we call heavenly lights "Flying Saucers" instead of "Flying Dragons"? Should we not examine our whole method of thinking, to see how scientific we really are? The evidence indicates that many people still are capable of dangerous misinterpretation of natural phenomena.

Some years ago, a completely imaginary flying saucer terrified millions of Americans. A realistic science-fiction radio drama caused a remarkable panic, and cast an embarrassing light upon our ability to distinguish between fantasy and reality.

Sunday, 30 October 1938, was a peaceful day in a turbulent year.

While Hitler was making heavy demands and light promises, the rest of Europe paradoxically prepared for war and cried for peace. The Japanese were carrying war into the heart of China. The United States was still absorbed in problems of economic recovery, but, as the international situation grew more and more tense, frequent and dramatic news reports slowly destroyed the myth of isolation.

At 8:00 P.M. on this peaceful American Sunday, Orson Welles and the Mercury Theatre presented a modernized radio adaptation of H. G. Wells's *War of the Worlds*.[1] Listeners will never forget the realism of the drama. Following the usual opening announcement, Orson Welles created the atmosphere with a brief prologue. He spoke as if he were living in the future and looking back to the year 1938, when men from Mars attacked the earth:

It was near the end of October. Business was better. The war scare was over. More men were back at work. Sales were picking up. On this particular evening, October 30, the Crossley Service estimated that thirty-two million people were listening in on radios.

Announcer cue: . . . For the next twenty-four hours not much change in temperature . . . Maximum temperature 66; minimum 48. This weather report comes to you from the Government Weather Bureau . . . We now take you to the Meridian Room in the Hotel Park Plaza in downtown New York, where you will be entertained by the music of Ramon Raquello and his orchestra.

After a few moments of Ramon Raquello the program was abruptly cut off.

Ladies and Gentlemen, we interrupt our program of dance music to bring you a special bulletin from the Intercontinental Radio News. At twenty minutes before eight, Central Time, Professor Farrell of Mount Jennings Observatory, Chicago, Illinois, reports observing several explosions of incandescent gas, occurring at regular intervals on the planet Mars. The spectroscope indicates the gas to be hydrogen and moving towards the earth with enormous velocity.

The radio audience had just been returned to the Meridian Room when another announcer broke in to broadcast an appeal from the Government Meteorological Bureau requesting all large observatories to keep watch on Mars. He stated that the network had arranged a special interview with Professor Pierson (Orson Welles), a famous Princeton astronomer. The interview followed almost at once.

Phillips (Announcer): Good evening, ladies and gentlemen. This is Carl Phillips, speaking to you from the observatory at Princeton. I am standing in a large semicircular room, pitch black except for an oblong split in the ceiling. Through this opening I can see a sprinkling of stars that cast a kind of frosty glow over the intricate mechanism of the huge telescope. The ticking sound you can hear is the vibration of the clockwork . . . I ask you to be patient, ladies and gentlemen, during any delay that may arise during our interview . . . Professor, may I begin our questions?

Professor Pierson then described the planet Mars, where the chances against life were "a thousand to one." The gas eruptions he could not explain.

Phillips: By the way, Professor, for the benefit of the listeners, how far is Mars from earth?
Pierson: Approximately forty million miles.
Phillips: Well, that seems a safe distance. . .

Reports from Canada soon confirmed the observations of the American astronomical stations. A special announcement from Trenton, New Jersey, "reported that at 8:50 a huge, flaming object, believed to be a meteorite, fell on a farm in the neighborhood of Grovers Mill, New Jersey, twenty-two miles from Trenton. The flash in the sky was visible within a radius of several hundred miles and the noise of the impact was heard as far north as Elizabeth." A special mobile unit was dispatched to Grovers Mill with Carl Phillips in charge.

Phillips: . . . This is Carl Phillips again, at the Wilmuth farm, Grovers Mill, New Jersey. Professor Pierson and myself made the eleven miles from Princeton in ten minutes. Well, I . . . I hardly know where to begin, to paint for you a word picture of the strange scene before my eyes, like something out of a modern Arabian Nights . . . I guess that's the . . . *thing*, directly in front of me, half buried in a vast pit . . . What I can see of the . . . object itself doesn't look very much like a meteor . . . it looks more like a huge cylinder.

As Phillips spoke, a faint humming began. He moved closer to pick it up on the microphone. Professor Pierson thought that possible unequal cooling of the surface produced the noise, but he could not identify the object itself. A sudden roar attracted their attention. "Just a minute!" exclaimed Phillips. "This is terrific! The end of the thing is beginning to flake off! The top is beginning to rotate like a screw! The thing must be hollow!" Something fell with a loud metallic crash.

Phillips: Ladies and gentlemen, this is the most terrifying thing I have ever witnessed. . . Wait a minute! Someone's crawling out of the hollow top. Someone or . . . something. I can see peering out of that black hole two luminous disks . . . are they eyes? It might be a face. It might be . . . (*Shouts of awe from the crowd.*)

Good heavens, something's wriggling out of the shadow like a grey snake. Now it's another one, and another. They look like tentacles to me. There, I can see the thing's body. It's as large as a bear and it glistens like wet leather. But that face. It . . . it's indescribable. I can hardly force myself to keep looking at it. The eyes are black and gleam like a serpent. The mouth is V-shaped with saliva dripping from its rimless lips that seem to quiver and pulsate. The monster or whatever it is can hardly move. The thing's raising up. The crowd falls back. They've seen enough. This is the most extraordinary experience. I cannot find words. . . I'm pulling the microphone with me as I talk. I'll have to stop the description until I've taken a new position. Hold on, will you please, I'll be back in a minute.

Announcer: We are bringing you an eyewitness account of what's happening on the Wilmuth Farm, Grovers Mill, New Jersey. We now return you to Carl Phillips at Grovers Mill.

Phillips: Here I am, back of a stone wall that adjoins Mr. Wilmuth's garden. From here I get a sweep of the whole scene. I'll give you every detail as long as I can talk. More state police have arrived. . . Wait! Something's happening! (*Hissing sound followed by a humming that increases in intensity.*)

A humped shape is rising out of the pit. I can make out a small beam of light against a mirror. What's that? There's a jet of flame springing from the mirror, and it leaps at the advancing men. It strikes them head on! Good Lord, they're turning into flame! (*Screams and unearthly shrieks.*)

Now the whole field's caught fire. (*Explosion.*) The woods . . . the barns . . . the gas tanks of automobiles . . . it's spreading everywhere. It's coming this way. About twenty yards to my right. . . (*Crash of microphone . . . then dead silence. . .*)

Announcer: Ladies and gentlemen, due to circumstances beyond our control we are unable to continue the broadcast from Grovers Mill.

A series of news bulletins, official statements, and eyewitness reports followed in rapid succession. Pierson escaped, but Phillips was burned to death by the heat-ray. Seven thousand troops moved in, only to be completely annihilated by one sweeping blast of the heat-ray. More cylinders landed throughout the country. The Martians departed from their ships in fantastic tripodlike robots that towered above the trees. Thus they began a devastating march northward.

Soon the first Martians arrived at New York City. The strange machines approached, belching forth a poisonous black smoke. Gas masks were ineffective. Throngs of people fled frantically, only to find all roads from the city hopelessly jammed. Others gathered in churches to pray. From the roof of a skyscraper a reporter vividly described the destruction of the city:

Enemy now in sight above the Palisades. Five great machines . . . First one is crossing the river . . . wading the Hudson like a man wading through a brook. . . His steel, cowlish head is even with the sky-scrapers. . . This is the end now. Smoke comes out . . . black smoke, drifting over the city. People . . . running towards the East River . . . thousands of them, dropping in like rats. Now the smoke's spreading faster. It's reached Times Square. People trying to run away from it, but it's no use. They're falling like flies. Now the smoke's crossing Sixth Avenue . . . Fifth Avenue . . . 100 yards away . . . it's 50 feet. . .

Operator: 2X2L calling CQ . . . 2X2L calling CQ . . . 2X2L calling CQ . . . New York. Isn't anyone on the air? Isn't there anyone . . . 2X2L. . . (*Middle Break.*)

Thus ended the first act of the drama. After station and program identification, Professor Pierson, the hero of the story, related the outcome of the disaster. He had hidden successfully and later had made his way to New York. There he saw nothing but the charred ruins of men and buildings. Finally he discovered a Martian machine. Cautiously he crept closer. There lay the Martians – all dead – killed by earthly diseases over which they had no power! In the end the human survivors regained earthly supremacy. Pierson returned to Princeton.

The play was over. Orson Welles appeared to explain its purpose:

This is Orson Welles, ladies and gentlemen, out of character, to assure you that the *War of the Worlds* has no further significance than as the holiday offering it was intended to be. The Mercury Theatre's own radio version of dressing up in a sheet and jumping out of a bush and saying Boo! . . . You will be relieved, I hope, to learn that we didn't mean it . . . and if your doorbell rings and nobody's there, that was no Martian . . . it's Hallowe'en.

Although Mr. Welles and his colleagues "feared that the classic H. G. Wells fantasy . . . might appear too old-fashioned for modern consumption," [2] they had greatly underestimated their talents. Four times station and program identification interrupted the hour-long drama, and yet the realistic presentation convinced at least one million of the six million listeners that the disaster was real. Their consequent fear led to widespread panic. Quite by accident, the program provided a test of peoples' understanding and reactions. Following the incident, a group of scientists from the Princeton Radio Project and the Columbia Broadcasting System, taking advantage of the unexpected experiment, set out to diagnose the causes and sources of the panic, by thorough examination of the reactions of the participants. The causes of the Martian panic and the current saucer scare seem to be comparable. Study of one should contribute to an understanding of the other.

Five million listeners realized that the story was entirely fictional. Those who at first were confused because they tuned in late or disregarded the preliminary announcements dialed other stations or looked to see if the program were listed in the paper. They withheld their conclusions until they could make adequate checks.

To the million who were fooled by the realistic technique, the fantastic seemed possible. They believed the accounts by the fictitious astronomer, the unnamed "government officials," and the numerous "eyewitness" reporters. Once convinced, they fitted everything into their established picture. One man, seeing much traffic from his window, envisioned mass evacuation. Another, finding his street deserted, imagined that it had been blocked off by the police. Normal traffic served only to convince a third that the invaders had not yet reached his vicinity. Several, noticing that less than two

minutes after the Princeton interview Professor Pierson appeared in
Grovers Mill, eleven miles away, rationalized that "the reporter was
excited and had made a mistake," or "they were relaying reports or
something."

Thousands of terrified people prepared for evacuation or prayed
earnestly for deliverance. A few momentarily questioned their faith
in the existence of Providence. Some thought the invaders were
Germans or Japanese. Hundreds called friends and relatives for a
last farewell; others ran about hysterically, spreading the alarm,
until they happened to learn the truth. The police received call after
call for help: "We can hear the firing all the way here, and I want
a gas mask," exclaimed a Brooklyn man. "I'm a taxpayer." [3] Roads
and telephone lines were jammed for several hours.

Fear often affected the senses. One man, from the roof of a New
York building, saw the flames of the battle through binoculars.
Another *heard* the swish of a Martian cylinder. Many *heard* gunfire.
Others *smelled* gas or smoke.

The truth soon spread. Although the panic subsided, controversy
flared for weeks. An indignant press attacked Mr. Welles for playing
upon public gullibility — especially for using radio, "a mechanical
device which in itself is still a little staggering to the common mind." [4]
Some people maintained that *ignorance* was *responsible* for the panic.
The Federal Communications Commission considered radio censorship because, among other things, the program dramatically demonstrated the dangerous power of Hitler's hypnotic weapon — the
disembodied voice.

Many critics, however, acclaimed the incident as a significant yet
harmless experiment, which exposed many of man's weaknesses. It
seemed that the fundamental difficulty lay in some cultural fault of
man rather than in the fact that a radio drama happened to be
realistic. After all, is the swindler responsible for the naïveté of his
dupe? If man could so easily accept this fantasy as fact, would he
not just as easily subscribe to the political propaganda of some
fanatic?

In order to discover the foundations of cultural delusions, the
Princeton examiners questioned hundreds of listeners. Comparison
of the results revealed several significant characteristics common to

the majority of those misled by the program. Although no single factor completely accounted for an individual's behavior, certain generalizations threw some light upon our cultural defects.

The level of an individual's education, in general, directly affected his reaction — even though some college graduates were fooled while some persons with little formal training correctly interpreted the drama. The more limited a person's knowledge of the world, the more likely he was to make a wrong snap judgment, and stick to it. Those with greater experience were more prone to question the evidence or to seek for other tests.

To say that the program *frightened* people is only partially true. Fear had long ago imbedded itself in the minds of men. On that Sunday evening the fictitious invasion merely served to ignite the smoldering terror. Regardless of education, persons who were dissatisfied or disturbed by economic conditions were readily thrown off balance, their tensions obstructing calm thinking. A large number of these were unable to find jobs or earn enough to live on comfortably.

The Princeton investigators also studied the personality traits of the subjects. Certain personality factors strongly influenced the responses of many. Irrespective of education and economic status, some people were more impressionable than others. Many lacked the self-confidence necessary to question the seeming authority of the scientist and reporters. Lacking convictions of their own, these insecure persons succumbed to the word of false prestige and suppressed what reasonable doubts they may have had. The superstitious, too, were highly suggestible, as were habitual worriers who were perpetually anxious about imagined unlikely problems. Some of these possessed severe phobias, such as unreasonable fear of darkness, death, or high places. Fatalists, certain of the inevitable destruction of humanity, promptly resigned themselves to await the heat-ray.

Ignorance, insecurity, and lack of self-confidence have fostered a tendency toward a blind acceptance of scientific authority that has apparently supplanted the similar faith in medieval demons and sea serpents, witchcraft and sorcery. The radio drama's scientific jargon, endorsed by ostensibly valid scientific authority, precipitated panic among the blind disciples of the "scientific faith." Persons who thus habitually defer to prestige without understanding its basis comprise a special group of suckers, always ready to subscribe to any claim as long as the advertisements display seemingly scientific credentials.

The manner in which a person heard the news naturally affected his reaction. Hundreds who believed the hysterical accounts of a terrified neighbor might have discredited the report if they had heard it firsthand from the radio. A group generally acted according to the behavior of its dominant member. Unfamiliar environment contributed to the deception, especially of those separated from their families. Persons geographically near the danger naturally took the invasion more seriously than those far away.

Some people believed the story primarily because they had some personal connection with some aspect of the event. Many had relatives or business in New Jersey. Some persons naturally participate emotionally in any disaster wherever it may be. A Princeton geology professor set out to get a sample of the meteorite.[5] Several avid science-fiction readers felt so intimate with Martians that the invasion seemed perfectly natural.

A few people apparently welcomed the disaster. Attack from another planet was one possible way to earthly unity. Some preferred total destruction to Fascist domination. One woman felt relieved because she would not have to pay her butcher's bill. An optimistic man exclaimed, "I knew it would at least scare ten years' life out of my mother-in-law."

Modern men, confident that they were successfully practicing the methods of science, thus carried germs of an invisible cultural disease — germs of inexperience, insecurity, and irrationality. Panic became the symptom, active as long as possibility of resistance or refuge appeared. The Invasion from Mars was the shock that made us aware of our faults and suggested a possible cure, namely, a better understanding of science and less emotion in the interpretation of nature.

Whether or not we have made progress is open to question. Well-defined tests like the radio drama are rare. I strongly believe, however, that a vivid flying-saucer hoax, concentrated into an hour and witnessed by millions, would reproduce the Martian panic on an even greater scale. Many persons would suspect fraud and examine evidence; others would unquestioningly grasp at any available theory, especially one masquerading as science.

Although the recent saucer scare and the Martian incident are unlike in form, they possess certain qualities in common. Both Martians and saucers are outside of our personal experience. The only easily understandable fact about saucers is that they fly. Flying objects within our experience are birds, airplanes, rockets, and supermen.

Saucers resemble none of these consistently, though observers have frequently used the simile of an airship or wingless plane to describe what they saw. However, they more frequently called upon their everyday experience to find unnatural comparisons, such as pie plates, hub caps, wheels, and — saucers. It is not the observers who have insisted that the objects must be interplanetary craft. They have contributed but little to the giant myth that has deluded so many. The fantastic theories have in fact come from the newspapers, journals, and books, which have sensationalized Saucers in the name of science, for obvious commercial reasons. Persons accustomed to believing what they read or hear did not notice gaps and inconsistencies, and thus came to believe the impossible. Millions find the concept of interplanetary saucers a source of pleasure.

On the other hand, I know of many instances where observers have not even reported to officials what they saw, either because they were skeptical or because they investigated and, unassisted, found a logical mundane explanation for the apparition.

Those who now maintain that saucers are interplanetary space craft do not realize that they are being exploited by the creators of this illogical myth. Those who were fooled by the Invasion from Mars learned of their error almost at once. The millions taken in by the myth of interplanetary saucers continue to be deceived by the ceaseless propaganda.

The unmistakable undercurrent of terror is today even stronger than it was in 1938. Another war carries the threat of atomic annihilation. Flying saucers furnish a convenient and, so far, a harmless outlet for our latent fears. Since emotions demand expression, those who fear most strongly may seek relief in the enjoyment of a sensational mystery.

The results of the Princeton study of the Mars drama suggest that the believers of the saucer myth also would be highly subject to suggestion. Captain Mantell's unexplained crash precipitated much worry and superstitious fear. Fire in the Mars incident frightened the fatalists who believed the "end of the world was coming by fire"; to some, the fiery saucers may likewise represent the destruction of civilization.

Now, more than in 1938, a variety of wishful attitudes prevails toward a possible extraterrestrial invasion. Many persons cling to the vain hope that a threat from space will at last bring unity and peace on earth. It is natural to prefer harmless little saucers to atomic bombs.

I received not long ago a letter that is relevant to the problem.

Dear Dr. Menzel:

For some time, I have been enjoying a beautiful dream which I have been hoping might materialize in some form one day. Now you have come along and shattered my vision. How could you be so cruel?

You know, there are no men left in Washington? The few nice ones are all married, and the rest are sailors, only boys, far too young!

It is not easy for a girl employed as typist in the Navy Department to meet a nice eligible man these days, so the only thing she can do is dream. Therefore, I have built up a wonderful and romantic idea, based upon the many articles I have read about flying saucers, which concerns a man from another world, tall, dark and handsome, highly intelligent, and very exciting, coming down in a flying saucer in my vicinity.

I have been contemplating writing a novel — the man comes down, to the dismay of a startled world — the world starts building flying saucers, and soon the sky is full of them, and the man meets a lonely government girl, marries her and takes her away to his planet which has a much higher civilization than Earth. After I finish it I want to send it around to publishers, but after reading your article in *Look*, I am not sure that publishers would want to read it.

Now, see what you have done! You've spoiled my whole beautiful idea by claiming the saucers are only reflections, pieces of paper, balloons, etc., and *not* interplanetary craft containing intellectual people from another world.

I realize how many people, after hearing a flying-saucer report, might think that any object they saw in the sky, even a kite, was a flying saucer.

Therefore, you have a lot on your side, but doesn't it seem reasonable that there should be other worlds similar to ours outside our solar system? Don't you think that there could be civilizations older and farther advanced, and even more civilized than us? Surely, with the billions of stars in the universe, the Earth cannot be the only center of life — that is what scientists are always pointing out these days.

Since Earth scientists are contemplating space travel, why shouldn't men from other planets do it, too, and if they are farther advanced than us, they might be able to overcome space. There is nothing frightening or supernatural about such a project. We, ourselves, will be going to the moon and beyond some day. . .

Sincerely yours,
          Shirley W———— *

We have seen how the listening situation affected reactions to the Martian story. Perhaps responses to saucers are sometimes determined by the circumstances in which we form our beliefs. Many people are more impressed by the opinions of their respected friends than by the printed word. The secretive attitude of the Air Force investigation has occasioned much unnecessary fear, especially in areas where saucers have been so numerous.

Unlike Mr. Welles's Martians, flying saucers have been around for a long time. Characteristically enough, as long as no one completely understands the mystery, people feel quite free to trust in their own interpretation or in that of the most convincing authority. The myth originated in papers, magazines, and pseudo-scientific publications. Counterfeit logic persuades those unable to detect its fallacies yet eager to accept the "scientific" dogma. Imposters know the commercial value of the "scientific faith." They use the most attractive decoy, paint it with false colors, place it strategically, then capitalize on public idolatry. If prosaic theory of legitimate science is sometimes disappointingly drab, the propaganda of sen-

---

* To which I replied:

Dear Shirley:

    Thank you for your kind comments about flying saucers. But for an expert on the subject, as you claim to be, don't you know that reports have the Saucerians ranging somewhere between 27 and 40 inches tall, blond, and beardless? Perhaps what you want is a date with a Cub scout.

    But don't let me spoil your illusions. Do write that book after all. Some day we shall have space travel. All I am saying is that the flying saucers of today have no relationship to the space travel of tomorrow.

sational sham is treacherous. Scientific pretenders today hold as much power over us as did the ancient sorcerer over our fore-fathers.

Only recently a dictator revised the science of genetics to support his doctrines. Contrary to the well-established findings of science, he proclaimed that offspring do, after all, inherit the characteristics acquired by their parents. Science, thus embroidered, was reduced to mere propaganda for the cultivation of a "master race."

Pseudo science thus contends with authentic science. Newspapers promote this conflict by refusing to distinguish between forged and valid authority. They invent "scientific experts" by the dozens. The science articles in many journals, too, are frequently written by men who obviously are incapable either of scientific thinking or of under-standing what they report. Some authors will write what they think the public would like to read, no matter how untrue the story may be.

No one wants press censorship. But freedom of the press imposes some responsibilities on the publisher. His own integrity should lead him to seek the advice of responsible scientists, if he is con-sidering a manuscript that deals with some phase of science. And, if the scientist warns that the manuscript is wrong or misleading, the publisher should either accept the advice or, if he suspects that the first report is biased, call in additional reliable referees. The scientist called on to give the advice also has a responsibility not to suppress a view merely because it does not agree with his own. There is and should be plenty of room in science for differences of opinion and occasional serious but legitimate disagreements.

There are of course examples of sincere scientists who have made mistakes. The notion that a race of superhumans lives on Mars arose from such erroneous reasoning. Early in this century, the noted astronomer, Percival Lowell, remarking the permanent patterns that show on the surface of the planet, concluded that they must be canals artificially made by living beings. No one can deny that this ingenious argument would account for the presence of the markings. But until we have definitely removed other possible natural explana-tions, we cannot say that the study proves that Mars is inhabited. Some of the authorities in the Air Force, perhaps confused by their

fears, likewise prematurely jumped to the conclusion that saucers
are also inhabited. The technique is unscientific, but the temptation
to follow it is high.

Against such overwhelming odds, how can the layman possibly
figure out the truth? How can he distinguish between science fact
and pseudoscientific fiction? Although he cannot expect to know all
the facts and background necessary to check each article he reads,
he must nevertheless guard against being deluded. There are in fact
two ways for him to evaluate scientific information without spending
years in the study of theoretical physics. One way is to scrutinize the
source and authority of the evidence. This approach will be illustrated in the following chapter. The second method is to test the
coherence of the details as they stand. By this I mean looking for
false premises, gaps in evidence, and illogical conclusions, thereby
being a "scientific detective." With a little thought, we can detect
fallacious logic, even when it is disguised with scientific vocabulary.
Basically, the reasoning of much pseudo science is like the example
of the table that turned into a dog: A dog has four legs; the table
has four legs; therefore the table is a dog. Here compare a similar
argument used by the ancients. "Animals have legs and muscles.
Animals can move. The earth has no legs or muscles. Therefore it
must be fixed in space."

Pure-food laws and narcotic acts protect us from potentially
dangerous medicines, foods, or drugs. Yet, exploitation of the minds
of the American public, feeding them fiction in the guise of fact
under the protection of a free press, or frightening people with
fanciful ghosts — these, too, are potentially dangerous. The public
is afraid of saucers — and we need only a match to set off a nation-
wide panic that could far exceed that of the Invasion from Mars. In
fact, if a foreign power were to pull off a surprise attack on the
United States, millions of Americans would conclude that the flying
saucers from Mars or Venus were finally landing!

12

The little men from Venus

▼▼

I referred briefly in Chapter 4 to an unusual tale associated with the University of Denver, a story of mysterious landings and crashes, of saucer craft manned by little beardless men from Venus. The tale almost immediately achieved world-wide circulation and many persons still believe it to be the "true story" of the saucers. The fact that I am a graduate of that University increased my interest in the reports.

I am especially indebted to my good friend Dr. A. C. Nelson, Vice Chancellor of the University of Denver, for putting at my disposal his complete files on the subject. Mr. Francis F. Broman, instructor at the University of Denver, has also kindly lent his extensive file of clippings and correspondence. I am, therefore, able to present the first complete and detailed picture of the startling story. None of the accounts printed to date gives all the facts. The only readily accessible statement of the incident appears in a book called *Behind the Flying Saucers*, by Frank Scully.[1] In this book, as in other accounts, the omission of certain highly significant details illustrates an apparent desire to sacrifice accuracy for sensationalism.

Mr. Broman, who was instructor in a class of general science at the time of the event, 8 March 1950, has kindly summarized the story for me:

The flying-saucer incident at the University of Denver occurred in a class of general science in which the subjects of astronomy, mathematics, biology, botany, geology, physics and chemistry, etc., are presented. While we were using the subject of astronomy in our class, students naturally inquired about asteroids, planets, comets, and the like; naturally, the subject of flying saucers came into the discussion.

One student in that class volunteered to bring an individual, who was reported to be an expert about flying saucers, to class. The class agreed, along with the instructor, that it would be an interesting experiment to listen to some one purporting to be an expert in regard to flying saucers and to evaluate the information this person would give us. This seemed especially valuable inasmuch as we had been evaluating all kinds of printed material in regard to flying saucers in the class. The class developed a basis upon which to judge authenticity and reliability of information.

The criteria that Mr. Broman and his class developed for testing information deserve the careful attention of anyone who thinks about flying saucers. They are excellent standards for judging impersonally whether or not a report is reliable. Information has the greatest value when it satisfies the five following conditions.

In the first place, the reports should be firsthand. Even the most reliable stories suffer from the retelling. Gossip and rumor stories should be viewed with suspicion.

Second, the material should be free from prejudice. He who presents information should have an unbiased view. Otherwise, censorship — be it conscious or unconscious — will distort the picture. In the extreme case, highly selected information, even if true, becomes propaganda, whose force we well recognize.

Third, the information carries much more weight from a trained than from an untrained observer. The untrained observer is much more readily deceived by his senses; he may observe the wrong things or interpret them wrongly. Abundant evidence of lack of skill in the saucer observations lies in the Air Force files. For example, the great majority of the reports estimate both size and distance, where a trained observer would know in advance that he could only measure size in terms of the angular span of the disk and that no ordinary method will enable the observer to tell how far away the object is. Even the most experienced observer is at a disadvantage when he encounters a flying saucer for the first time. In retrospect, as I know from my own experience, one can always think up tests or observations he should have made, but which did not occur to him under the stress of the moment.

Fourth, the data should be available for double-checking. Courts of law have generally ruled out hearsay as a form of evidence. Saucers themselves, as long as we just see them in the sky, can be noted only as the result of observation. A check, if any, depends on reports by independent reliable observers. But suppose that the report refers to an actual saucer crash. If we are prevented from inspecting the evidence ourselves, and thus have to rely only on secondhand reports, we should regard the report with suspicion. "Hush-hush" information, purporting to be "inside dope," is often most unreliable of all.

Fifth and finally, statements must be, in effect, signed, and thus backed by the reputation of the person who makes them. Newspapers generally refuse to print anonymous letters, except under very special circumstances. The unsigned statement carries no implied responsibility for its correctness.

I should emphasize again that these criteria for judging reliability of information were set up by Mr. Broman's class before they ever contemplated calling in a guest to speak about saucers. Moreover, there was no advance guarantee that the guest's story would be "true." The students were expecting to evaluate it in terms of "fact or fiction."

At this point a series of mysterious episodes began to occur. The original "authority" — a Mr. George Koehler — declined to speak, though he offered an unnamed substitute who would identify himself at the proper time, a man reported to be a scientist and a graduate of two European universities. After some hesitation, the instructor agreed to this irregular procedure, explaining that the lecture would have to be evaluated by the rules given above.

When the lecturer arrived, he brought no diplomas or certificates to establish himself. Mr. Koehler introduced him to the instructor merely as Mr. Newton. He presented one or two articles from what appeared to be a trade magazine in the field of oil prospecting, as evidence of his scientific attainments, but even these were indefinite. In the press of the few minutes before the lecture, Mr. Broman does not recall having noticed any special authorship or the exact title. The article probably was a blurb advertising Newton's questionable ideas about magnetic oil prospecting. The instructor had to make a snap decision — one dictated in part by the prior publicity given to the lecture. He decided to go ahead with the program.

He then reiterated the five points that would be used to evaluate the lecture, and secured Mr. Newton's agreement to speak under these conditions. Mr. Broman continues:

The class decided not to prohibit visitors from attending; friends of members of the class might be invited.

Upon arrival at the lecture room, we found the room overcrowded with many strange and eager faces listening to hear what our guest would have to say about the flying saucers. For fear that the guests at the lecture would not be primed for what might occur, the instructor introduced the lecturer and emphasized the fact that he was brought here to talk about flying saucers to those in our science class, and it was hoped that those who were guests also would be very analytical in evaluating the information that he would divulge. The instructor requested visitors especially to be careful to apply the criteria developed by the science class to the lecture; these criteria were given to the group as a whole as part of the introduction of the speaker.

Needless to say, all ears in the lecture room, save those of the science class, were deaf to this admonition and most visitors eagerly believed, because believing was thrilling, as the speaker progressed.

Within thirty minutes after the close of the lecture, telephones began to ring in the instructor's office. These calls were eager inquiries from newspapers in regard to the lecture just completed at the University of Denver. It was apparent that the class's attempt to secure a living situation on which to apply criteria of judgment to propaganda and other types of information had backfired, and that across the city there seemed to be a wave of incredulous acceptance and wonderment at the apparently sincere and fantastic story related by our guest speaker.

Without doubt, the lecture was fascinating. The speaker talked brilliantly, convincingly, and — according to all reports — with apparent authority. When some of the students declared, "He talked like a university professor," I hope they intended to be paying him a high compliment. Or did they only mean that his apparently sincere delivery of highbrow technical language lent an aroma of authority to the talk, even though no one could afterward be found who claimed to understand the speaker's "scientific explanations"?

The man was introduced to the instructor of the course simply as "Mr. Newton." He was anonymous otherwise. Near the end of the lecture, Mr. Koehler interrupted to say, "You will have to come now, or you will miss your plane." The two men left abruptly; no one had the presence of mind to check the license number of the automobile. For some days the question, "Who is Mr. Newton?" loomed almost as large as "What are the Flying Saucers?" One of the students in the class solved the mystery. He recognized the lecturer as Silas

Newton, described as a Denver oil magnate, for whom he had once caddied at the country club.

According to Vice Chancellor Nelson, Mr. Koehler made a tape recording of the lecture for his own use. The diagrams drawn on the blackboard were not lacquered over and preserved, as Scully claims in his book, *Behind the Flying Saucers.* Mr. Broman confirms, however, that Scully's account of the lecture itself is otherwise substantially correct.

My chief source of information has been accounts that appeared in the Denver newspapers,[2] which included published interviews or even signed stories by Newton. The following account has been pieced together largely from these sources. The statements assigned to Mr. Newton represent what the newspaper stories quoted. They agree essentially with other reports about the subject matter presented by Newton in his lecture at the University of Denver.

The speaker claimed to have gained his information about the mysterious crashes through chance meetings with government experts on magnetism, with whom he was discussing problems of "magnetic oil detection." During various conferences, the subject of flying saucers "sailed into the conversation."

"To my amazement," Mr. Newton later confirmed to the *Rocky Mountain News*, "the men said they knew all about them and knew where two which had crashed were located." The government scientists at first were cautious, but they later took Mr. Newton into their confidence and led him to a government laboratory where flying-saucer fragments and the bodies of the little men recovered from them were under scientific scrutiny. Although Newton never admits having seen a wrecked saucer, he describes them and their operators vividly.

"The little men," Newton explained, "were tiny creatures, from 38 to 44 inches long and had the same physical characteristics as we, except they did not have beards." They had no cavities in their teeth.

"They were not midgets. They were perfectly developed. They wore 1890 dress, of cloth that was not wool or cotton but which couldn't be torn." Some reports state that the men wore shoes of a material that resembled human skin.

"The first saucer which landed contained sixteen men who had been burned a dark brown, apparently because one of the nine-inch portholes in the ship had been broken.

"It was a fortunate thing the porthole was broken," Mr. Newton observed. "By means of a long pole, the invisible magnetic doors in the thing were opened. A small knob with a smaller knob affixed to it was jabbed and the invisible door flew open.

"The second ship which landed came down unharmed. But when its two operators tried to get out, they must have been killed by the change in atmosphere here from that of their own planet. They were found as they died, one at the door, the other slumped over the control board of the pilot's seat."

The first disk crashed near Aztec, New Mexico, and the second near Durango, Colorado. The government military agencies assumed immediate control and did everything in their power to keep the matter quiet.

A third craft contained sixteen men — also dead. These men were all blond, as fair complexioned as the Anglo-Saxon. Except for their small stature they closely resembled men from earth, with one major difference. They had no beards — just "something resembling peach fuzz."

Mr. Newton referred to a fourth landing. A group of scientists, near some unidentified government proving ground, almost stumbled over the craft which, at the time, was unoccupied. Nearby they saw several of the little men. The scientists gave chase, but the little men were fast runners and evaded capture. When the scientists came back to the point where they had seen the saucer, the ship had vanished.

Mr. Newton described in considerable detail the characteristics and mode of operation of the saucers. And here we find phrases of mere scientific double talk, which has no significance at all except to give the impression of authority. He asserted that the machines employ magnetic lines of force as a source of power and as tracks to guide them through space. He attributed the various crashes to huge "magnetic faults," which happen to lie near Aztec, New Mexico, and other places where the accidents occurred.

The term "fault" is a geological expression, signifying a place where a rock layer has first cracked and then slipped along the crack. Sometimes a miner, following a rich vein of ore, will come to a disappointing dead end, where faulting has broken across the vein. Somewhere the vein continues — above, below, or to either side. But the search for it in a mine is often fruitless.

By the expression "magnetic fault," Mr. Newton apparently wished to suggest that the magnetic lines of force came suddenly to an end, like a railroad track on a bridge that has been half carried away by a flood. A train following such a track would be wrecked if it fell off the bridge. And the implication is clear that a saucer would meet a similar fate if it came to the broken end of a magnetic line of force.

But this is nonsense. Magnetic lines of force are never completely broken. There is a law of magnetism, as firmly founded as Sir Isaac Newton's law of gravitation, which states, in highly technical language, that "the divergence of the magnetic induction is equal to zero." Only a mathematical physicist can fully understand what that sentence means. But this law does mean something and one of its major consequences is simple enough.

Suppose that we have a magnetized iron bar, with a north pole at one end and a south pole at the other. Imagine further that we hand this bar to the strong man of a circus, who breaks it into two pieces, which he then hands back to us. What will be the magnetism of the two bars? Will we have a north pole on one, a south pole on the other, and fractured lines of magnetic force at the break? No! Two new poles, one south and one north, have appeared at the break. Two magnets exist where we had only one before, and the magnetic lines of force show no sharp angles at the broken ends of the rod. Magnetic faults simply do not exist. A large body of iron ore, a steel ship, or a magnet can make a line of force bend, but nothing can make it come to a dead end.

Mr. Newton maintained, however, that the saucer operators, after the crash, sent a "whole armada of saucers to explore the Durango area" and find some way to get around the fault. As "proof" of his contention, he offered the evidence of newspaper reports of saucer sightings in these areas. Then he further said that U. S. scientists were themselves studying magnetism as a source of power, which he predicted would be cheaper and more revolutionary than atomic power. Here, by associating the idea of saucers with our various atomic developments, Mr. Newton implied that the government had reasons for keeping the entire project secret.

He further said that magnetic lines of force emanate from the sun and other bodies at twice the speed of light. Hence ships can travel from here to Venus and back in a matter of minutes. They can cross magnetic lines and propel their machines by power and energy released by the crossing.

Hidden in the foregoing paragraph is a statement fully as revolutionary — if true — as the advent of space ships from Venus. This is the casual statement that magnetic propulsion can be twice as fast as light, in utter contradiction to Einstein's famous theory of relativity, which is based on the hypothesis that no body in the universe can move faster than light.

Scientists do use magnetic fields in various experiments, including some of the atomic variety. In the cyclotron, perhaps the most famous of all atom smashers, individual charged particles move in spiral paths around lines of force, though the energy that the atoms attain requires the use of vast quantities of electric power. The particles do *not* slide along the lines of force, like beads along a string. And the magnetic lines of force are *not* in motion, like the ropes of a ski tow, so that all one needs to do for propulsion is hitch on to a moving line of force.

The phrase "crossing lines of force" has a familiar sound. For example, any wire moving through a magnetic field will have an electric current induced in it as a consequence of the motion. If a person were to "jump rope," using a length of flexible wire instead of a rope, a very weak current would flow along the closed circuit formed by the wire and the person's arms and body. This current arises from the fact that the wire is cutting across the lines of force of the earth's magnetic field.

This wire swinging in a magnetic field is a crude sort of dynamo. The generated power, if the wire is turned fast enough, will run an electric light or turn a motor. But in the final analysis, the energy that lights the lamp or runs a vacuum cleaner came from the effort used in swinging the wire — not from the magnetic field. A dynamo does not produce power by itself. It merely converts one form of energy — coal, water, atomic — into electrical energy. You get back only the energy you put into it in the first place. If we could get something for nothing, we could achieve perpetual motion, which is impossible — even on the planets Mars or Venus.

Mr. Newton further commented that the theory of magnetic control was logical because "the entire universe is controlled by magnetic force." This statement is so much jargon; it omits the role played by gravitation, which is all-important for the motions of planets, meteors, and other solid bodies in the solar system.

On 10 October 1950, Newton reviewed the very excellent science movie, "Destination Moon," for the *Rocky Mountain News*. Mr. Newton and I agree that the movie, which portrays a fictional rocket trip to the moon, is excellent. I have shown the film to my astronomy classes at Harvard because of its "documentary" character, asking the students to pick out the several minor scientific "boners" that appear.

Mr. Newton agrees with me on this point too, since he suggests that Denver University science professors bring their classes to see the picture and "then tomorrow have a quiz on fact or fiction." I wonder what grade Mr. Newton would get on such a quiz — especially when he devotes the last half of his review to plugging flying saucers and magnetism. He said, "Now that 'Destination Moon' has gone and done it, why not cross over into the magnetic fields that surround the other planets in our solar system and visit them? We might find a people, say on Venus, that have discarded war for planetary peace. What a dream!"

Mr. Newton described the saucers themselves in some detail. The two larger ones measured, so he said, 99 feet and 72 feet, respectively. The smallest one was 36 feet in diameter. The largest possessed a central cabin measuring 72 inches in height.

He assigned a special, mystical significance to the numbers, because they seemed to be tied up with the number 9. He particularly pointed out that $3 + 6 = 9$ and $7 + 2 = 9$. But why did he express the height as 72 inches instead of 6 feet, except to support the numerology? Why should the people from Venus use either feet or inches for measure? Conceivably the "foot" of a man 36 inches high might be only four "inches" long, in which event the business of the nines makes no sense at all. This sort of numerology is convincing evidence of the unreliability of the account.

Mr. Newton further commented that the material comprising the saucer contained two elements previously not known to man. The metallic shell was "extremely light" and had resisted all attempts by scientists to cut through it with welding torches. Though raised to "10,000 degrees of heat, it defied decomposition." These statements are also clearly designed for scientific window-dressing; in the light of modern science they have no meaning.

But Mr. Newton, in his efforts to impress, piles detail on detail. The saucers defied our early attempts to enter them because of the alleged resistance to heat. Except for that fortunate fracture of one window and the accidental locating of push-button controls that opened the doors, we might not have been able to enter at all. For there was not "a single rivet, or bolt, or screw in the entire mechanism."

A revolving ring of metal encircled the outer edge of the craft. Mr. Newton vaguely described the process of landing as controlled by a maze of push-buttons, and, perhaps, completely automatic in its final stages. Since the landing gear consisted of three large balls instead of wheels, set in the form of a triangle, the saucer could take off or land in any direction.

The articles found in the space ship included some device for measuring magnetic fields, paper of unfamiliar composition covered with hieroglyphics of undetermined significance, a peculiar form of radio, and a clock operating on a 28-day lunar cycle.

According to Drew Pearson,[3] Koehler produced some of this material as evidence, but "it turned out to be a mundane product of this planet, stamped with the Roman numeral VI. His space radio was a chunk of metal that utterly failed to pick up a message or even a wheeze from space."

How Newton or Koehler or the scientists fixed upon Venus as the probable home of the saucers has never been at all clear. The clock supposedly had something to do with it, but the argument is cabalistic.

Mr. Newton referred indirectly to the Mantell disaster, and implied simply that Captain Mantell had come so close to the saucer that its occupants had "demagnetized" him, in self-protection. Otherwise, Mr. Newton reassures us, the Venusians are not in the least hostile. "The little men are simply scouting the earth, mapping out its magnetic lines in preparation for the day when they will land here and take up life." The word "demagnetization" as employed here is without scientific meaning.

When confronted by the direct question, asked by Pasquale Marranzino, writer for the *Rocky Mountain News*, "Did you see the men, Mr. Newton?" the reply was somewhat amazing: "Don't ask me that question. For reasons I can't explain, I can't say."

I insist that this reply is amazing, coming as it did from a man who had told a fantastic tale of a supposedly secret investigation. Here was a man who had told this story because he felt that the world should know these epoch-making details that, he said, the Air Force was trying to keep so secret. And now, this man who had revealed so much refused to answer a simple question: "Did you see the men, Mr. Newton?"

His refusal can mean only one thing. I believe that the story was a hoax, and meant to be a hoax, perhaps not malicious. We might say, rather, that the story was a yarn or tall tale, filled with many clues to its fictitious nature. Perhaps Mr. Newton was surprised at how gullible the public proved to be.

Tall tales are part of our existence. Some of the more familiar ones begin, "There once was a traveling salesman who . . . ," and no one is expected to believe that the rest of the story is true. There are the legends of the North Woods, where the giant Paul Bunyan and Babe, his blue ox, had miscellaneous fantastic adventures. We don't believe these stories, even though we enjoy them. Why, then, should we believe a tale no less tall, where the supporting evidence is so clearly packed with misinformation?

I have never met Mr. Newton, but I take my hat off to him in one respect. Few people other than the famous P. T. Barnum have had the distinction of fooling so many of the American public. Newton's assertion that oil deposits radiate microwaves is completely untrue, and any oil company making such claims would lay itself open to prosecution under Federal laws.

People who indulge in the spinning of yarns adhere to a rather special code of ethics, which resembles that followed by both amateur and professional magicians. We go to a magic show expecting to be fooled. In the course of the evening the magician makes a woman disappear and we are properly mystified. If we are so naïve as to approach him later and ask the question: "Did you really make her disappear?" we must not be surprised at the reply. The magician will almost never give an outright "yes" or "no." To say "yes" would be lying. To say "no" would detract from his artistry. Besides, we ought to know that she didn't disappear! A combination of natural and Federal laws will not permit it. So he hedges — "That's a special question I can't answer now."

I feel that Newton's actions are analogous to those of the magician. He had been advised that the students would judge his story on the five points already mentioned. The tale failed to meet a single one of the requirements, but even so, many persons believed it to be the truth. He must have given a convincing performance!

"But where did he get so many facts?" is the primary question that believers tend to ask. The answer is simple: "From the same place that Jules Verne or H. G. Wells or other writers of similar fiction get their facts — from an active and vigorous imagination!"

The University of Denver incident occurred in March of 1950. Approximately six months later Frank Scully's book *Behind the Flying Saucers* appeared, headlining the story of the little men from Venus. The jacket of the book carries the blurb:

To some this book may appear as an exciting and swiftly-paced story of interplanetary high jinks — wonderful entertainment. To others it may appear as a serious and extraordinary recounting of experiments and phenomena in new methods of air travel. To others it will be a combination of both. Which is it?

The book makes for entertaining reading — especially if one has no scientific background for separating fact from fiction. Roland Gelatt, in a review,[4] raises the question whether Scully's book is serious or a deliberate hoax. He checked with the author, who indicated that the presentation was intended to be serious. Koehler backed the claim. The publishers stated, "If it's a hoax, we'll be the biggest suckers of all." The *Saturday Review*, its "curiosity still

piqued about Silas Newton . . . checked with the American
Petroleum Institute and learned that he is neither a member of the
American Association of Petroleum Geologists nor of the Geological
Society of America. According to our informant, Newton is not the
key figure in the oil industry that Scully would have us believe."

Nor was Scully really so complimentary, for he described Newton
as "a man who had never made more than $25,000,000 nor lost more
than $20,000,000." Read those lines carefully, and consider whether
they add authority to Scully's claim that Newton was "a man of
substance."

The *Saturday Review* appraises the book as quasi-scientific, and
concludes, "It seems plain that we are in for a deluge of humbuggery
calculated to exploit popular superstition and ignorance." It seems
significant that nowhere in Scully's book is there a reference to
Broman's five tests, which the book itself completely fails to pass.
Instead, it is Mr. Scully who complains against censorship by newspaper editors or even by the Chancellor of the University of Denver.
Scully himself holds forth on the subject of hoaxes.

It is generally believed that to be any party to a hoax spells ruin, once
the hoax is exposed. Nothing is further from the facts. The exposure of the
Locke hoax did not ruin *The New York Sun*, any more than Lincoln
Colcord's exposure of Joan Lowell's *Cradle of the Deep* ruined Simon and
Schuster or Orson Welles's realistic broadcast of H. G. Wells's *The War
of the Worlds* destroyed either C.B.S., Trenton, N. J., or Orson Welles.

Nevertheless, no one wants to be either a collaborator or a dupe in such
a literary lollypop if he can avoid it.

In general a fair backlog of believable data has to be accumulated
before a hoax can be tried with hope of any degree of success. You just
can't pull off a practical joke about something no one ever heard of
before.[5]

The book and later events proved that Newton, Koehler, and
Scully were friends.

In a later interview for the *Denver Post* (9 October 1950) in
which both Mr. Scully and Mr. Koehler participated, Mr. Newton
added some further details. First he announced the landing of a
"fifth saucer," this time in northern Africa, which also was under
scientific study. He referred to four previous crashes in the United
States, but kept the total number of bodies at the same figure as that

of his earlier versions when only three crashes had occurred. He specifically mentioned "crashes" and did not apparently refer to his account of "an actual landing."

Mr. Newton, elected spokesman for the group, prognosticated that saucers soon would land on the earth, because they had evidently nearly completed their survey. He set the date as winter 1950, or at least by fall of 1951. And then he repeated his "scientific" arguments about saucers flying on magnetic lines. He readily admitted that "the trick is to harness this force."

Here he made a statement whose incorrectness should be apparent to everyone. "Magnetic force — this is the force that keeps the planets of the universe in their restricted, mathematically precise orbits. It is a sensitive force; when disturbed even slightly, floods and physical disaster swim in the wake." The error in his argument? Simply that gravitaton, the true force that holds the planets in their orbits, in no way depends on the existence or nonexistence of magnetic fields.

As usual, Mr. Newton refused to answer the direct question: "Have you seen the saucers? Have you seen these men from a foreign planet? Do you have pictures?" He would only say, "All will come out in time. Don't press questions. I won't answer."

But the greatest inconsistency of all has never been emphasized. Mr. Newton told how he met the government scientists and how they took him into their confidence. But admission to secret laboratories is never made on so casual a basis. Surely Mr. Newton does not expect us to believe that he and he alone has this information. For note that no one else has stepped forward to back his claims.

But even if one were to admit that Mr. Newton's first story of the government laboratories and the crashes were true (which I do not), his statement about the fifth crash then becomes absolute nonsense. If the Air Force really wanted to keep this type of information as quiet as he implies, then the very last man on earth who could gain admission to a laboratory to find out about the African crash would have been the man who announced the secret to the world.

In his book, Mr. Scully refers to an unidentified government scientist, an expert on magnetism, the mysterious man whom Scully calls "Dr. Gee," as the person who gave out the original information. Many persons gained the idea that Newton and Gee were professors in the University of Denver and wrote in for additional information or for confirmation.

Out of fairness to Mr. Scully, we should note that he specifically states, "I have never seen a flying saucer . . . and to the best of my knowledge and belief I have never participated in the perpetration of a hoax on flying saucers." He refers to Dr. Gee as his primary source of information. Mr. Scully, therefore, takes the position of merely relaying information, the correctness of which depends on the reliability of the unidentified man hiding behind the alias "Dr. Gee," whose credentials we are not allowed to examine.

J. P. Cahn of the *San Francisco Chronicle*, writing in the September 1952 issue of *True*, recounts a series of interviews that he had with Frank Scully, Silas M. Newton, and George T. Koehler, in an effort to find out whether there was any truth in Newton's assertions that flying saucers with little men from Venus had actually landed and been examined. (In January 1950 *True* had published an article about flying saucers in which it announced its "reasoned conclusion that they were interplanetary in origin.") During his interviews with Newton, Cahn obtained from him, by a sleight-of-hand substitution of another piece of metal, one of the coin-sized disks that Newton said came from a flying saucer. Cahn had the metal analyzed in a commercial testing laboratory, and found that it consisted of "plain old aluminum, 99.5 percent pure."

In the course of his investigations, Cahn found that Newton had frequently telephoned from San Francisco to Leo A. GeBauer, proprietor of a Phoenix, Arizona, radio and television parts supply house. Cahn obtained from Scully an admission that GeBauer was the mysterious "Dr. Gee" whom Scully and Newton had described as a great scientist whose time was spent on highly secret government research. GeBauer denied in writing that he was "Dr. Gee," and Scully then refused further comment.

Cahn concludes that Scully's book was a complete hoax, conceived by Newton for reasons that are not clear, and carried out by Scully, perhaps unwittingly, as a result of his long-standing friendship for Newton.

On 14 October 1952, according to the *Denver Post*, District Attorney Bert M. Keating of Denver accused Newton and GeBauer of "defrauding Herman A. Flader . . . out of $50,000 in a swindle involving oil well exploration tests with electronic 'doodlebugs,' one of them represented as costing $800,000. . . Two similar machines have been examined and declared to be war surplus items worth about $3.50, the district attorney said."

Mr. Broman has made available some further comments relative to the evaluation tests made by students and instructor. The day following the lecture, application of the evaluation procedure to at least eight classes of students

gave a value of zero to the lecture in terms of acceptable authentic information, but a very high score in entertainment.

A few of the ideas used in the evaluation of the guest speaker's talk in terms of the criteria developed by the class are as follows:

1. At no time did the speaker refer to the first person singular; rather, he insisted on referring to "we." In response to a direct question, "Were you there?" he answered with "We were there."

2. In regard to prejudice, it became perfectly clear that the speaker felt at odds with the United States Air Force. At no time was it made perfectly clear why. It seemed, however, that if complete belief in flying saucers could be secured on the part of a great many people, some kind of personal victory over the USAF would have been achieved by our speaker.

3. In regard to trained observation, our speaker suggested that the material out of which flying saucers were made was like nothing familiar to us. He suggested a new element. Anyone familiar with the scheme and system inherent in the Periodic Table of Elements and isotopes could not so glibly suggest a new element; what would its number be, what properties are predicted for it, etc.? Another example in connection with trained observation was in regard to his inference that we human beings have gained an insight into the numbering system of these little men. He referred to our system of nines in which it is perfectly obvious that 1 plus 8 equals 9; 2 plus 7 equals 9, etc. Then he drew a connection between this system and the measurements taken of flying saucers. These measurements were always such that the sum of the digits in the measurements produced 9. For instance, the cabin on the flying saucer was 72 inches high. The length of the saucer was 99 feet. The class immediately picked up the fallacy of this thinking and emphasized that feet and inches as units of measurement were culturally developed on this

planet and are in no wise a specific measurement of length in the universe.

4. In regard to public information for double-check, our speaker emphasized over and over again that this lecture was the first exposé of the truth about flying saucers and that all information contained in the lecture had been constantly suppressed or censored by the powers that be.

5. Last of all, our speaker insisted upon remaining anonymous. Our class suggested that to remain anonymous in a situation like this may be analogous to a man writing a sizable check on some bank and refusing to sign the check. Was there any money in the account?

Those students who had the prior training in the course were the ones who in general recognized that Mr. Newton had purposely been telling a tall tale.

The publicity attending the lecture was embarrassing to the University of Denver. Chancellor Albert C. Jacobs of the University cautioned the faculty to use utmost care in screening guest lecturers. To his weekly council of deans, shortly after the lecture, he said:

You are well aware, I am sure, that I consider it absolutely imperative that academic freedom, the very foundation of learning and of our free society, be fully preserved and maintained at the University of Denver.

I have, I am confident, in my several public utterances, made my views on this point very clear. I have, however, also stressed the grave responsibility which academic freedom entails, pointing out that it is a trust of the highest sanctity.

Each teacher in our university is responsible for what goes on in his class, for assuring himself that the persons who are permitted to appear before our students are qualified to express their views in regard to a particular field of learning. . .

I have been much concerned over the recent appearance on our campus of an individual, whose name I still do not know and whose qualifications have never been established, who presented his views, purportedly scientific, to our students on the "flying saucer." This situation has subjected the university to considerable adverse criticism and must not happen again.

I request you, as the dean of your faculty, to take such steps as may seem most feasible to prevent a recurrence of this situation. You will, I am sure, invite the attention of your faculties to the high trust which accompanies a teaching post in our university.

Scully calls this statement by the Chancellor "sounding off." Yet, any fair-minded person must admit that universities have a high responsibility to their students and to the nation, to see that the speakers and teachers are qualified to present their subjects. To open up the classroom to everyone would make a mockery of education. Communists and other crackpots in various fields could take over. The screening of lecturers is not censorship, or dictatorship, or suppression of free speech. Such restrictions are a necessity if the university is to fulfill its basic function: education of students and advancement of human knowledge.

But the idea of the little men is extremely hard to combat. It crops up here and there, most recently in Berlin, 1 July 1952. The story hit the world via the *Sunday Graphic* (London). Although the details differ slightly from other reports, the basic pattern is recognizable. The saucer was 50 feet across and shaped like a warming pan, with a 10-foot cylindrical conning tower. Two operators, "clothed in a kind of shimmering, metallic substance," climbed back into the machine and set it in motion. It swirled away like a spinning top. The implication was that the object was a new war machine. The primary proof of the truth of the story is an affidavit, "sworn to " by the eyewitness.

13

Sight and saucers

▶▶▶

> 'Tis the eye of childhood
> That fears a painted devil.
> — *Macbeth*, Act II, Scene 2

If the human mind were constructed as simply as a garden rake, we should gather knowledge as we gather grass. By a simple operation, we should learn whatever information happened to catch itself in the prongs. Such an elementary tool, with no moving parts to wear out, would generally be precise and solid.

Human understanding, however, is not so simple a process. One single moment of mental activity is, in fact, far more complicated than the operation of any man-made machine. There are, therefore, many more chances for error in thinking and learning than there are chances of breakdown even in an automobile of many parts. Nevertheless, just as we may drive a car without considering its mechanics, so may we take for granted our methods of understanding the world, even though analysis shows how obscure these methods are. We cannot visualize how mere brain tissue makes us aware of ourselves and the world. When we try to be conscious of an automatic activity, it ceases to be automatic, and then we no longer observe naturally occurring processes. We cannot "try on" other minds in order to test our strengths and limitations by comparison. Instead of looking for faults in our mental habits, to check the accuracy of our understanding, we generally prove our beliefs simply by finding other people in the world who agree with us. Sometimes we do not bother to check at all! As we have seen in the two preceding chapters, reliance on external impressions alone, or failure to allow for possible inaccuracies, often lead us to irrational conclusions. When we become aware of the limitations as well as the capabilities of our minds, we minimize the chances of misinterpretation.

We have examined two major examples of contemporary irration-

ality. The radio "War of the Worlds" unwittingly produced mass
panic among vast numbers who mistook drama for news. The University of Denver incident was a conscious and obvious hoax, con-
cocted for purposes of publicity, perhaps with facetious humor.
The wide acceptance of these extreme fantasies demonstrated how
irrational we can be in spite of the advancement of so-called scientific reasoning.

"But by far the greatest hindrance and aberration of the human
understanding proceeds from the dullness, incompetency, and de-
ceptions of the senses . . . speculation commonly ceases where sight
ceases. . . The sense by itself is a thing infirm and erring; neither
can instruments for enlarging or sharpening the senses do much." [1]
Despite this wisdom of three centuries ago, we still continue to
credit our senses with more ability than they in fact possess. Although today no one believes that thunder is noise caused by
Hendrik Hudson and his crew playing at ninepins, many still believe that it results from the collision of two clouds. This modern
notion is scientific in so far as it represents an attempt to find a
physical explanation based on observation. From three facts alone
— the noise of thunder, the presence of thunder clouds, and the fact
that collisions produce noise — we can easily deduce the bumping-
cloud theory. These three facts are, however, insufficient for us to
develop a reasonable description of the occurrence of thunder.
Our simple theory collapses completely when we add one more
fact: rain clouds, however highly concentrated, are not solid
enough to make noise when they bump together. Furthermore, there
exist other sources of noise than mere collision of solid bodies;
explosions, for example, also make noise. An adequate description
of thunder requires far more evidence than our five senses can discern unaided. We cannot *see* the electricity that heats the cold air
when a lightning flash leaps from cloud to cloud, or cloud to ground.
We cannot *see* the heated air expand rapidly. We can only hear the
reverberations produced by the explosive expansion.

Difficulties inherent in the events themselves thus often compli-
cate the understanding of natural phenomena; in other words, the
five senses are incapable of perceiving all of the factors necessary for
complete understanding of the world. Because we can best under-

stand a description that provides us with a clear mental picture, we assume that seeing is identical with believing. Just as a child "believes in" the glass slipper and the pumpkin coach, so may we believe in Martian machines "wading the Hudson like a man wading through a brook," and blonde, 36-inch Venusians with peach fuzz on their faces.

The senses, our initial contact with the world, are on the whole reliable informers of experience. When we look at a tree, we do not mistake it for a house. When we smell hay in a barn, we do not think that the barn is on fire. We may sometimes mistake a tree stump in a dark wood for a bear, but our senses are not responsible for the error.

The functioning of the senses constitutes only a limited portion of our total learning process. The messages they send to the brain would be unintelligible if our brain did not organize them and interpret them in the light of human experience. Consider the following example. A man leans out of his window. He sees four trees, a long street, several large buildings, a motorcycle, cars, three flags, and a number of men dressed in white; he hears music and drums; he smells dust and automobile exhaust. He then turns to his wife to report the sight, but he does not list his perceptions individually. He organizes them according to his experience and says that he has seen a parade. If he happens to know that the day is a holiday, he may deduce the reason for the parade. But if he knew nothing whatsoever about parades, his senses might deceive him into thinking that the town was being invaded.

Of the various operations of the mind, the senses are the ones most available for study. Although perception never actually operates completely apart from motivation, thinking, and the other departments of mental activity, we can nevertheless reconstruct part of the sensory processes.

Isolated from the other operations of the mind, perception becomes a purely physical process. Light stimulates the rods and cones on the sensitive surface of the retina of the eye; sound waves set in motion the diaphragm within the ear; nerves in our fingers respond to pressure, heat, or cold. Stimulation sends impulses to the brain, where in some way they affect the tissue. The brain thus receives a mosaic of sensations. Each element in the mosaic, being a fragment of a total image, has no meaning in itself. The senses do not supply understanding. Other mental activities select and organize the impressions. In so far as these are familiar, they become meaningful in terms of experience. But if we were to receive a set of impressions entirely outside our experience, we would not understand them.

Men commonly tend to confuse means with objectives. In this case the *means* are the senses; the objective is understanding. Accurate understanding of most natural events requires more than simple perception. The story of the blind men who went to "see" an elephant illustrates that understanding is distorted if we accept a single sensory impression as valid proof. One blind man happened to grasp the tail; he decided the elephant was like a rope. The second, feeling the leg, thought the elephant was like a tree. Each man in turn encountered one part of the animal and formed his conclusions from one limited, though nevertheless accurate, observation. The conclusions were not *wrong*; they were nevertheless far too incomplete to be *right*.

A significant fallacy lies in the maxim "seeing is believing." The eye is only the intricate and marvelous instrument that communicates the external world to our intellect, yet we often consider this instrument as identical with understanding. With Othello, we cry, "Be sure of it. Give me the ocular proof." [2]

Understanding, as I have said above, is not the task of the senses. We rely on memory of past experience to give meaning to perception. When we see a chair, we know what it is because we have experienced chairs before. Similarly, flying saucers, so foreign to our experience, possess no meaning until we find something within our past experience to serve as a basis for understanding. If we conjure up memories from science fiction for our basis, we may accept the space-craft hypothesis.

The total experience of each person is, of course, unique. That it so profoundly influences understanding implies that no two persons possess identical ideas about the world. Plato even doubted that men can know the real world at all. He believed that they observe only shadows, although what they are seeing appears to be real. The significant fact is, however, that the relation between previous experience and interpretation permits many chances for error.

Superstition results from a misapplication of logic. Today we should know that a black cat cannot bring bad luck. Only the superstitious believe in this type of causality. A superstitious person habitually endows events with totally irrelevant causes. Thus he may "lay his goatish disposition on the charge of a star!" [3] Human reason thus often rests on illogical foundations, permitting very serious mistakes. The explanation of the source of flying saucers is an example of this kind of irrationality. Although they appear to be "new" to human experience, it does not *necessarily* follow that they are extraterrestrial.

Still another extremely powerful force influences perception and experience. This force is motivation or feeling. The role that feelings play in understanding is obscure but critical. Attitudes are never absent from mental activity. Even the simplest events of our lives are accompanied and hence affected by an attitude such as love, hate, fear, aggression, or even indifference. The influence that emotions can exert varies from person to person. One man may disagree categorically with anyone he dislikes. Another may insist that an ugly person whom he loves is actually beautiful. A third may be ignorant of some law he wants to break. The baseball enthusiast may read the sport page in the paper and omit the travel section. We all, perhaps, are guilty of "not remembering" to do a disagreeable chore.

Although the effect of emotion on understanding is complex, the influence is unquestionably a strong one. Suppose that some woman buys a dress of bright red, purple, and orange. The color combination may start a controversy among her friends. One may approve because gaudy colors happen to be in style. Another may disapprove only because he dislikes purple. A person who dislikes the woman may consider the dress "bad taste." The color clash may hurt the eyes of another. The differences in judgment are due to differences in individual feelings; the colors themselves do not change.

In the case of saucers, the predominant feeling that distorts understanding is fear, sometimes combined with wishfulness and expectancy. The flying-saucer believer is somewhat like a man forced to spend the night in undesirable quarters, say in a dirty hotel; expecting to find bedbugs in the bed, he begins to notice every tiny twitch of his body. Characteristically, he is afraid because he is uncertain whether or not any bugs are there; he almost hopes that one will bite, so as to remove his uncertainty. Thus do attitudes and emotions rule behavior. No wonder so many people welcome the "proof" that saucers are truly invaders from Venus! The theory extinguishes all fears that they might be a mysterious threat from Russia. Although fear of the unknown is a natural response, irrational fear can be treacherous. One discerning answer to the problem of such fear lies in Plato's definition of courage. Courage is "knowledge of what is truly to be feared." [4]

Expectancy often controls thinking. When we are searching for a certain friend in a crowd, we may pass by other friends although we may look directly at them. The attitudes that are uppermost in our minds affect our perception and thinking most easily. The following incident, which occurred soon after the first saucer reports, illustrates the effect of expectancy. The motion picture "Fantasia" had returned to Boston. The first section is devoted to abstract, colorful designs that move rhythmically with the music. The audience listened and watched. Suddenly a flock of little white ellipses skated across the screen. Everyone in the theater burst into spontaneous laughter. Many exclaimed: "Flying saucers!"

Innumerable problems of understanding the world lie, then, in the processes of perception, thinking, and motivation. The problems I have mentioned here represent fragments of the integrated process of understanding. The various components that I have artificially isolated for the sake of simplicity are, in actual practice, inseparable. Motivation, learning, thinking, and perception are interdependent. Each requires the others; each affects the others. If we can misinterpret observations made with perfect vision, how much more can we misinterpret observations if our eyes contain imperfections that we do not recognize.

During the past several years I have had correspondence from a woman who is eighty years old and nearly blind. She has the unusual and extremely dangerous hobby of looking directly at the sun with the unaided eye. She describes what she sees: "Bright spots of many colors detach themselves from the sun and float about in a most beautiful pattern. They must represent something important happening on the sun. I am sure you could see them for yourself because I see them every day."

Poor old lady! If she had not been blind originally, she has completed the destruction of her eyes by looking at the sun directly. The lens of her eye has as surely burned holes in the retina as a reading glass will burn a hole in a piece of paper. The weird blots of color that she reports are the impressions that her brain reports of the sensations sent from a badly damaged eye. The mysterious spots of color are the burned holes in the retina, and perhaps droplets of blood inside the eyeball. As long as the optic nerve can function, it still will try to interpret whatever stimuli it receives. Here, brain tissue has no experience to draw on. But a senile mind still tries to endow the images with reality and insist that they represent something on the sun rather than in the eye.

The foregoing case is, of course, extreme. But most of us have occasionally seen objects that exist on the surface of the eye or even within it. These take various forms. Some, which show up as shimmering globules of light, are only tiny specks of dust, motes, floating on the outer surface of the eye. If one of these specks, preferably illuminated indirectly by an intense light source, happens to be on the pupil, it will appear as a large, out-of-focus blob of light. If viewed against a dark sky or other dark background, this bright image can appear spectacular. The motion of the particle, as it floats across the pupil, may make it look like a flying saucer. These so-called "entoptic" phenomena are responsible for many saucer reports.

Numerous related apparitions can occur, all arising from sensations produced on or in the eye. That such phenomena occur was recognized by Hippocrates about 400 B.C. and later interpreted by Galen in A.D. 200 as caused by the presence of minute opaque bodies within the eye itself.

The reported images, some of them much discussed throughout history, have been described as gnats, flies, flying ants, insects, shining spots, glowing disks, chains, strings of pearls, cobwebs, hairs, or pieces of wool. I am indebted to James A. Hamilton, M.D., of San Francisco, for pertinent information on this important aspect of physiological optics. Dr. Hamilton has been studying such phenomena for the Air Force.

If any foreign objects in the eye are illuminated, they can cause a type of flying saucer. The "chains" or "strings of pearls" are actually minute blood capillaries in the surface of the retina and 'the "pearls" are the tiny corpuscles themselves, which become visible under special conditions of illumination.

Fig. 21. Lights projected on the sky may originate from defects within the eye.

A related and perhaps more familiar phenomenon is the after-image. A sudden flash of light will momentarily affect a part of the retina so that we continue to "see" a dark image of it for some time afterward. One can induce a remarkable phenomenon by cutting a model saucer from black paper, putting it under intense illumination against a white background, and looking at it fixedly for at least a minute until the eye feels perceptible fatigue. Now if one turns out the light and sits in darkness, he will see the image of a bright space ship seemingly floating in the air. If one uses a colored instead of a black saucer, the flying image will also be colored, in the complementary color. Hence, a red saucer will produce a blue-green image and *vice versa*.

Many reports of lights or saucers in the sky refer to a peculiar rocking or wobbling motion. One August evening during the saucer maximum of 1952 a loud and almost hysterical conversation woke me from a sound sleep. I caught detached phrases like "There it moves again!" "Look at the color shift." "Is it in distress?" So I struggled into robe and slippers, grabbed a flashlight, and went out of doors. Some of my neighbors were pointing skyward toward a bright object that seemed to be gyrating and performing celestial gymnastics. It was only the star Arcturus, perhaps twinkling somewhat more wildly than usual — the day had been a scorcher — but the color changes were those common to twinkling objects. The rocking motion the viewers thought they saw was all in their own eyes. No eyeball is absolutely stationary and no one can keep his gaze fixed perfectly. The motion can increase under hysteria. And thus another potential flying saucer vanished.

These phenomena within the eye are especially hard to eliminate. One should particularly distrust any observation so fleeting that he cannot really analyze it, at least unless it is confirmed by an independent observer.

14

How far away is a rainbow?

▀▀

Why, in the midst of a discussion about flying saucers, do I ask "How far away is a rainbow?" What can rainbows and flying saucers possibly have in common?

Let me say now what I hope to establish later, that the flying saucer is indeed an optical phenomenon, a sort of cousin of the rainbow. Neither one is an optical *illusion.* You can see a rainbow and you can see a flying saucer.

The majority of those who have reported seeing a saucer have made some statement about its size, its distance, its speed. Hence, if we can talk about the distance of a saucer, it is certainly legitimate for us to talk about the simpler problem, the distance of a rainbow.

There is another reason why we should discuss the rainbow. We have seen that the heavens are filled with many wonders: the stars and planets, eclipses of the sun and moon, comets, fireballs, and shooting stars, a wide variety of cloud formations, the aurora borealis, rings and halos of great beauty. Before we admit that a flying saucer must be an object from another world, should we not first explore the possibility of its being perhaps one of the rarer forms of astronomic or atmospheric apparitions? We can start with the rainbow — which in itself is a startling apparition to anyone not familiar with the way it originates. What we know about the rainbow will help us, in turn, to resolve the saucer problem.

And so I repeat, "How far away is a rainbow?"

Before going any further, stop, think about some rainbows you have seen, make an estimate of distance, and jot it down for future reference. Most of us have had the experience of seeing the rainbow apparently lying between us and some not-too-distant object, a tree, a house, a mountain, or a meadow. We may have seen an even more localized rainbow at the foot of a waterfall or in the spray from a garden hose. Our impression of location may be so definite that sometimes we can almost swear that we know exactly where the "foot of the rainbow" lies. But if we try to look for the legendary pot of gold hidden there, we perceive that the rainbow moves tantalizingly ahead, never allowing us to get nearer.

As a preliminary step in our attempt to interpret the rainbow, let me ask another somewhat simpler question. Consider this situation: A man sitting in his own home, facing a mirror 5 feet away from him, sees in it the image of a nearby street lamp. He turns and looks at the lamp directly through the open window. He knows that the lamp is exactly 100 feet away, perhaps because he has measured it before. Now, then, as he turns again and views the lamp in his mirror, how far away will its image be? Or, if my use of the word "image" seems too ambiguous, let me rephrase the question and ask, "How far away will the lamp *appear* to be?"

If the man uses some accurate means of gauging the distance of the street lamp as seen in the mirror, he will find that the light appears to be at a distance from him of 110 feet, which is 100 feet plus twice the distance from himself to the mirror. If, therefore, he walked 5 feet behind the mirror and looked at the street lamp he would see that it had the same apparent size that it would have as viewed in the mirror from his original position.

Many persons to whom I have talked seem to think that a mirror is something like a picture — that the image resides in the surface. To prove otherwise, try this simple experiment. Stand at arm's length from a picture and touch some detail of the surface with your finger. Now take a couple of steps to one side or another, continuing to indicate the same definite spot on the picture. No matter where one stands, the finger will always point to the spot on which it rests.

Repeat the same experiment with a mirror, pointing toward the street lamp or some other distant object, with the finger touching the glass surface. As one walks sideways, the distant lamp will appear to move, to keep pace. To indicate its direction, one will have to drag his finger across the mirror surface, with the arm sweeping in a path nearly parallel to itself. The more distant the object indicated, the more nearly parallel will be the successive positions of the arm. The image does not lie on the mirror surface. It is just as far behind the mirror as the original object lies in front of the surface.

And now we see the rainbow difficulty clearly. Each drop of rain is a sort of mirror, reflecting the image of the sun in its own special way. Not one but many thousands of such tiny mirrors are contributing at any one time to give us the rainbow pattern. The water-drop mirrors lie somewhere in the volume of space between the eye and the distant rain cloud. Thus we do not even have a distinct mirror surface. But in any case, all of these individual mirrors reflect the sun's rays. Hence, the rainbow must be as far away as the sun itself — 93,000,000 miles!

If this statement sounds unbelievable, a simple experiment will be convincing. Suppose that a man stands with his back to the sun and lets the spray from the nozzle of a garden hose come within a few feet of his face. If he now reaches out and points to the rainbow, blinking his eyes alternately, looking at the rainbow first with the right eye and then with the left, he will discover that only one of his eyes sees the rainbow indicated. Actually he sees two rainbows, one with each eye, as long as he focuses his eyes on the spray itself. But if he focuses his eyes as if the bow were very distant, the two rainbows will fuse into one.

As in the case of the mirror, a man may point to the rainbow in the sky, a waterfall, or a hose spray, and then start walking to one side or the other. The rainbow will keep pace, stopping when he stops, moving when he moves, and in the same direction.

No one is concerned or frightened by the fact that the rainbow seems to dog his footsteps. No one attributes to it some special intelligence that enables it to follow, or concludes that it must possess a sense of curiosity because it seems to be so personal.

But note, in passing, how this behavior resembles that of the docile variety of foo ball. In this similarity we get one of our first clues to the true nature of a flying saucer.

This characteristic of the rainbow contains a warning for every potential observer of a flying saucer. If the saucer is not a solid object, not something that we can really reach out and touch, but an optical effect something like a rainbow, then our ordinary procedures for estimating distances and sizes do not apply. If we happen to guess that it is 10 feet or 1 mile or 50 miles away, we can judge its size and speed accordingly.

Even though two or more people may have the same illusion that a certain rainbow is near, the mere fact that all arms pointing to it are essentially parallel shows the fallacy of estimating distances.

Perhaps we should be more accurate if we assigned no special distance to the rainbow, or regarded the distance as meaningless. The rainbow is, in truth, a "direction" and not a "thing." We generally see rainbows only in the early morning or late afternoon, because the sun must be less than 42° above the horizon before we can see the primary bow elevated against the sky.

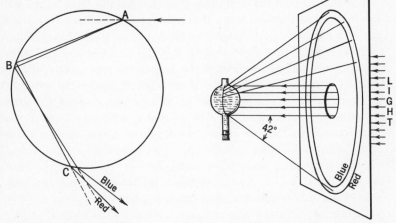

Fig. 22. Formation of a rainbow. Light is refracted and dispersed within a spherical drop of water.

Fig. 23. Diagram to show a method of producing an experimental rainbow.

I might also ask, "How big is a rainbow?" But now we realize that the apparition depends upon a combination of two factors: first, we must have a source of light, and second, we must have some way of reflecting or focusing or otherwise changing the direction of the light beam. With such simple devices we can explain a large variety of natural phenomena — including the flying saucer.

Reports from observers indicate that many of the flying saucers possess peculiar color effects. Since these probably arise from a process very much like the one that gives color to a rainbow, we should know something about color.

A light ray that strikes the surface of some denser but transparent substance like glass or water will in part be reflected by the surface and in part transmitted through it. Reflection is very simple. The light simply bounces off at the same angle that it struck, like a billiard ball rebounding from the side of the table. But the path of light entering a denser medium is a little more complicated. The light ray bends where it meets the surface. We call this phenomenon "refraction of light."

White light is a mixture of all colors. When white light is refracted, the blue light is bent more than the red; the other colors are bent by intermediate amounts. It is this unequal bending that gives color to a rainbow. Each drop of water is a tiny globe. The situation is approximately that illustrated in Fig. 22. Light strikes the drop at the point *A* and passes through the drop to the rear surface, where it suffers a mirrorlike reflection at *B*. Next it strikes the external surface at *C*, where red light emerges at an angle of about 43° with respect to the entering beam. Consequently, when we look at the light from such a drop or from a multitude of drops, we see a red band 43° from the point directly opposite the sun. Blue light, being bent a little bit more, emerges at an angle of 41° and hence the blue bow lies inside the red. The other colors lie between these two, and we see the rainbow colors in their normal order.

A secondary rainbow also is fairly common. It is somewhat less brilliant, with the colors more spread out and appearing in the reverse order, at an angle of 51° for the red and 54° for the blue.

A simple demonstration, easily performed at home, requires only a clear, spherical glass container of some sort. The upper half of a glass coffee maker is ideal. To make a large-scale model of a raindrop, put a cork in the bottom of this globe and fill it with water. Next take a piece of cardboard and cut a hole in it with a diameter about 10 per cent larger than the globular flask. Use a distant source of bright light — the sun itself, a very bright lamp, or a projection lantern — allowing the light to pass through the hole and fall on the flask. As shown in Fig. 23, the ordinary rainbow will appear clearly in the proper position. If the room is dark and conditions are just right, the secondary bow will also show.

This property that liquids and solids possess of splitting light into its rainbow colors appears in many different ways. One of the simplest methods of demonstrating this effect is shown in Fig. 24. Prop up a hand mirror (or mirror from a compact) on a slope in a washbasin. Light a match and hold it so that its reflection is visible in the mirror. Now fill the washbasin to the level of the top of the mirror. Another lighted match held in the position of the first will not show any reflected image. But lower the match slowly, and its

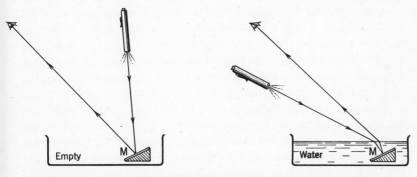

Fig. 24. Refraction of light. The eye is in the same position in both cases, but note how much lower the flashlight must be held if the light is to reach the eye when the basin is filled with water.

reflection will again come into view. Now the flame will have a distinct blue color on top and a reddish hue on the bottom. The effect will be even more striking with a point flashlight (fountain-pen type) used instead of the match, because an intense red image flares out at the bottom — *like the exhaust from a rocket jet.* Does the description recall some of the word pictures of flying-saucer observations?

We observe the rainbow with our backs to the sun. When the sun is very low and the ground covered with dew we can sometimes see the rainbow spread out flat on the lawn, its edges curving away into the distance. This so-called "dew bow" is rare except where the drops are almost as spherical as they would be when falling through the air, for example, when fine cobwebs or feathery plant fibers support them.

Sometimes little droplets of fog or dew may float on the surface of a pond, perhaps deterred from uniting with the main body of water by a thin oil film. Under such conditions the dew bow can be very brilliant.

Under these conditions, if a person stands with his back to the sun and looks at his shadow stretching out long before him on the grass, he will see the grass glitter and sparkle. (If not enough dew is present, one can enhance the effect by giving the lawn a light sprinkle with a fine spray from the hose.) He will also see a brilliant halo surrounding the shadow of his head! The shadows of other persons standing near will not possess such a halo. But each person will see a halo around the shadow of his own head. According to legend, some people have interpreted the brilliance of their own personal halo, and the absence of any such halo around the shadows of others, as a sign of their own special genius or sanctity. The curious fact is that each person on the lawn sees only his own halo; his companions are all haloless. Similarly, in a photograph of the phenomenon taken with a camera held at arm's length, the halo appears around the shadow of the camera and not around the head of the photographer. Meteorologists call this phenomenon the *heiligenschein*, German for "holy shine."

Reflection by waterdrops is one of the important effects for the production of flying-saucer phenomena. If a ray of light is sent out from any object — a flashlight, the windows of a plane, the sun, or the moon — any globules of water on the grass will tend to reflect the light back upon itself. At night, hold a flashlight at eye level for the source, and note the brilliance of the reflection from dew drops on the lawn. Now move the flashlight to one side and see how rapidly the illumination falls off. The effect is closely associated with the one that makes the eyes of animals seemingly glow in the dark, when actually they are merely reflecting light rays.

The nature of a rainbow and the character of these reflections depend to a marked degree on the size of the water drops. A normal-sized drop gives sharp, mirrorlike reflections and produces a highly colored rainbow. But as the drops approach microscopic size, so that we have fog or mist instead of rain, the rainbow colors begin to fade, the rainbow contracts, and we have a white rainbow instead of a multicolored one. The circular band has an orange tint at the outer rim and a bluish one on the inner. And sometimes we get rainbow colors in between.

As the density of the mist increases, a most remarkable and sometimes frightening apparition appears. The effect is occasionally visible in daylight, but the most striking ones occur on a dark night when the fog is dense and heavy, of the type you can "cut with a knife." Stand in front of a brilliant lamp and face the shadow that stretches away into the distance like a long, dark hall. The shadow possesses a distorted human shape, but it moves with the observer. If he raises his arms on high, the shadow grows a pair of protruding horns.

This phenomenon has a name, the "Specter of the Brocken" (Fig. 25). The Brocken is a mountain in the Swiss Alps where the "specter" appears on occasion, when the sun breaks through the mist at the peak. The strange appearance results from the fact that no single surface is responsible for producing the shadow. The shadow occupies a large volume of space and stretches away into the distance as far as the

Fig. 25. The Specter of the Brocken, with halo.

eye can see into the dense fog. To produce a reasonable imitation of the phenomenon, hang up a dozen layers of gauze or cheesecloth, an inch apart, and then look at the multiple shadows of some simple object on the gauze.

When the fog droplets are nearly uniform in size, the shadow around them will possess a striking halo — a "glory." Aviators flying over clouds often see them around the shadow of the plane — the so-called "pilots' halo." Like the Heiligenschein, each person sees a halo around only his own head. The shadows of his companions are drab by comparison. No wonder that medieval artists have tended to put such halos around the heads of saints. Since the halo is a type of "glory," we can understand the Biblical reference to the rainbow itself as the "Glory of the Lord."

To observe the colored halo, breathe on the lenses of your spectacles or on the surface of a mirror, to form a fine fog, and view a small, bright light through it. Or, better yet, dust a mirror or piece of glass lightly with lycopodium, the powdery spores of the club moss. (Druggists use this material as a coating for certain types of pills.) Any bright source viewed through the dust will be surrounded by a remarkably brilliant halo.

15

Ice crystals in the sky

▀▀

Drops of water in the air are pretty much alike: round. Large drops and drops of intermediate size give the beautiful rainbow. Fine mists give the white fogbow. In addition, they can provide the other wide range of effects discussed in the previous chapter, from the specter of the Brocken to the *Heiligenschein.*

Ice crystals, on the other hand, present a wider range of possibilities, in shape and in orientation as well as in size. The simplest ice crystal of all, and probably the most common variety that occurs naturally, is a tiny needle or prism.

These simple shapes tend to stick together and build up formless clumps, especially when the temperature is a little above the freezing point. But when the temperature is lower, stars and plates begin to grow, and we get the more complicated forms of snow crystals, many of them quasi-regular and symmetrical crystals of great beauty: the six-sided snowflakes like those shown in Fig. 26. The hexagonal star is characteristic of many crystalline forms of ice.

Light entering one of these crystals is reflected one or more times within it and finally emerges at an angle very different from that at which it entered. In consequence, we can have almost innumerable patterns of halos and other phenomena produced by ice crystals in the atmosphere. We have already discussed some of these effects, without trying to understand in detail the physical situation that caused the particular pattern of light.

The ice crystals that produce the most significant optical effects are those possessing regular forms. A small, flat snow crystal, fluttering to earth, will fall something like a feather or a fragment of tissue paper. It will tend to lie flat, parallel to the ground, to a greater extent than it will fall down edgewise. Needles behave similarly.

If the sun is low in the sky and if the flakes are almost completely horizontal, reflection from their upper or lower surfaces will produce one of the simplest of all of the solar apparitions: a vertical pillar of white light (Fig. 27). One can see a somewhat similar column if he stands before a window covered with a Venetian blind, its slats horizontal (Fig. 28). The reflected sunlight will form a column. If the sun is very low, the pillar will generally possess the sunset colors and show a reddish light.

Sometimes, oscillations of the falling snowflakes, especially when needles rather than flat plates are involved, can produce a horizontal as well as a vertical strip of light. The two arms meet at the sun, and we see a most startling apparition — much rarer than a rainbow

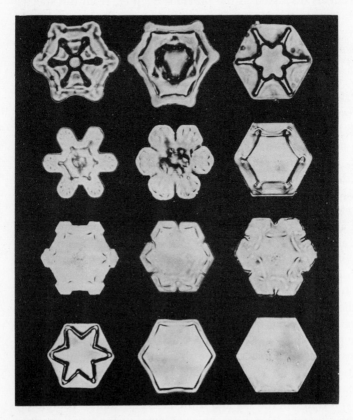

Fig. 26. Hexagonal ice crystals.

— of a cross, sometimes of fiery hue, suspended in the air before us. When the storm is very distant, the cross may appear to hang against the sky. But if the flakes are concentrated in a narrow curtain close to us, with the sun shining through from the opposite side, the cross may appear to be only a few hundred feet away. Like the rainbow, the cross moves as we move, and stands still as we stand still.

Fig. 27. Pillar of light reflected from horizontal crystals of snow.

Indeed, it was probably such a celestial apparition that led the Emperor Constantine the Great to acknowledge Christianity in the year A.D. 312. He adopted the cross as his emblem with the words, "*In hoc signo vinces*," that is, "By this sign conquer."

These columns or crosses, themselves composed of sunlight reflected from falling snow crystals, have a peculiar feathery texture. At the same time, a glowing scintillation like a shower of sparks lends realism and makes the column stand out seemingly more brilliant than the rainbow. Sometimes the pillar will appear to be only a few yards away. But if one tries to pursue it, it retreats, and then vanishes almost instantly at the moment one emerges from the snowstorm into the sunlight.

We should mention, however, that the ice crystals need not by any means be as densely packed as in a snowstorm. Sometimes they

Fig. 28. Column of light reflected by the horizontal slats of a Venetian blind.

form cirrus clouds (Fig. 29). Again, they can be so thinly spaced that the atmosphere is transparent, except in the direction that the "pillar of fire" appears.

The floating ice crystals can cause another phenomenon — a pair of halos, one whose radius is about 22° and the other about 45°, both centered around the sun. These halos, which are not at all uncommon, are sometimes wrongly called "rainbows." Actually, as we have already mentioned, one has to turn his back on the sun to see a rainbow. These halos lie relatively close to the sun, and, in addition, their coloring is very different from that of the ordinary rainbow. The inner edges of both of these bows have a warm, ruddy tint. The outer edges, instead of being blue or violet, possess a pearly iridescence, glowing almost as if the halo were self-luminous. The halos and the cross are essentially independent phenomena. We can have one without the other. Their simultaneous occurrence is rare.

When the upper air is so highly tranquil that the minute flakes of ice tend to lie flat, the portions of the inner halo whose altitude equals that of the sun display an increased luminosity, which on some occasions almost approaches the brilliance of the sun itself.

Fig. 29. Feathery cirrus clouds, containing ice crystals.

Thus the sun appears to possess on either side brilliant, glowing, mock suns, commonly referred to as sundogs and technically known as parhelia (Fig. 30). These images are colored like the halos, red toward the sun and white or amber on the side away from the sun.

The rings occasionally show a bright spot above and also one below, so that the complete apparition of a cross centered in two beautifully colored circles, with the mock suns glowing like "burnished brass," is one of the most spectacular sights in all of nature

Fig. 30. A display of halos with only inner rings and associated mock suns.

Fig. 31. A full display of rings and mock suns.

(Fig. 31). Add to it a few of the other arcs and horns that sometimes appear and a selection of other false suns, shining like "eyes" on the rim of the outer circle, and you indeed have an apparition that would frighten the ignorant and alarm the superstitious.

Fig. 32. Subsun, photographed from the Zugspitze, Bavarian Alps.

A short arc that curves upward like horns, from where it touches the uppermost edge of the outer circle, possesses a special characteristic that distinguishes it from all of the other circles, because it is the only one that resembles a rainbow. It is red on the side toward the sun, and blue, a real sapphire blue, on the upper edge. On rare occasions, especially in a very clear sky at a high altitude, the uppermost portion is a rich violet. A brilliant white ring may encircle the entire sky at the same altitude as the sun itself.

From a plane, balloon, or mountain top another phenomenon is sometimes visible: a brilliant reflection of the sun in the mirrorlike layer of flat ice crystals (Fig. 32). The image, called the "subsun," lies just as far below the horizon as the sun lies above the horizon. The mirror is imperfect and the reflection tends to be drawn out into a vertical ellipse, which may suffer even further distortion and

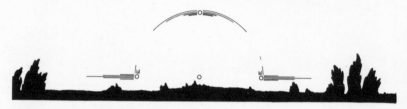

Fig. 33. Mere fragments of a mock-sun apparition, as seen near sunset. Often the upper arcs are absent.

Fig. 34. Mock suns seen at sunset.

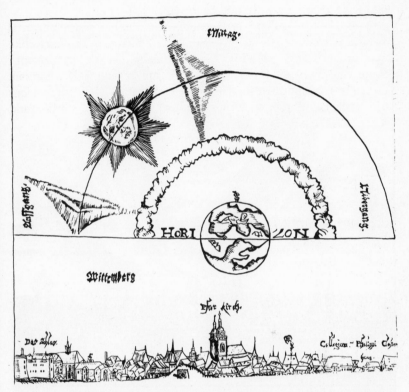

FIG. 35. Mock suns as seen in Wittenberg, Germany, in 1556.

look like a parachute or balloon. The subsun can also develop sub-
sundogs and halos, to produce a still greater complication of pattern.

These peculiar reflections are, like the rainbow, centered on the
eye of the observer. They require a luminous source and the intervening orientated ice crystals. In the daytime the source is usually the
sun and at night, the moon, in which case we refer to the "moondogs" or "paraselenae." But any bright light can show these peculiar
refractions and reflections, though usually only the more brilliant
aspects appear. I have seen them surrounding a distant street lamp,
when the snow was gently falling.

Fig. 36. Rare halos and sundogs seen over Nuremberg, Germany, in 1530.

The pattern can become even more complex because each sundog can act as a source and thus acquire what we might call "a litter of sun puppies," though the extremely rare phenomenon has no technical name. In this event, the pattern of lights and rings in the sky becomes so extremely complex that we find it difficult to distinguish the sun itself from the multitude of glowing images.

Fully developed sundogs and moondogs are quite rare. In my life I have seen only one complete apparition of each. However, I have seen many examples of the partially developed phenomenon. Indeed, the average person is unaware of how frequently sundogs occur, without the accompanying halo that assists in the identification. Sometimes one of these mock suns looks as real as the sun itself. When the ice cloud is near, the reflection may look like a ball of fire floating between you and the background of a nearby tree. In my opinion, many of the so-called reports of ball lightning, a phenomenon never fully explained and still not generally recognized, are due to these mysterious sundogs that occasionally interpose themselves between the observer and some nearby solid object. One may be unaware of the fact that any ice crystals are in the atmosphere, and the major feature that will identify the object is a slight trace of red coloration on the side toward the sun.

Even the 22° distance from the sun is not sacred. A cirrus cloud near the sun will often develop a small part of the arm or upright of the cross, and thus appear like a detached sundog, glowing brightly.

Naturally, sundogs that give the illusion of nearness require the presence of frost or ice crystals in the lower atmosphere and hence are seen only in winter. But ice crystals in the upper air can occur at any season of the year, so that any cirrus formation is a potential source for bright patches of reflected or refracted light.

Sundogs or the subsun are attached to the observer in exactly the same way we have described for the rainbow or other solar-induced halos. The very brilliant reflection from a nearby cloud of frost crystals chases after a plane in realistic foo-ball fashion. As long as we maintain a straight course, that ball of light will stay in exactly the same position relative to the plane. In daytime we see clearly what it is and recognize it as a reflection (see the Frontispiece). If

Fig. 37. Mock suns as a reflection phenomenon, illustrated by the reflection of the man in the mirror.

Fig. 38. A fireball floating in the air, as seen from Hamburg and other places in northwestern Germany, on 4 November 1697. Probably a mock-sun phenomenon.

we veer course, the ball of light will move from its original place and turn to meet the change of course. If we face into the sun, the foo ball will show dead ahead. However, in view of the fact that we are then flying against a layer of snow crystals, usually the brilliance increases enormously as part of the light pillar. This light pillar may seem to race on ahead, sometimes lagging behind and approaching the plane if the ice crystals become denser, or moving on ahead as in Fig. 39, or even vanishing completely as the frost thins out.

Fig. 39. Subsun reflected in hexagonal ice crystals.

If we did not see so clearly exactly what was happening, we might be deluded into thinking that we were chasing a bright, metallic object or one with glowing lights suddenly taking off at an enormous speed — for thus we tend to interpret the sudden disappearance of what seems to be a solid craft.

The great majority of the foo fighters and flying saucers are caused by refraction or reflection in crystals of ice. Any luminous object can give mock images of itself. Though I have never seen the phenomenon myself, there is no reason at all why the bright luminous sunset glow on the horizon, or a bright patch of auroral radiation, could not give "horizon dogs" or "aurora dogs." And, by the same token, cities or searchlights can give similar peculiar reflections. Our experience with the solar and lunar prototypes of this mystery convinces us that the image can be at times almost as intense as the original source appears to be. This statement disposes of one widely publicized criticism, namely, that reflections could not be intense enough to produce the observed saucers.

Many of the saucers reported from the ground have all of the basic characteristics of sundogs. Flying ice-cream cones, some of them topped with red, are characteristic formations of ice crystals. An authoritative German book on the optics of the upper air [1] shows some very convincing conelike formations associated with various appearances of mock suns.

The saucer that Captain Mantell chased to his death presents some special problems of interpretation. Observers from the ground stated that the object, as reported in Chapter 1, looked something like "a red-tipped ice-cream cone." An alternative simile was "circular, but with some of the appearance of a parachute, with the sun strongly reflecting from it." As seen from the plane, the object glinted like metal in the bright sunlight.

The bearing of the craft, reported by Mantell before the crash, was 210°, that is, 30° west of south, substantially on the same bearing as the sun, which had an altitude of about 20° above the horizon. We can assume that Mantell could distinguish between the sun and the nearby saucer. Slight inaccuracies in the estimates of altitude and azimuth make it uncertain whether the object Mantell was chasing was the sundog 22° above the sun or some part of the vertical beam of the cross nearer the sun. There is reason to believe that Captain Mantell saw the subsun on the same bearing and mistook it for the sun itself. The image can look almost as real as the sun. He may then have pursued the true sun, which, partially dimmed by crystals of frost, could easily have appeared as recorded in the fragmentary reports of Captain Mantell.

I have a number of other reports of objects seen from the ground which are very clearly either sundogs or moondogs. And when some observer reports that he sees the stumps of wings and a reddish glare beneath, he is only seeing part of the phenomenon described by Ezekiel. For the stubby wings of a modern saucer are only the vestiges of the fully developed outstretched wings of Ezekiel's beasts. The amber light in both cases is the glowing of the mock sun. And the redness underneath, which we now know to be merely the inner red part of the halo, is built up by the imagination to be the "red exhaust of the jet," the same warm redness that Ezekiel took to be the outstretched arms of the angels. So do our imaginations endow with life the shadowy apparitions that suddenly rise like ghosts out of the dark.

The fact that the plane itself may contribute to the manufacture of a cloud of ice or mist that in turn can reflect light from some distant object seems not to have been previously considered. If a plane has had some injury to its wing, such as damage from anti-aircraft fire, the nonuniform flow of freezing air over these broken patches may produce sharp changes of density and pressure that will cause droplets or frost to condense within a seething bubble of turbulent air. The fact that the foo fighters were generally not recognized until the later stages of World War II, after planes had had a number of such injuries, perhaps with imperfect repairs, suggests that sometimes the formation of the crystals may be due to the plane itself. However, since ice crystals do occur naturally, this is not in itself a necessity.

I am indebted to Dr. Vincent Schaefer, of the General Electric Company, for his photographs of ice formation. Dr. Schaefer, I should say by way of identification, is the man most responsible for the modern science of "rainmaking." Though many of us may have looked skyward at large masses of billowing clouds and asked, "Why doesn't it rain?" Dr. Schaefer is the man who has done more than merely give us the answer. He has been able to produce the rain.

Air grows colder with height, at a rate of approximately 5.5 degrees Fahrenheit per thousand feet of altitude. Hence, air that is just completely saturated with moisture at ground level would be oversaturated — supersaturated, we call it — at the higher, cooler levels. Thus, at these levels, the air squeezes out its excess humidity in the form of tiny droplets, to give us clouds or mist. At the center of each droplet we usually find a tiny speck of dust or even a tiny particle of salt left over from evaporated ocean spray, to form a sort of seed on which the water can condense. Without these seeds or nuclei, the air will remain supersaturated and clouds will not form at all unless the temperatures get very low and the excess of moisture very great.

Thus, even if the temperature at the surface of the earth is 90°, it will be freezing at a height of approximately 11,000 feet, or 2 miles. And here, at these low temperatures, we usually find the tremendous, billowing, rain-bearing clouds, which will produce rain if certain other conditions are satisfied.

In the first place, the tiny droplets of fog will have to adhere one to the other and gradually grow from many tiny particles to a few large drops — drops so large that the sheer updraft of the air currents can no longer support them. Then down they splash to earth to give us rain.

The problem is to make the tiny droplets adhere to one another. But they are singularly uncoöperative in this respect, so that we often have day after day of rain clouds and still a heavy drought.

And here is where Dr. Schaefer's laboratory experiments solved the problem. The simplest way of causing droplets to grow requires freezing them, to make tiny needles of ice. These needles, in turn, stick to one another, giving snowflakes. Finally, the snowflakes form clumps and start falling to earth, and melt to give the rain — a complicated process, but apparently a necessary one.

The temperature falls below freezing at some height far above the surface, from 2 to 3 miles, even on a fairly warm summer day. One might think that the tiny drops of moisture would freeze under these low temperatures, like miniature ice cubes in a refrigerator. But ordinarily they show a high resistance to forming ice and, unless something is done to help the process, these little droplets will not actually freeze until the temperature gets down almost to 40°F below zero! Water drops that remain liquid even below freezing are said to be supercooled. The problem of rainmaking, then, is one of forcing the droplets to crystallize out in the form of tiny frost particles.

One way of accomplishing this result is simply to lower the temperature, perhaps by squirting into the clouds large amounts of extremely cold material like finely divided carbon dioxide snow (dry ice), whose temperature is approximately 70°F below zero. This will cause all the water droplets to condense upon the cold nuclei and start the formation of larger crystals with eventual snow or rain.

Carbon dioxide snow causes this effect by virtue of its own extremely low temperature. Schaefer has found, however, that other finely divided material can be just as effective, at temperatures only slightly below the freezing point of water itself. One of the most efficient materials found to date proves to be silver iodide. If a small amount of this substance, in a state so finely divided that it is almost in the form of a smoke, is injected into one of these super-cooled clouds, the crystallization into fine needles occurs almost instantaneously. The necessary fine division of the material can be produced by the burning of a strip of paper upon which a few drops of silver iodide solution have been placed.

Modern rainmaking usually employs an airplane to fly through or close to the clouds whose temperatures are below freezing. Then the silver iodide vapor shot out from behind the plane causes the widespread formation of crystals throughout the entire area.

Figure 40 shows a photograph of a long, straight valley in the clouds where a plane has just flown, sprinkling silver iodide en route. In this region ice crystals have already formed and a rain-storm is in the making. Looking backward on this strip, one sees in it two very bright patches: the bright patch immediately below the sun is the subsun; the one on the right is a sundog, not of the sun itself but of the bright reflection. I previously called it a sun puppy. This secondary reflection, 22° away from the first, is characteristic of ice-crystal phenomena and clearly shows that ice crystals have been formed in the region.

An interesting report of the subsun, observed from a balloon in 1850, appears in *Travels in the Air*.[2] "When near their highest point, the bed of clouds which covered the sun having become less dense, the two observers saw the sun dim and quite white, and also at the same time a second sun reflected as from a sheet of water, probably formed by the reflection of luminous rays on horizontal sides of crystal ice floating in the clouds."

One of the early records of a flying saucer seen from the air occurs in a record of a flight made 22 March 1868, in a balloon called the "Entreprenant." This flight, with many others, is described in *Travels in the Air*, published in 1871. This book, which is beauti-fully illustrated with engravings and colored lithographs, contains many important early observations from high altitudes.

Fig. 40. Optical effect observed in a dissipating cloud area seeded with dry ice. The bright spot on the left is part of a reflected sun pillar; that on the right is a sundog 22° from the sun's reflection.

Fig. 41. The shadow of a balloon and the subsun.

In the flight of the "Entreprenant," the shadow of the balloon fell on the white cloud layer below (Fig. 41). The recorder of the flight commented,

It [the shadow] follows us rather obliquely, for the sun is already far from the zenith, it being now past five o'clock. Our car comes out in black upon this brilliant white surface, together with our three heads and our two guide ropes. If we had the proper apparatus, we might take a photograph of ourselves.

The author goes on to speak of light reflected uniformly from the balloon, as from a metallic mirror.

This reflected beam of light falls upon the layer of clouds above which we are sailing, but in its path it has taken a most singular form. I will endeavour to describe it, but will leave its explanation to those who are cleverer than I am — at least until I make my next ascent above the clouds.

In the centre of the strange reflected image a black point is very distinctly seen: its tint is soft and graduated, and its diameter a quarter that of the moon. Around this disc we perceive a circle of rainbow colours, the diameter of which is about sixteen times greater; and around this first coloured circle is a second, the diameter of which is about double that of the first, and also tinted with the colours of the spectrum.

I made a rough sketch of the phenomenon, just sufficient to permit our friend M. Albert Tissandier to execute a chromolithograph of it.

The spectacle was certainly curious enough. On one side of us, the dark shadow of our aërostat; on the other, the marvellous reflection which travelled along with us over the white surface of cloud.[3]

The explanation that the writer gives is almost certainly wrong, as far as the bright patch was concerned. Light reflected from the balloon could not possibly have caused it. The bright spot was the subsun, and the two colored circles are the halos caused by snow or ice crystals.

Had this apparition occurred today, the observer, if possessed of any imagination whatever, would have doubtless visualized it as a flying saucer — probably one with a small black window. We still cannot explain this effect in all detail. But does our failure to do so make imperative the conclusion that the object is a saucer?

Although the deluxe apparition of mock suns or mock moons is by far the most outstanding characteristic associated with refractions and reflections from ice, a few secondary effects are worthy of notice, when they happen to appear. Under some circumstances, cirrus clouds containing fine ice crystals will show brilliantly colored edges. We call these the "coronae" or crowns. I have seen such clouds frequently in the mountains of Colorado and New Mexico. They are somewhat rarer in the East, but occasionally show with a fairly intense coloring.

Similar colors occasionally appear in frost crystals deposited on a window pane through which one views a bright source of light on the outside.

Dr. Vincent Schaefer has also called my attention to an associated phenomenon, which has caused occasional wonder, especially since the saucer scare has conditioned us. One evening, shortly after sunset, Dr. Schaefer and his family were driving through west Texas, when one of the children "shouted that a bright orange flame was passing through the sky. Stopping the car, we were amazed to see a brilliant orange streamer emitted from an object moving westward. The glasses showed the mysterious object to be a high-velocity jet plane at perhaps 40,000–50,000 feet, causing a condensation trail in fairly dry air which was evaporating some 500 feet behind the plane. The plume of ice crystals formed by the spontaneous freezing of the condensation of water from the exhaust was being illuminated by the sun which, although it was below the horizon for us, was still capable of illuminating objects at the altitude of the jet plane. A similar occurrence in upper New York State was headlined in our papers several years ago as an unexplainable fiery trail that couldn't be a meteorite because of its long persistence."

16

Lenses of air

▰▰▰

The human eye is a sort of miniature camera, beautifully designed for the operation of seeing. The outer surface of the eye contains a tiny lens, liquid or jellylike in character. It lies just behind the visible surface, imbedded in the dark "pupil" and surrounded by the colored "iris" diaphragm, which changes its diameter to admit more light in darkness or less light in brilliant illumination. The lens is a remarkable mechanism, controlled by tiny muscles that actually change its shape according to the distance of the object at which you are looking.

If you are reading a book or a newspaper, the eye muscles make the lens surfaces bulge out and bring the object into focus. If the object is distant, the muscles flatten the lens markedly. If your eye did not possess this remarkable ability to change focus, you would probably have to carry at least half a dozen pairs of spectacles, one for near, one for far, and others for intermediate distances.

Most of the lenses used for spectacles are made of the best glass and polished to the highest degree of precision. However, in the broadest sense of the word, any piece of glass whatever, even a piece of window glass, is a lens.

All of us have had some experience with lenses of glass. Even though we may be fortunate enough not to need spectacles, we have perhaps looked through those of a friend, or have used a magnifying glass. The world we see through lenses not specially fitted to our eyes is a distorted one, sometimes seeming fantastically unreal.

A piece of window glass is intended to be a lens that possesses no magnification whatever. The high-quality plate glass in the windshield or windows of an automobile is very nearly perfect, so that it produces negligible distortion. Although average window glass contains many irregularities, they are not too important for the most important function of a window, namely, to let in light from outside. But if you carefully examine the outside world through a piece of ordinary window glass, you will find it usually somewhat distorted. Bubbles in the glass or ripples in its surface cause these distortions.

When you see a telephone pole twisted and bent by the window, you do not suddenly get excited and think that the pole is about to fall. Slight motion of your head will make the broken place move up or down the pole, but again you have no concern that the pole is about to crash on you. Further, if you call somebody else's attention to the phenomenon, he will generally be unable to see it unless he places his eye reasonably close to the point from which you saw it yourself.

Thus, even though the world outside may seem to be warped and twisted, there is nothing about the effect that really startles us. And if one of these defects in a pane of glass happens to throw an unexpected streak of sunlight on the floor, we do not immediately exclaim "flying saucer," or postulate that a searchlight from some space ship is shining through the window, merely because we know that a perfect pane of glass would not have produced the light pattern we have seen. We recognize these distortions for what they are and we are all confident that when we go out of doors and look at the world without the intermediate window irregularities we shall see it in its real and undistorted form.

But are we so sure that the outside world is undistorted? True, the nearby trees and houses no longer show the seeming imperfections that we saw through the window glass, But if the day happens to be unusually hot, distant objects may seem to writhe and twist as if alive. Look at them through field glasses or binoculars and again you will see the distortions, some of them many times greater than you observed through the window glass.

The unsteadiness of the images of distant objects is, perhaps, even more startling in the nighttime than in the daytime. Distant lights will seem to twinkle, changing both in color and in intensity, as well as to dance around, or to alter their size and shape. Sometimes we forget that air is like glass in some respects. It is usually transparent in small thicknesses, but in large thicknesses and where irregularities are present, it can give appreciable distortions. A few miles of air can give as great or even greater distortion than a few inches of irregular glass produce. The air, then, proves to be a lens of a sort, usually a bad lens, but occasionally fairly effective.

We have already noted how a light ray striking a glass surface splits into two parts. One part is reflected as from the surface of a

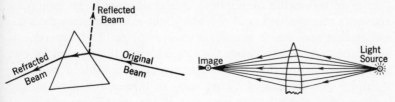

Fig. 42. Refraction of light by a prism.

Fig. 43. Image formation by a lens.

mirror. The other enters the glass but the beam is bent at the point where it enters. Physicists term the bending that light suffers when it leaves or enters a denser or a less dense medium "refraction." A prism or triangle-shaped piece of glass will cause light rays to follow a path as in Fig. 42. A convex glass lens will bring the rays to a focus (Fig. 43).

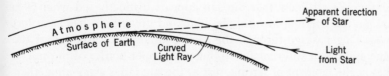

Fig. 44. Normal bending of starlight in the earth's atmosphere.

A secondary effect of considerable importance also occurs, namely, the fact that light rays of different colors bend at different angles. We have already briefly mentioned this point in Chapter 14, because the color effects of a rainbow depend upon it. Since this splitting of light in different directions *disperses* the colors that make up white light, we call the effect "dispersion."

The earth's atmosphere is densest at the surface and the density and pressure both decrease with height. This change in density makes a light ray passing through the atmosphere bend more and more as it approaches the earth's surface, as shown in Fig. 44. Light entering the earth's atmosphere, from the sun or a star, curves in the same direction as the curvature of the earth's surface, though its normal curvature is somewhat less.

There are two consequences of the combined refraction and dispersion of the earth's atmosphere. A star appears to be somewhat above its true position, and the blue light is raised more than the red, so that each star is actually a small rainbow. The dispersion is not particularly marked when the star is high in the sky, but for one low on the horizon the color effects can be noticeable. I have, for example, seen the planet Venus with an intense red glow on the bottom edge and a bright blue tint at the top. These effects, of course, are most pronounced when one views the planet through a telescope. In fact, someone not knowing the real reason for this peculiar coloration might easily conclude that Venus was a saucer, and perhaps attribute the redness of the bottom edge to the glow of jet engines.

There is a third effect that the atmosphere can produce. Although air in small quantities is clear, in large amounts it is distinctly blue. Hence the blue of the sky. Air transmits red light, but scatters the blue. These color effects are enhanced at the time of sunrise or sunset. We all know that the sun appears distinctly red when it is low on the horizon. Most of the blue and green light has been lost in its long passage through the earth's atmosphere. Enough of the blue and green still remains to tinge the upper border of the sun so that at the moment of setting, just as the sun fades away altogether, the last color to disappear is a flash of green or, more rarely, a flash of blue.

This phenomenon, called the "green flash," is best observed from the top of a high mountain or on the ocean, where one has an unobstructed view of the distant horizon. I have frequently seen it from the summit of Mount Hamilton, at Lick Observatory, in California. But one cannot always expect to see the color effects. One has the best chance of seeing the green flash on afternoons when the setting sun remains round or only slightly oval, with a minimum of distortion. On some days the setting sun presents a remarkable series of distortions, taking the form of a Chinese pagoda, a mountain with numerous precipitous slopes, or a bell pepper. Some of these distinctive formations, recorded by J. F. Chappell, of Lick Observatory, appear in Fig. 5.

The prism effect actually raises the sun approximately half a degree in the sky, when the sun is just on the horizon. Since the sun's diameter is about half a degree, when we see the sun with its lower rim just touching the horizon, actually the upper rim, instead of the lower, is at the horizon. The air has lifted the whole image, the lower portion of the sun more than the upper, so that it will appear partially flattened on the bottom instead of round.

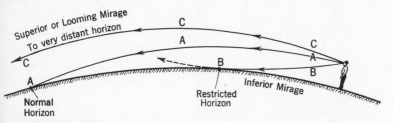

Fig. 45. Formation of mirages.

When the rising or setting sun suffers distortions like those shown in Chappell's photographs, we conclude that the earth's atmosphere is not perfectly regular. Like the piece of window glass, it has layers that distort, producing irregularities when the sun is low.

Normally, as we learned in the last chapter, the air is warmest at the surface and the temperature decreases upward at a rate of approximately 5.5 degrees Fahrenheit per thousand feet. The normal or standard refraction of the earth's atmosphere is calculated on the assumption that the temperature follows this simple law. However, one sometimes encounters very appreciable departures from this average distribution of temperature.

On an excessively hot day, especially on the desert, the air close to the ground can become extremely hot; it expands or becomes less dense. In such an atmosphere light rays would be somewhat less sharply curved than normal; in an extreme case they can be concave upward and follow along path *B* rather than the standard path *A*, in

Fig. 45. At the other extreme, the earth's surface may be extremely cold, with perhaps an overlying layer of warmer air, so that the temperature may even increase instead of decrease upward. Then the bending becomes greater than normal and the path may be even more curved than the surface of the earth, as in C.

If we are standing out on the desert on one of these hot days, a remarkable phenomenon occurs. Light from the very distant horizon never will reach the eye. Or, to phrase the problem somewhat more accurately, the horizon seems to be phenomenally contracted. In an

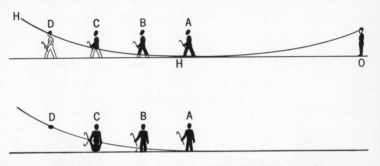

Fig. 46. Mirage effects. The horizon is shown at *HH*. An observer at *O* sees a man walking over the horizon; his appearance, with mirage effects, is shown at *ABCD*. Finally, the man's head has become a flying saucer, floating in an ocean of blue.

exceptional case, it may even seem to be only a few hundred feet away. The world has become an island of sand a few hundred feet across, and an ocean of silvery blue flows in, breaking up into waves. The edge of the "shore" is indefinite and rapidly changing. "Pools" of shimmering blue "water" twinkle in and out of one's vision. Their appearance may be very sensitive to the position of the head; moving about, or even nodding the head from side to side, can cause one "pool" to appear to dry up and others to come into view.

This phenomenon, caused by the upward curvature of the beams of light, is somewhat more than the senses can grasp. They are not accustomed to seeing the sky below eye level, except when it is reflected in water. Hence the eye will interpret this shimmering blue as a lake or ocean. In many instances, a distant, elevated horizon will appear almost normal and, rising above the foreground sky, will enhance the illusion of nearby water.

But if a person tries to walk toward this lake — if, for example, he is a traveler lost on the desert, his mouth parched — he will never reach the "shore," because it recedes ahead of him and closes in behind. One gains the impression of walking on dry land through the midst of a sea. When the mirage is perfect, the continued recession of the sea seems to be little short of a miracle.

If the traveler has a companion who walks away into the distance, the sea will often appear to "swallow him up." As he strides along, his feet disappear first, and then gradually more and more of his body gets "covered up" as he disappears beyond the restricted horizon (Fig. 46). Often some remarkable mirage distortions occur: his legs may appear to be lengthened and other parts of his body may be squashed down in comparison. An unsteady atmosphere can cause remarkable reelings and writhings.

If the conditions are just right, that is, if the air is very calm and steady, an inverted image of the man's head and shoulders may join on to the visible portion sticking up above the horizon. Under average conditions, this lower image is distorted. It may writhe and twist or break into little nodules, intermingled with bits of blue sky. Indeed it looks not unlike the reflection of a man in a disturbed pool of water.

Very distant objects, like mountains or trees — if trees are found in such surroundings — will show this inverted image. Hence, the mountains or parts of them will appear like cigar-shaped islands floating in the sky. (Fig. 47).

Although most of us are unable to go to the desert to see this full-scale mirage phenomenon, we can often see it along a highway. On a clear, hot, calm day, with the sun shining down on the dark asphalt pavement, a layer of intensely heated air often lies directly over the road. Hence, on a straight, level stretch you will see this mirage phenomenon both before you and behind you as you travel along in your car. The road several hundred feet ahead appears to be wet, covered with a layer of water, but as one approaches, the large puddles turn to small ones and disappear completely when one comes near. These puddles are merely an image of the sky against the dark pavement. The phenomenon does not require, as some people have thought, reflection from nearby bodies of water.

Many reports of flying saucers have to do directly with this phenomenon. The following excerpt is from the *Denver Post* for 19 October 1950.

Fig. 47. Mirages of distant mountains. Note how fragments are detached from the tops and float like dark saucers in the air. What does That prove

Five southwestern Wyoming oil-field workers said that a gleaming flying saucer apparently controlled by a U. S. Air Force plane briefly followed their automobile, and then streaked away at high speed when they stopped to watch it. Louis Mandrich of Rock Springs made the report. He said the bright, silvery disk swooped to within 300 yards of his automobile as he and four other oil-field workers drove on the highway near Beryl Springs, Wyo.

"The disk stayed near the car as long as it was in motion," he said. "It appeared to be about 15 feet across and was saucer shaped. It was so bright in color it glared."

Mandrich said the disk streaked away "at terrific speed" when he stopped the car.

According to the oil-field worker, the twin-engined plane bearing Air Force markings was flying near the disk when it first was sighted.

"The plane and the disk were in full sight of each other and appeared to be operating together," he said. "The plane flew off just as the disk disappeared."

. . . Mandrich said he sighted the disk first and shouted to his companions that "There's one of those things you keep reading about."

Now here is a sort of flying disk that almost anyone will meet under certain circumstances — that is, if "meet" is the right word to use for an object that chases after you down a long highway.

Conditions must have been just about right for an intense mirage on the highway, but in front of the car the mirage seemed far enough away to cause no special comment. To the rear of the car, however, the hot air was effectively stirred up and lifted. As a consequence, the mirage, though still 300 yards or so away, was elevated by the disturbance of the air due to the car's motion until a bright, gleaming saucer, an image of the sky, seemed to chase after the men. This image, viewed against the darker background of the highway, would have all of the characteristics reported and would definitely follow the car as stated. And it would have disappeared as the car stopped, because the air was then no longer stirred up.

Mirage effects that would be small on the ground can sometimes be enormously magnified in a plane or a balloon. A saucer like the one that chased the automobile can also occur in a plane and give the operators the impression that a metallic lens-shaped object is either following or fleeing from the plane, and moving at the same speed. The appearance of this image is very sensitive to the position of the plane. Move up or down by only a few feet and the lens-shaped object inflates or deflates, without appreciable change of shape. Thus the pilot gets the impression of rapid accelerations and extreme speed (Fig. 48). Some of the reports of nearby daytime saucers may be attributed to this type of mirage.

We do not require an immense expanse of desert to see this mirage effect. You can produce something like it yourself along a hot brick

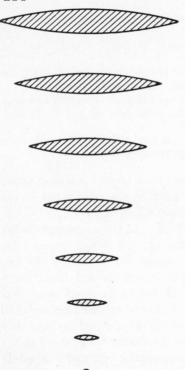

Fig. 48. Sometimes only a few feet difference in elevation can cause one of these cigar-shaped mirages to change markedly in size or even to vanish. If the eye interprets this image as a solid object, like a flying saucer, it also interprets the change in size as due to enormous velocities.

sidewalk. Simply have someone hold an object — a pencil, a pen, or a key — close to the heated surface, 30 or 40 feet away if possible. If conditions are right, an inverted image of the key, lying below the direct image, will appear when you place your eye near the surface. Sometimes you can see even two or three images, some erect and some upside down, standing one on top of the other.

We call the reverse conditions a "temperature inversion," when a layer of extremely cold air lies close to the ground and the temperature increases upward. If the rate of increase of temperature is rapid, a striking effect occurs, which is just the opposite of the desert mirage. As we have noted, hot layers below cause the horizon to press in, but hot layers above make the horizon expand. Light rays bend in the opposite direction and follow along the curved surface of the earth. If the conditions could be made just right, with an extremely steady atmosphere, and with the temperature distribution chosen exactly right, we could theoretically see all the way around the world. For under these idealized conditions, the light rays would follow parallel to the surface of the earth and indeed the earth would then seem to be flat except for the peculiar fact that no matter in what direction you looked, you would see only the back of your own head.

We never can expect so ideal a condition to hold over tremendous ranges. However, we do occasionally get unusual steadiness over distances from 300 to 400 miles. A distant coast may therefore "loom" up above the horizon when you well know that you would otherwise not be able to see it at all under normal circumstances.

Occasionally, the distribution of temperature in the horizontal as well as vertical direction is sufficiently uniform to give a lens that

Fig. 49. Mirage effects.

images a ship both above and below the real image (Fig. 49). And the real image itself can shift appreciably from its normal position. Sometimes we see the ship highly magnified and at other times extremely distorted. These occasional mysterious mirages, which suddenly appear and fade away into nothingness, gave rise to the legend of the "Flying Dutchman" — a ghost ship supposed to appear most commonly off the coast of southern Africa. According to legend, the captain of the ship was condemned forever to sail the seas without touching port, because of blasphemy. Wagner used the story as a basis for his opera "Der Fliegende Holländer."

The Flying Dutchman, therefore, should be definitely relegated to the realm of flying saucers. The ship's captain, playing dice with the devil of his soul, is particularly appropriate for this type of object.

The temperature inversion also accounts for observations of the kind made by the Montgomery, Alabama flyers previously mentioned. In these reports a saucer, turning to avoid a collision, rocks the plane with a blast from its jet engines, then speeds up and disappears. How can a mirage possess powerful exhausts? Does not this observation prove that the saucers are real craft?

The atmospheric lens that causes the associated mirage consists of a layer of cold air sandwiched between two layers of hot air. Air in the upper half of the lens is steady, but the lower part is unstable. A plane flying through the dividing surface between layers will suddenly encounter sharp up and down drafts. These currents or "pockets" are what the pilot feels — not a blast from the jet engines of the vanishing saucer. The saucer disappears because of the atmospheric irregularities in this region.

Mirages occur more frequently than most people realize. I have seen two and sometimes three independent horizons, partially overlapping. Mirages from the air are even more spectacular than those from the ground or ocean. In our desire for speed, in the modern airplane, we miss some of the beauties of nature that the old-time balloonist frequently saw and had time to explore. Many of these optical forms change so fast with position that a man in a speeding plane does not have a chance to study them in detail. If some atmospheric conditions happen to produce an unfamiliar form, the image usually vanishes before we have a chance to analyze it.

On a balloon voyage that occurred in August of 1868, Tissandier describes an unexpected mirage seen from an altitude of 5,900 feet (Fig. 50). He says:

We turned to look for the coast of England, but it was hidden by an immense veil of leaden-colored cloud. Raising our eyes to discover where this cloud-wall terminated, we perceived above it a greenish layer like that of the surface of the sea, and soon we descried upon it a little black point, the size of a walnut shell. Fixing our eyes upon it intently, this little moving spot turned out to be a ship sailing upside down upon an ocean in the sky. In a few moments a steamer made its appearance —

it was the image of the boat from Calais to Dover, and by the aid of my telescope I could distinguish the smoke coming out of the funnel. Then two or three other vessels came upon the scene . . . projected into the air by a fantastic effect of mirage.[1]

Dr. Vincent Schaefer, of the General Electric Laboratory, has told me that "while climbing in a United Airlines plane from La Guardia, I saw an amazing example of a mirage in the Hudson

Fig. 50. Mirage from a balloon.

Valley. In the region toward the Catskills was a mountain range that would rival the Himalayas. As I watched, tremendous U-shaped canyons appeared and disappeared and jagged peaks were in a state of rapid evolution . . . Radiosonde records show the presence of a strong inversion and very dry air up to about 4,000 feet."

Charles Lindbergh, on his epoch-making flight to Paris in 1927, records that he noted the Irish Coast projected upward by mirage, several hours before he expected to see it.

There is thus abundant evidence that refraction has occasionally played peculiar tricks upon our senses. Mirage sometimes lifts land areas high into the sky. If these land areas are dark, they will seem like black islands projected against a sunset. And the cigar shape is always characteristic. In many cases a luminous region on the earth, such as lighted fog over a distant city, or towering cumulus clouds shining in the sunset, can also be lifted and the images carried several hundred miles. In the darkened sky we lose all sense of perspective and could readily imagine that such objects were close to us, especially since their appearance changes so rapidly as we shift our position by a small amount.

Simple mirage is by no means the only phenomenon that aviators can see. There are all sorts of peculiar cloud reflections and refractions that produce surprising images and apparitions that the eye cannot interpret readily.

I have already discussed how a heated desert surface produces an inferior mirage in the daytime. As all inhabitants of the New Mexico or Arizona deserts will testify, the ground cools rapidly as soon as the sun sets. The air close to the ground also cools faster than does the air at higher levels. A temperature inversion sets in, therefore, and tends to persist all night. Hence, where inferior mirages are the order of the day, superior mirages are the order of the night.

Distant city lights, automobile headlights, or searchlights can thus shine against the sky (Fig. 51). The natural astigmatism of the lenses of air will spread out the light into the characteristic cigar-shaped pattern. Usually, these images will be low on the horizon. But if a layer of haze is present, reflections from that layer can be intense.

Thin layers of dust or smoke often occur naturally with some kinds of temperature inversions. Smoke rising from a chimney or factory will often attain a certain height and then flow sidewise to form such a haze layer, at the height where the temperature reaches its *minimum* value, below the inversion region.

The Wave Propagation Committee of the Joint Chiefs of Staff, an organization of which I was first acting chairman and later chairman during World War II, carried out special radio experiments in the Southwest. These studies made direct use of the nighttime

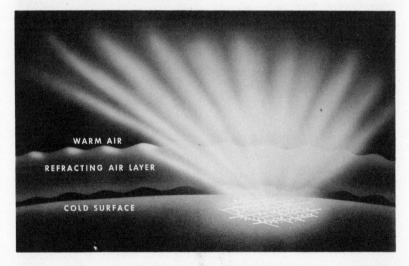

WARM AIR

REFRACTING AIR LAYER

COLD SURFACE

Fig. 51. Effects of refraction: (*a*) normal atmosphere; (*b*) a temperature inversion carries light to a long distance, apparently lifting the lights of a distant city into the sky.

Fig. 52. Artificial mirage of a tree.

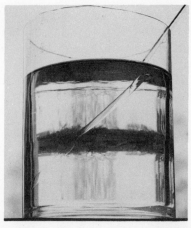

Fig. 53. Mirage and distortion.

desert inversions to show that radar waves, like light waves, can also produce mirages. Further details will appear in Chapter 19. Here the chief point is that temperature inversions in arid regions were well-known phenomena.

I have tried to test some of these theories experimentally in my laboratory. Since it is difficult to control amounts of air large enough to produce measurable bendings or distortions, I used a liquid equivalent to a few miles of air. I filled a glass jar half-full of benzene, and then gently floated a layer of acetone on top. Benzene acts like cold air, having a high refractive index, and ace-

Fig. 54. Mirages of the author's face. At least five are visible, as evidenced by the conspicuous deep shadow on the left.

tone like warm air. The region where they mix represents the temperature inversion.

The mirage effect produced shows clearly in Fig. 52; note the trees growing down as well as up. The apparent distortions of what is actually a straight glass rod, Fig. 53, illustrate the irregularities of refractive index in the liquid, as does the mirage of the author's face, Fig. 54, with images alternately erect and upside down, some fairly clear and others badly blurred.

Fig. 55. Experimental setup of refraction. Note how the beam of light is deflected by the liquid.

I produced saucers experimentally by projecting light through a tank of benzene and acetone, Fig. 55. Any disturbance of the liquid made the saucers dance or move. Images from a multiple source produced the Lubbock light effect already shown in Figs. 6 and 7.

A simpler though less realistic setup substitutes reflection at a water surface for the internal refraction. Fill the kitchen sink with water. Set a light, for example, a burning candle or pen light, as

Fig. 56. Flying saucers in a coffee cup.

close as possible to the water on the far side, and view the reflection, with the eye near the water surface. Now stir the water gently with a spoon and the light reflections will dance all over, like flying saucers. One can even perform this experiment in miniature, in a cup of coffee, as in Fig. 56. The reflection from the match, viewed in the ruffled surface of the liquid, often shows the saucer-shaped light pattern.

Although horizontal irregularities are the most important, vertical irregularities also appear and sometimes these can co-operate to produce phenomena of the flying-saucer variety. We have all noticed that the stars twinkle more violently on some nights than on others. Although the sun as a whole does not appear to twinkle, examination of its surface with a large telescope will often show that each minute area is twinkling individually. The effect is most pronounced during a total solar eclipse, when all of the sun is covered except for one or two tiny spots, which shine like beads of molten silver. At this moment, if the observer looks at a white sheet or a white bank of snow, he will often note a pattern of shadow and light moving rapidly, the so-called shadow bands.

The atmospheric waves that produce the shadow bands and cause stars to twinkle are most intense at the boundary between layers of cold and warm air. The differences of refractive index between such layers can produce distorted images of objects seen through the wavy surface. These distortions can, theoretically at least, be sensibly increased when a layer of cold air lies above a warm one. A weather balloon breaking through the top of the inversion will carry with it a bubble of hot air. The overlying cold layer will sag into the hotter level and momentarily act like a big lens, focusing

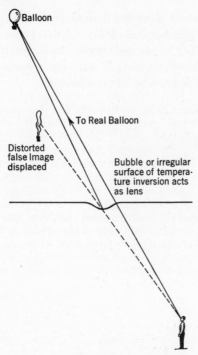

Fig. 57. Distorted image of a weather balloon formed by a lens of air at a temperature inversion.

whatever happens to be above it. Thus it may produce a distorted image of the balloon (Fig. 57).

This phenomenon, I believe, can explain the peculiar balloon effect reported and previously mentioned in Chapter 3 as the mysterious sausage-shaped saucer snooping around our balloon experiments. I understand that similar ghosts have also accompanied some of the ascending V-2 rockets. The phenomenon is entirely a natural one and not too complicated optically. Calculations show that the known difference in temperature between the two layers can produce the imaging effect.

If the saucer devotee thinks that his view of the universe, peopled with beings from another planet, is in any sense modern, I should like to give here some thoughts that de Fonvielle had on a balloon ascent that he made back in 1867. As the balloon rose to great heights, he was able to see the moon more clearly than from the ground. He examined its surface with his telescope and saw the great craters and mountains whose summits

appeared to shine like a chaplet of pearls. Are they capped by perpetual snow, or are they virgin rocks which no water has ever moistened? I cannot say what beings may people this world which our globe seems to have bound to itself; but neither Fourier nor the whole of the French Academy will ever make me believe that this is a desert and an inanimate globe which follows ours in its track through space. Who knows but what the moon may be peopled by a race of beings more intelligent than ourselves, and who may someday conquer us as Columbus conquered the Indians of South America? Is it true that the moon acts upon our reason more powerfully than upon the waters of the ocean? Is it true that it dissipates human reason and the gay projects of lovers, as, tonight, it hides from our gaze the trains of the meteors? No; let us banish from our thoughts these relics of superstition and fear no longer to contemplate its soft white light! [2]

17

The aurora borealis

Few apparitions in the sky are more beautiful or have caused more wonder than the aurora borealis. About the only people who seem to have taken this phenomenon for granted are the Eskimos and the inhabitants of Scandinavia. As the name implies, the "northern lights" are indeed most common in the far north. We usually associate glowing skies with the intense cold and arctic snow fields, but occasional displays appear in temperate latitudes. In past centuries these unexpected auroral apparitions have taken their turn in frightening the people. The association of the aurora with the great saucer of 1882, previously recounted, justifies our considering the phenomenon here. Even though no direct evidence exists to connect aurorae with modern saucers, some persons have taken the green color of the New Mexico fireballs as indicating an auroral phenomenon.

The northern lights, by virtue of the relatively higher abundance of habitable places in the north, have had the wider publicity. But their southern counterpart, or aurora australis, likewise exists and has furnished a natural illumination to the famous Byrd and other Antarctic expeditions.

Primitive ideas about the aurora have in general been extremely far from the truth. The Eskimos, for example, have regarded the glow as light reflected from arctic snow fields still illuminated by the sun, as certain gods intercepted it at the western horizon and carried it around under the northern sky, so that it would be ready to rise again the following day. A rather amusing theory — but completely wrong.

A much more common view, apparently widely held by the ancients, was that it depicted events on the surface of the earth. The superstitious and imaginative could see kings, armies, beasts, great processions, battles, and funerals — in addition to other apparitions like angels, devils, and dragonlike monsters the like of which never walked the earth.

Reinzer, in his *Meteorologia Philosophico-Politica*, previously referred to, writes:

One should remember the year 1568 when on one bright night, as Fomianus Strada testifies, two armies in the sky met in real order of battle, encountered with shining spears; now retreating, then advancing;

Fig. 58. Northern lights, as seen in Germany, Switzerland, and France on 17 November 1605.

Fig. 59. "Fighting armies in the air," an auroral display, recorded by Lycosthenes, Basel, 1557.

PRÆLUDIT OLYMPUS.

Fig. 60. An aurora.

with shields colliding, and fighting, as when a new race of giants had risen up to storm the heavens. This strange apparition caused no unreasonable fear and terror to the Duke of Alba; thereafter it came to light that this work was heaven's charity — a warning given to rouse the Duke's foresight. The portent prognosticated, as the historian has observed, the approach of the armies of the Prince of Orange, the horrid pillaging and massacring, and a long, miserable war.

Although the farther one goes from either the north or the south poles, the less frequent the aurorae become, intensive study of the occurrence of the auroral lights has established that the maximum of intensity does not occur at either the north or the south poles of rotation.

Careful experiments have determined that the earth is a magnetized sphere. It is this magnetism that makes the compass needle "seek" the north and thus guide the traveler. But the magnetic poles do not coincide with the geographic ones. Instead, they lie roughly 12° from the poles of rotation. The earth's north magnetic pole, which we should really refer to as a "south-seeking" pole because it attracts the "north-seeking" end of a compass needle, lies near Baffin Island, north of Hudson Bay, on the continent of North America. The south magnetic pole lies on the Antarctic continent. These poles, however, are not precisely fixed. They wander slowly and with some regularity in a roughly circular path around the poles of rotation.

Study has shown that the aurora borealis occurs most frequently on a circle about 23° away from the magnetic pole. From this zone of the auroral maximum, the numbers of visible aurorae decrease both toward the magnetic pole and away from it, toward the equator. At the present time, we on the continent of North America are much more favorably located for observing the aurora borealis than the people of central Europe, for instance.

Although the forms and patterns of the auroral lights vary as widely as those of summer clouds, we nevertheless can recognize certain definite types. The aurorae fall into one or the other of two main classes, those with and those without appreciable ray structure. One of the most common forms is the arc, a circular belt of light girding the northern sky. Some of the arcs merely glow and show no marked internal features, whereas others display a series of rays, like the teeth of a comb. Usually the patterns of light shift slowly, but occasionally the brightness flickers and flashes like rays from a burning bonfire. Thus we get three important classes of auroral forms: the homogeneous arcs, the ray arcs, and the pulsating arcs. When the arcs are so far away that their brightest portions lie below the horizon, only a faint glow indicates the presence of an

Fig. 61. Auroral drapery. Fig. 62. The auroral crown.

aurora. Occasionally the rays themselves appear individually or in bundles, sometimes steady, at other times flickering. Not infrequently the auroral light comprises a drapery, which hangs in graceful sweeping folds that may move back and forth like a curtain or a long skirt swaying in the breeze (Fig. 61).

When the arcs are not well defined, the northern sky may be traversed by homogeneous or rayed bands. Occasionally we see only a uniform, diffuse, pulsating surface.

In very intense displays, the auroral glow will sometimes reach to the zenith or beyond and form the beautiful crown or corona (Fig. 62). The corona usually appears as a series of streaks radiating from a dark center, which lies in the direction toward which a compass needle would point if it were free to move vertically as well as horizontally. We call this point the "magnetic zenith."

The auroral glow arises from various atoms and molecules that occur in the earth's upper atmosphere. The characteristic green glow comes mainly from oxygen. This atom, however, under certain circumstances can also contribute a reddish hue. Nitrogen, the most abundant constituent of the earth's atmosphere, also can produce a deep red glow. Auroral displays occasionally show radiations from the very light atom, hydrogen. These observations indicate that the hydrogen gas, instead of being stationary in the earth's atmosphere, is rushing at us with a speed of from 200 to perhaps a couple of thousand miles a second.

The development of commercial fluorescent lighting has made us all familiar with glowing gas. Many advertising signs, like the red neon lights, shine because electrons, driven through the gas, smash into the neon atoms with sufficient force to make them radiate.

Explosions on the sun and other types of solar activity are responsible for the aurora borealis. We now have evidence of the clouds of gas coming in to the earth from the sun, the fast-moving hydrogen referred to above. But, for a long time, the evidence for a solar cause was indirect.

A compass needle points toward the north magnetic pole. If our compass is very sensitive, we soon discover that the needle is never really still. It swings first to the east and then to the west, making a fairly regular progression in the course of 24 hours. But the total amount of the swing and the smaller fluctuations associated with it change markedly, sometimes from just one day to the next. Days when the needle shows a big fluctuation, we call "magnetically disturbed." Intense auroral displays often accompany these big disturbances. In fact, great magnetic activity had caused many scientists to watch the northern sky, back in 1882, as related in Chapter 7, in Maunder's comments about the presence of a large sunspot group, when the great auroral beam behaved like a flying saucer.

Scientists generally like to make observations about any natural phenomenon, and record their measures for later use. Thus we have accumulated detailed information about magnetic activity for well over 100 years. Astronomers have likewise watched the sun and have noted the black spots that show on the solar surface (Fig.

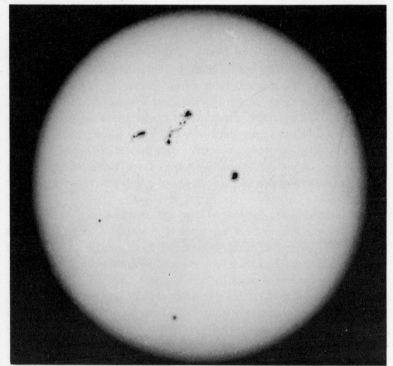

Fig. 63. Sunspots.

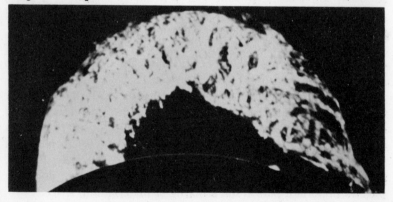

Fig. 64. The largest solar prominence ever photographed. This great cloud of gas erupted from the sun on 4 July 1946. How much material left the sun completely is not known.

63). Records of the size and number of these spots, from day to day and from year to year, have disclosed the remarkable fact that sunspots come and go with a high degree of regularity. A surge of spots is not quite as predictable or as accurately periodic as tides on the earth, but we do see the sunspots increase in number for a time and then decrease almost to zero, before a new cycle gets under way. Records going back over 200 years show clearly that the average interval between successive spot maxima is about 11 years. There has been considerable variation from this average figure, however, with intervals as short as about seven years and as long as sixteen.

A remarkable fact, discovered long ago, was the close correspondence between the curves of magnetic activity and of sunspot activity. They rise and fall together and have continued to keep in step ever since the first magnetic records became available.

Motion-picture records of the sun disclose a surface that is highly turbulent. Great geysers of hot, shining gas shoot upward from it for hundreds of thousands of miles. These streams are sometimes ten or even twenty thousand miles across and they move with speeds up to 50 miles a second, sometimes higher (Fig. 64). These tremendous surges are most common in the vicinity of sunspots, and probably are associated with spot activity. A sunspot is a storm area on the surface of the sun, a region where the temperature and pressure are much less than in the sun's shining surface. Indeed, that is why the spots appear dark; being cooler than the surrounding surface, they send out less light and heat. But that does not stop them from being eruptive.

Of the great masses of gas ejected, the greatest portion probably falls back to the solar surface. A continual rain of down-falling gas on the surface of the sun is one of the outstanding observed features of solar activity. But some of the ejected material must escape from the sun, and some of this must reach the earth. The solar spicules, peculiar bubbling jets in the neighborhood of the poles, may also play an important part in the shooting of material into space.

Study of the sun is becoming more and more important, for economic as well as for purely scientific reasons. If we could forecast when the sun will erupt, we should then be able to predict when magnetic storms will occur. Such forecasts will be useful, because magnetic storms sometimes produce a number of unfortunate consequences on the surface of the earth. Chief of these is the interruption of radio communications, because the aurora borealis seems to knock holes in the layers of the upper atmosphere that ordinarily reflect radio waves from the transmitter to a distant receiver. In fact, during a severe magnetic storm, many types of radio communication become impossible. Anyone who owns or operates a radio station can plan his schedule of transmission much more effectively if he knows in advance when interruptions of the service are most likely to occur.

We also have occasional trouble even with land lines. Here, the rapidly changing magnetic fields can produce strong surges of electricity, which can cause relays to chatter or trip, and on some occasions even make the teletypes print out unintelligible ghost messages. On several occasions, large areas of the country have been without light and power as a result of these magnetic disturbances.

Most of the clouds of gas shot from the sun fade in brilliance before they have traversed more than a small fraction of the distance from the sun to earth. We have no direct way of finding out what happens in the intermediate zone of 93,000,000 miles that lie between earth and sun. At the time of total solar eclipse, we do see a magnificent halo of gas surrounding the sun — the solar corona — and have traced some of its faint streamers out to four or five solar diameters. Thus we infer that gas can completely escape from the sun and that the earth probably intercepts it some hours or some days later, depending on the speed of travel.

Sometimes photographs of the solar surface, taken with a special kind of filter that allows only the red light from hydrogen gas to fall on the photographic film, display a brilliant flash or "flare." These can form in a matter of seconds and disappear minutes later. We still do not know exactly what they are, but they seem to be some sort of major explosion. The blast of ultraviolet light that accompanies the visual manifestations of the flare can cause radio disturbances, which differ somewhat from those produced by the clouds of gas that strike the earth.

The type of radio disturbance that accompanies a flare is termed a "fade-out" or a "sudden ionospheric disturbance." I have occasionally listened to a distant radio program, say from London, coming in plainly on short-wave. Almost in a matter of seconds the program fades away. Has something happened to the radio? No! The peculiar electrification produced in the atmosphere by the ultraviolet light from a solar flare is responsible for the fade-out. Radio waves are absorbed in their path from transmitter to receiver. Some of these flares, which may accompany very intense surges, also seem to eject material from the sun. Hence, twenty-four hours or so later, we may often encounter a magnetic storm and associated aurora borealis.

The distribution of the aurora borealis on the surface of the earth clearly suggests that magnetism has something very definite to do with the phenomenon. Theories of the aurora borealis based on solar and terrestrial magnetism go back to the early 1900's, when the Norwegian scientists, Birkeland and Störmer, were carrying out basic studies of the aurora and its behavior, in the laboratory, in the field, and by mathematical calculation.

Störmer worked out in detail how an electrically charged particle — say an electron — could traverse the distance from sun to earth and get caught in the earth's magnetic field in such a way as to produce the aurora. He showed clearly how electrons would tend to spiral around the earth's magnetic lines of force and how magnetism could guide the electron to earth. Some of the mystical jargon adduced by the persons who make claims for magnetism as a motive power for saucers has been taken from the work of Störmer and distorted to fit the saucer needs.

It is particularly important to emphasize that the electron speeding in its path from sun to earth, on any theory of magnetic control, derives no motive power at all from the magnetic field. The electron must be able to come all of the way on the initial shove it gets from the sun. The magnetic field is just the "track" about which the electrons spiral. Where the field is weak, the spiral is large; where the field is strong, the spiral is much tighter. The faster the particle moves, the fewer loops it will take in its path from sun to earth.

Low-energy particles shot from the sun would move along tracks

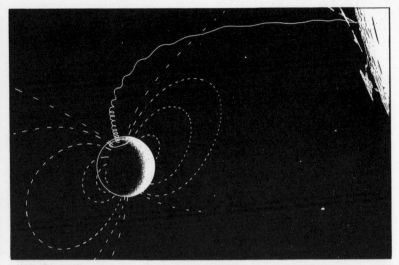

Fig. 65. The path of a low-energy electron in the earth's magnetic field, according to Störmer.

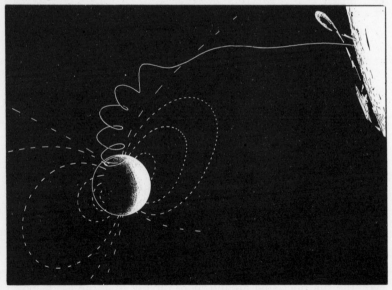

Fig. 66. The path of a high-energy electron in the earth's magnetic field, according to Störmer.

much like that of Fig. 65. The charged particles would never reach
the earth's equator. In fact, they would be concentrated in a very
tiny ring around the earth's magnetic pole. Störmer quickly saw that
his elementary theory needed elaboration to explain the auroral
zone. Thus he postulated greater energy for the electrons, so that,
instead of falling close to the pole, they would settle down along a
circle about 23° from the pole — the auroral zone, as shown in Fig.
66.

Sydney Chapman of England showed that Störmer's idea of a sun
shooting large quantities of electrons to the earth was inconsistent
with other facts. Each electron, for example, carries with it a negative
charge when it leaves the sun. Thus the more electrons that have
been ejected from the sun, the greater the positive charge that the
sun would have. It is well known that opposite electric charges
attract one another. Very few electrons would leave the sun before
the positive charge on the solar surface would be great enough to
prevent any further escape of the electrons. Indeed, the total number
of electrons that could escape from the sun would be able to run a
one-cell flashlight for less than one minute. Thus, this theory could
not possibly account for the enormous energies and luminosity of the
aurora borealis.

Chapman and his colleague Ferraro theorized about the clouds
of gas escaping from the sun. They reasoned that, since gases were
escaping, each negative electron must be accompanied by the
positively charged atom from which it was originally torn. An
atom that has lost an electron we call an ion, and these great clouds
of ionized gas, in Chapman's theory, replaced the stream of electrons
that had appeared in Störmer's calculation.

Chapman showed that if such a cloud of particles were shot out
from the sun, like water from a slowly rotating fire boat, we should
have a situation that develops something like that shown in Fig. 67.
The sun rotates once about every 27 days. Since the equatorial
regions move a little more rapidly than those of intermediate latitude,
no single figure can represent the time of the sun's rotation. However, the sun does spin around more rapidly than the earth moves
forward in its orbit. Hence, any cloud of gas shot from the sun would
curve as shown in the diagram and strike the earth from behind.

At considerable distances from the sun, as Chapman and Ferraro showed, and also as D. F. Martyn of Australia later proved in greater detail, the clouds would move almost unhindered. The magnetic fields in space are so weak that they could not possibly serve as a guide rail, as Störmer had hypothesized. As a matter of fact, the moving gas would tear through any magnetic field present, and, to continue with the "track" analogy, "rip up the rails" and sweep through space almost unhindered by the magnetic lines of force. More accurately, the "rails will stretch," but never will an "open track" occur. About the only effect that the magnetic field could have would be a minor focusing action, which would tend to keep the cloud from dispersing.

Such a cloud of ionized gas could not penetrate all the way to the earth. At a distance of three or four diameters from the surface, the cloud divides, leaving the earth in a hollow. It is the earth's magnetic field that produces this effect, raising a sort of "cosmic umbrella" to keep off the rain of ionized gas from the sun. Thus, if conditions were absolutely perfect, none of the material would ever penetrate to the surface of the earth, and we should never have an aurora borealis.

I have recently made calculations based on a new theory called magnetohydrodynamics. These studies indicate that the simple conditions exist only when the cloud of gas is absolutely uniform, without any appreciable clumps of gas within it. If one of these clouds possesses a sharp irregular edge, it will put a severe strain on the earth's magnetic umbrella. The magnetic lines of force are flexible and give. Like an umbrella in a howling gale, the magnetic field can sometimes turn "inside out," and if this happens, the umbrella no longer can protect the earth from the storm of solar gas. An umbrella that is blown inside out becomes a "funnel" as shown in Fig. 68.

The weakest portion of the umbrella lies on the afternoon and evening side of the earth, since the ion clouds tend to overtake the earth from that direction. But the greatest caving will occur in the polar regions where the lines of force — the ribs of the umbrella — extend farthest. Thus the earth's magnetic umbrella is almost completely gone within the auroral zone. And when, during a phase of

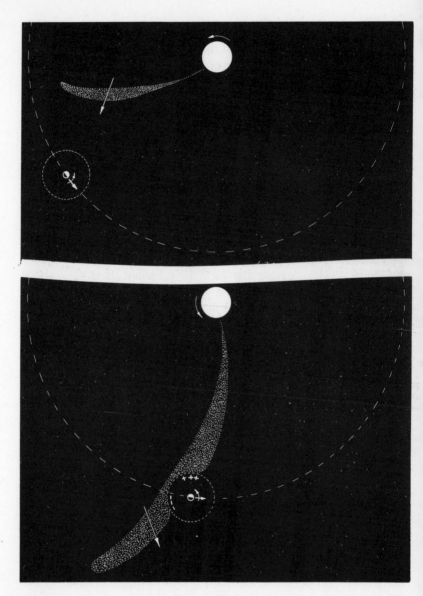

Fig. 67. Three stages, according to Chapman, in the envelopment of the earth by a surge of gas from the sun. Note that the earth's magnetic field forms a protective envelope. The third stage appears on p. 239.

particularly great solar activity, any exceptionally heavy or dense cloud of gas reaches us, the magnetic lines of force can be damaged to a lower latitude, the funnel opened more widely, and more material "sucked in" by what is a sort of gigantic vacuum cleaner (Fig. 69).

The end of the funnel near the earth has a long narrow opening, roughly parallel to a magnetic line of latitude. Thus the material shooting down through the funnel is concentrated and tends to appear as a curtain.

The beauty of the aurora polaris, with its wide variety of forms and its ever-changing appearance, is something that everyone should see. But when the auroral light glows in the sky, we should recall the superstitious horror that such apparitions have occasioned throughout the ages. We can enjoy and appreciate its beauty, because we know and understand what forces produce it and realize

Fig. 68. A more detailed analysis shows large and small clouds of gas shooting in all directions. A specially dense one encounters the earth and bends its magnetic field inward.

Fig. 69. Gas from the sun flows through the hornlike gap left where the earth's magnetic field has caved in.

that it is not a supernatural apparition or sign in the sky. As yet, we cannot predict it as accurately as we can solar eclipses, which have also caused their share of fear and horror. Nevertheless we are making progress in our understanding of the sun and of how solar and terrestrial magnetic fields control the motions of gases in their flight from sun to earth.

An interesting sky phenomenon, about halfway between the aurora and a saucer, and possibly related to the great saucer of 1882, is the occurrence of the so-called mother-of-pearl clouds, iridescent clouds whose nature is still unknown, except that, like aurorae, they tend to be more frequent at higher latitudes.

18

Comets, meteors, and other astronomical apparitions

▀▀

Comets, or "hairy stars," were generally regarded by the ancients and the superstitious as the most terrible of portents.

Our telescopes have shown that comets are by no means the rare objects that naked-eye observations would lead us to believe. For every really bright comet that we see, there are literally hundreds of smaller, fainter ones whose cometary character we deduce from the shapes of their orbits or from a trace of haze surrounding them. Only the brightest comets, the ones that come fairly close to the sun, develop appreciable tails.

What men do not understand, they usually fear. And these "blazing stars," with tails stretching sometimes halfway across the heavens and looking like a curved sword or scimitar, would astound the person who had never seen one before or who had no knowledge about the nature of comets.

The early scientists generally regarded the comets as being an exhalation of the earth, and with good logic according to their mode of reasoning. The great astronomical authority, Ptolemy, in explaining the motions of the planets and stars, imbedded each of the seven recognized astronomical bodies — the moon, Mercury, Venus, the sun, Mars, Jupiter, and Saturn — in a crystal sphere, each turning on a special axis according to a particular rule. The spheres were supposed to be of the finest crystal and thus perfectly transparent. Outside of these seven spheres was an eighth, which carried the background of stars in the sky.

Men believed that these crystal spheres really existed. Hence, a comet could not possibly come in close to the earth, say from a distant region of space, simply because it would have to break

Fig. 70. Cometary influence.

Fig. 71. A comet.

Fig. 72. Many comets and snakes.

Fig. 73. A comet.

through the crystal to do so. Since there was no evidence of crystal breakage, the comets would have to lie between the earth and the nearest sphere, that is, between the earth and the moon.

"Exhalations" were of various sorts. Some of them carried pestilence, some the seeds of war, and others death — especially to persons in high places. Shakespeare has Calpurnia say to Caesar: "When beggers die, there are no comets seen. The heavens themselves blaze forth the death of princes." [1]

There were some who held that the great comet of 43 B.C. was the soul of Julius Caesar, enroute to its heavenly abode.

One of the earliest records we have of a comet occurred in the boyhood of Aristotle, in 371 B.C. — a comet described by contemporaries as "a blazing torch."

As for the disastrous effect of a cometary apparition, one quasi-natural explanation asserted that the "appearance of a comet is followed by plague, pestilence, and civil war; for the nations are deprived of the guidance of their worthy rulers, who, while they were alive, gave all their efforts to prevent intestine disorders." So said Bodin, sixteenth-century French lawyer.

Not every person believed in the efficacies of comets to bring catastrophe and death. Vespasian, in A.D. 79, is credited with having said to his associates who were worried about possible disaster: "That hairy star does not portend evil to me. It menaces rather the King of the Parthians. For he is hairy, and I am bald."

Kepler established the fact that the orbits of the planets are somewhat elliptical, not circular. But the paths of comets, by comparison, are very long ellipses indeed. Comets spend by far the greater portion of their lives in the distant realms of interplanetary space, perhaps even beyond the orbits of Neptune and Pluto, where the gravitational force is so weak that many hundreds or thousands of years are necessary for the object to complete a circuit. By contrast, the comet usually spends only a few days or at most a few weeks in the vicinity of the earth and the sun, during which portion of its orbit it is moving very fast.

Scientific researches have by now established that a comet really is a celestial body in its own right. Although there is some disagreement about the details of a comet's structure, authorities generally agree that one of its major constituents is finely divided solid matter: dust, sand, gravel, rocks — of all grades and sizes. In addition, the observations clearly show that a comet, as it swings in toward the sun, develops a gaseous envelope that surrounds the "gravel bank" to form the head of the comet and then grades into the long, luminous tail that stretches into space in a direction away from the sun. Thus, as comets come in toward the sun, the tails follow behind. But as the comets leave, the tails precede them on the return trip. The tails are composed of extremely rarefied gas, glowing because of ultraviolet light absorbed from the sun. Presumably the force that drives the tail of the comet away from the head is the pressure of radiation, which, weak though it is for most purposes, can still act on so tenuous a medium as a comet's tail.

The "gravel-bank" theory of a comet presents some difficulty with respect to the origin of the gaseous aura that develops each time the comet approaches the sun. The implication is that heat from the sun, shining on the gravel, causes the gas to exude from the solid and thus form the extensive train.

My colleague, Dr. Fred L. Whipple, of Harvard University, has suggested what I regard as an important improvement on the older model of cometary structure. He still retains the "gravel-bank" concept, but he supposes that the individual particles, instead of being entirely free from one another, like a dust cloud in the wind, are held together by a substratum of snow or ice. To change the simile, we may regard the comet as a sort of plum pudding, with the rock and perhaps metallic granules for the "plums" and the great bulk of the comet's ices for the "pudding."

The ices of a comet probably contain such substances as carbon dioxide snow (dry ice) and frozen methane and ammonia, in addition to ordinary solid water.

This model improves our understanding of how a comet may act. At great distances, to which the sun imparts scant warmth, the ices are frozen. And in this stage the comet has little if any aura surrounding it. However, when it swings in close to the sun, melting and evaporation of the ices produce the atmosphere and, at the same time, release the outer layers of gravel, which then are free to escape from the comet because the very low gravitational force of the body cannot hold on to the fragments.

The spectroscope tells us that a comet has considerable hydrogen in its make-up. In addition, we find traces of such lethal gases as cyanogen and carbon monoxide. In the spring of 1910, when Halley's comet came so close to the earth that a collision was imminent, newspapers played up the presence of these poisonous components. Though I was only nine years old at the time, I can still quote, almost verbatim, the words from a sensational piece of journalism telling of the possible effects of the cometary collision on the earth. "There is a distinct possibility that, the following day, the sun will rise on a world that is lifeless and soundless save for the ghastly popping of swollen bodies." No wonder that so many people committed suicide rather than face death in the comet's lethal gas chambers. And what nonsense too! For the gases, admittedly lethal in high concentrations, are so highly rarefied that the concentration of carbon monoxide from the exhausts of automobiles in a city street far exceeds that in the comet. We need not fear, therefore, comets as a source of poisonous gases.

Halley's comet put in its last appearance in 1910 and is due again 75 years later, in 1985. It possesses the shortest period of all the really bright comets. Such comets generally have periods so long that we have no direct way of determining the time required for a complete revolution about the sun, except that it may be well in excess of a thousand years. These comets are the really bright objects, the spectacular "nine-day wonders" that show up unexpectedly, spend a few days in the vicinity of the sun, and then fade to their former invisibility as they recede into the depths of space.

Occasionally such comets are bright enough to be visible even in daylight, as was Comet A–1, 1910, a brilliant object that competed with Halley's comet for recognition. If one of these long-period comets happens to come close to Jupiter, the largest and most massive planet in our solar system, the resulting gravitational action may switch it from its original very large orbit into one so small that the comet may then require only 5 or 10 years instead of a thousand to circle the sun. But, once a comet has been thrown into this small orbit, the great banks of ice disappear quite rapidly. In a relatively short time, cosmically speaking, the ices will have completely disappeared and the comet will have reduced itself to a flying gravel bank, without the possibility of forming an appreciable tail. At least one known comet is apparently completely "bald."

The concentrated solid matter, ices and gravel, that goes to form the nucleus of a comet is generally small, probably not more than a few miles in diameter. But the hazy mist that makes up the entire head can be extremely large. Some comets are known whose gaseous heads have been larger than Jupiter and some even larger than the sun.

Although comets still present many interesting and unsolved scientific problems, modern analysis has completely stripped from them any possible aura of superstition. If a great comet appeared today, we should all enjoy its superlative beauty. No longer would we quiver and quake before the apparition. We should immediately recognize as sham any claims that the comet was responsible for various malign influences, such as the statement made as recently as 1818, in England, that "flys became blind and died early in the season," and "the wife of a London shoemaker had four children at a birth."

Since 1947, no one has included a comet as a flying saucer. One rather significant reason why no one has done so is the simple fact that no bright comets have appeared in this interim. For I confidently believe that if some astonishingly beautiful comet were to show up, some persons on the lunatic fringe, or, more probably, exploiters of human credulity, would try to make a case for comets' being super space ships, inhabited by beings who want to come in and get a good look at the earth.

But even if active, bright comets are not responsible for the modern saucers, some of the fragments of these frozen gravel banks have been responsible for various saucer reports. When the ices have melted and evaporated away, the bank gradually thins out, until the once-dense cloud of dust and rocks has dispersed itself through almost the entire elliptical orbit of the comet. Thus, even though we do not see the clouds of dust moving through space, we do have some evidence for their existence. The earth's orbit touches or intersects some of these old cometary orbits. And when the earth reaches one of these points of contact, the heavens are lighted with showers of sparks — the so-called "shooting stars." A speck of dust or a chunk of rock, moving through space, occasionally encounters the earth. The earth's atmosphere strikes it with a speed of from 10 to 20 miles a second. As the particle plunges through the atmospheric layers, friction heats the surface until it becomes red-hot and luminous, perhaps sending a shower of sparks behind it.

Faint shooting stars are common. If you stand outdoors on a clear, moonless night and look upward, you will rarely have to wait more than 5 or 10 minutes before you see a tiny flash of fire dart across the sky. These shooting stars are, of course, not stars at all; real stars are suns like our own sun, faint only because they are so far away.

Most of the flashes across the sky are caused by particles no larger than a grain of sand. One as large as the eraser in a lead pencil would cause a flare so brilliant that we should term it a fireball. Larger masses, ranging from a few pounds in weight up to a number of tons, occasionally encounter the earth. And when these large masses crash, they cause a big explosion, devastating sometimes hundreds of square miles of territory. One such collision occurred in 1908, when a large meteor crashed into the bleak Siberian tundra. A number of meteor craters, the fossil remains of such crashes, are known on the surface of the earth. Perhaps the best known, though by no means the largest, is the Canyon Diablo Crater in Arizona.

When a meteor is large enough to reach the earth without being consumed entirely in the atmosphere we call it a meteorite. Study of such objects has enabled us to divide them into two major classes: the rocklike masses, which we call aerolites, and the chunks of iron-nickel steel, which we call siderites. The two types are distinct, and fragments should show major differences in color as they fall through the atmosphere.

Although the aerolites are probably far more abundant, we recover a greater percentage of the siderites, simply because their metallic composition assists in the identification. We find it difficult to distinguish between the aerolites and common rock.

These stony meteorites have shown nothing extraordinary. With minor exceptions, their chemical composition accords with the average sample of rock we find on the surface of the earth. They contain an abundance of silica, magnesium, calcium, and similar substances. They show traces of a large number of other substances, including copper. Two known meteorites have shown tiny specks of metallic copper imbedded in them.

Then there is the highly controversial "meteorite" that came from Eaton, Colorado. This object consists of copper, zinc, and lead, alloyed, according to H. H. Nininger,[2] in a form of "natural brass." Nininger feels that the fall is authentic, for he himself questioned the people who recovered the object and is convinced of their sincerity. However, the unusual chemical structure of this object makes me want to withhold final judgment until additional studies and analyses become available. I have seen the "meteorite" and have concluded that its unusual form and composition are opposed to the postulated celestial origin. More probably, the object is a brass bedpost or perhaps a knob off of such a bed, melted in a flame. I could perhaps accept a meteorite of iron-nickel-copper composition. One composed of pure copper would be easier to understand than one of brass. But why should only copper, lead, and zinc have combined in nature to form brass, an alloy whose composition is a man-made discovery?

I should not even mention so controversial an object if it were not for the implications that various persons have made concerning the alleged coppery nature of the now famous green fireballs seen over the New Mexican desert. Although these spectacular globes of fire are clearly very different from any of the lights and apparitions we have thus far discussed, they seem to have caused more furor in military circles than all the other apparitions put together. These objects, by definition, are also flying saucers.

I regret to say that some of the scientists working on the problem have frightened one another to the point where some of them are willing to accept the spaceship identification.

I believe that these objects are merely bright meteors and that the arguments others have advanced against this interpretation are completely invalid. I shall first present the evidence in favor of the flying saucer along with the refutation of that idea. The first question asked is: "Why are these green fireballs not seen elsewhere than in New Mexico and the Southwest?" Here, the answer is extremely simple. Green fireballs have been and are being seen in many locations. The frequency of sightings happens to be somewhat greater in the Southwest because the atmosphere is so very clear. Distant objects show plainly. We can expect to see mountain ranges

Fig. 74. Limited horizon near a city.

Fig. 75. Extended range of vision in desert areas.

more than 100 miles away, whereas in the East objects only 5 or 10 miles away tend to be lost in the haze. As a result, we can observe a much larger volume of atmosphere in the Southwest, and consequently see many more fireballs, especially low on the horizon, than we do near cities or in regions where the sky transparency is less (Figs. 74 and 75).

"Well," ask the saucer enthusiasts, "why were they not seen prior to 1947?" To this I reply that green fireballs were common before 1947. Of course, the clearer the atmosphere the more brilliant will the green color appear. A meteor shower I observed in 1940, from the High Altitude Observatory at Climax, Colorado, contained a number of bright green fireballs. Thus, the Southwest is not getting anything new. More fireballs are being seen chiefly because more people are looking for them.

About 10 miles from the White Sands proving ground, where these objects have been recently reported, Dr. Fred L. Whipple of Harvard maintains two special stations for the observation of meteors and the recording of fireballs. They are equipped with the most powerful meteor cameras ever built (Fig. 76). He has operated these stations since 1948 and has recorded many meteors during this time. The shutter on the camera rotates rapidly, breaking the trail into a series of dashes (Fig. 77). The fact that two stations are available enables one to determine the height of the meteor. The dashes define its velocity, so that we possess all essential information about the meteor and its path through space. It is particularly impressive that, in all of this time, not one object has been recorded whose characteristics would in any way suggest that it was other than a meteor.

"But," argue the unconvinced saucerites, "Dr. Whipple's installation is, after all, 10 miles away from White Sands. What is happening at White Sands, therefore, can be very different from what happens at their stations. In fact, does not Whipple's failure to detect these green saucers prove that they are interplanetary craft making special inspection of the White Sands region and other neighboring secret government laboratories?"

Here the answer is very clear. Whipple's meteor cameras, recording meteoric effects, frequently sweep through large volumes of air directly over White Sands, and even farther to the East. Failure to

Fig. 76. Baker Super-Schmidt meteor camera in place at Las Cruces, New Mexico.

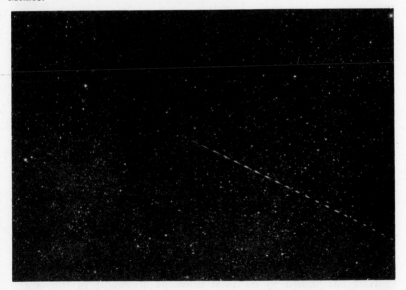

Fig. 77. Meteor trail taken with the Baker Super-Schmidt camera. The dashed appearance results from a rotating shutter in the camera that interrupts the exposure 60 times per second, so that the velocity of the meteor can be determined. A second picture taken simultaneously from another location also permits measurement of heights.

detect anything but meteors proves that nothing unusual is present. The saucer enthusiasts refer again to the color of the object, which they identify with the greenish glow of burning copper — the color that flashes momentarily at a short circuit of electric wires. And they hark back to the Eaton coppery meteorite, implying by indirection what they would not dare say outright, that this melted-down brass bedpost was a fragment from a flying saucer that crashed somewhere. They do not know where the rest of the saucer is, of course. But the occurrence of this brass suggests that unusual objects are flying in space close to the earth.

In other words, the saucer die-hards also cannot explain the existence of brass on natural grounds. But where I regard the object as a hoax, they accept without question that the brass nodule came from space and thus draw conclusions about space ships of brass — space ships moving fast enough to melt their brass trimmings when they swing in close to the earth!

What is brass doing in this story? It scarcely accords with the reports that space ships were composed of "two metals unknown to men on earth."

And here they try to establish an additional point. Some recent analyses of the chemical composition of the air over White Sands has shown the presence of a small amount of copper. The techniques of making these quantitative chemical analyses make me ready to accept this statement. Copper is indeed in the atmosphere. So what!

"Well," the saucerites exclaim, "analyses prior to 1945 do not show the presence of copper at all. Hence this copper must be new, and put in by the green fireballs. Green fireballs are new, and since the greenness can be due only to copper or brass, and since brass is rather an 'unnatural' thing to find in the universe, it must be a form of space ship."

First of all, I want to emphasize that burning copper is not the only source of green light. Glowing magnesium, which chemical analysis has shown to be 1400 times as abundant in the stony meteorites as copper, can also produce an intense green radiation, whose color differs only imperceptibly from that of copper, as far as the eye can detect.

The spectrograph, of course, enables us to tell the difference between copper and magnesium; of all the spectra secured of meteors to date, many have shown the presence of magnesium. None has shown the slightest trace of copper. This result means only that copper is generally much less abundant than magnesium and that the copper must be a rare substance by comparison. I should like to quote from a contribution by Dr. Peter Millman, of the Dominion Observatory at Ottawa, Canada. Millman refers to the identification of magnesium in meteoric spectra and specially comments that "evidence exists to show that a meteor with magnesium particularly strong in its spectrum appears visually of a green color." [3]

Let us return to consider the reports that copper is now more abundant in the air over White Sands than it was prior to 1947. Here is a simple calculation that anyone can verify.

A room $12 \times 10 \times 10$ feet contains as much as 96 pounds of air. A large lecture hall will hold 25 or 30 tons of air — perhaps more. About thirty million tons of air per square mile or a hundred billion tons of air are over the great Tularosa basin, which includes the White Sands region. This air must contain many thousands of tons of copper. If the saucerites are correct in their claim that this excess occurs only over the Tularosa valley, not even extending as far as Las Cruces, the fact that the winds sweep this valley clear at least once a day would require that thousands of tons of copper be reëvaporated each night.

Actually, if the green fireballs were of pure copper, the amount evaporated to account for their luminosity would amount at most to a fraction of a pound per day. No matter how we try to stretch the figures in favor of the brass saucers, we cannot come up with any reasonable figures to account for the copper content of New Mexican air.

Acting on a hunch, I called the Kennecott Copper Company, to ascertain the extent of New Mexico copper developments. I received the information that not one but four great copper smelters lie west of the Tularosa valley — where prevailing winds can carry the waste gas and dust over the desert areas we are discussing. The Cottrell precipitators are not 100 per cent efficient, and allow just about the right amount of copper dust and vapor to escape to account for the observed copper in the air.

The final argument that the saucer enthusiasts trot out relates to the reported low speed of the green fireballs. They cannot possibly be meteors, so the argument goes, "because they take so long to traverse the space of sky." Here again the clearness of the New Mexican atmosphere is confusing. Meteors are moving at their usual speeds, but their greater average distance makes them appear to move more slowly. Speeds of meteors commonly range between about 7 miles a second for the evening meteors that have to overtake the earth to about 44 miles a second for those that smash head-on in the early morning hours. The brightest meteors usually occur between 40 and 60 miles above the surface of the earth, although under some circumstances they will occur at still greater heights.

Under circumstances that we do not completely understand, a meteor can induce a special glowing in the various regions of the ionosphere. The E layer, at 70 miles above the surface, is particularly sensitive, though occasionally the still higher F layer can respond. I have already mentioned in Chapter 7 that the great saucer of 1882 may have resulted from the effect of a meteor upon the highly active upper regions of the earth's atmosphere. The meteor simply acted as a "seed" to excite a luminous glow over a wide region. It is possible that an occasional green fireball may result from similar action. However, New Mexico is extremely far away from the magnetic pole and therefore particularly unsuited geographically for any type of auroral displays.

There is no question but that the green fireballs are being highly overemphasized, because of saucer hysteria and lack of understanding of the whole meteor problem. Most of the reported saucers are slowly moving meteors. The Air Force official files contain many references to some of the most commonplace fireballs.

Flying-saucer enthusiasts have made much of an unusual meteor display that occurred on 9 February 1913. A great procession of slowly moving meteors moved diagonally across the United States and Canada, from Saskatchewan to Bermuda (Fig. 81). It caused, as usual, great consternation among the superstitious. The records clearly show that the objects, which various people estimated at hundreds or thousands, were truly meteoric, though they moved with exceptional slowness.

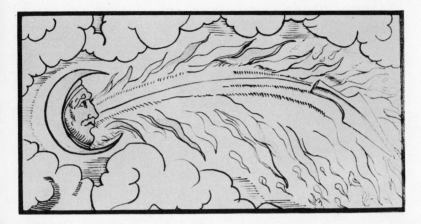

Fig. 78. A fireball, passing in front of the moon, as observed at Salon and St. Chamas, France, in 1554.

Fig. 79. A strange meteor that appeared after a violent thunderstorm in the sky over Esseck, in 1687.

Fig. 80. Exploding fireball observed on 9 June 1866 at Knyahinya, Hungary.

The occasional great meteorites that strike the earth sometimes put up a spectacular display of fireworks. Throughout history, we find that bright meteors have frequently spread fear among the superstitious.

Two other apparitions of distinctly astronomical character — eclipses of the sun and eclipses of the moon — have occasioned their share of fright among the ignorant. The moon, in its circuit of the

Fig. 81. The great meteor procession of 9 February 1913. A portion of the display as observed by Mr. and Mrs. Gustave Hahn, near High Park, Toronto. The spaces between succeeding clusters were actually somewhat greater than shown here.

earth, passes near the sun once each month, but only two or three times a year does it come sufficiently close to the position occupied by the sun that it can obscure the glowing solar disk. We can have a partial eclipse when the moon hides only part of the sun from view. Or the eclipse can be total when the moon completely hides the sun. The eclipse can be annular, or ring-form, if the eclipse occurs when the apparent size of the moon is a little less than that of the sun, so that a circular ring of bright sunlight encircles the black lunar disk.

Small wonder that such spectacular apparitions have spread fright among those unaware of eclipses. We have to recall that primitive people, ignorant of the sun's true nature, generally associated it with health, warmth, and abundant food. Seeing it about to vanish from the sky, and having no assurance that it would return, they would naturally be fearful — afraid of facing a future without the sun.

During the eclipse of 1922, the aborigines of Australia, hired to help erect the towers of the Lick Observatory eclipse expedition, vaguely understood something about the phenomenon and concluded that the astronomers were going to climb the tower and catch the sun in a net while it buzzed by. They were not too apprehensive, but they thought it would be better if the astronomers would not interfere with such fundamental things as the sun. The chief of the aborigines, having delivered himself of this thought, returned to digging holes for the piers and regaling himself on beetles and other insects turned up by the spade.

To the uninitiated, eclipses of the moon are sometimes even more spectacular than eclipses of the sun. These events occur when the earth moves between the sun and the moon, throwing its own shadow upon the latter. Sunlight, working its way through the earth's atmosphere, attains a ruddy, sunset glow. Hence the moon, during totality of the eclipse, never completely disappears; but it does possess a hue that suggests to the superstitious a moon bathed in blood.

Despite the sensational appearance of eclipses, we see nothing in them that merits fear. Few phenomena can be forecast with greater accuracy. We can predict to the nearest second and tell to within a few hundred feet on the surface of the earth the exact circumstances of solar eclipses in the near future. With slightly greater leeway, we can forecast eclipses thousands of years in the future. If what we fear, then, is something that appears to be outside of ordinary law — like the flying saucers — eclipses should cause the least fear of all, because of the exactness with which we can calculate every detail of the apparition.

19

The galloping ghosts of radar

▬▬

The saucer scare reached maximum proportions in July 1952. Head-lines proclaimed the sighting of a saucer armada flying over the Nation's capital — saucers seen by eye, saucers registered by radar, saucers sighted simultaneously by eye and radar.

The radar sightings led to a questioning of the theories advanced in previous chapters, that most of the hitherto unexplained saucers are only reflections or refractions. The argument, which happens to be wrong, runs about as follows: "Radar is a machine, and machines have no imagination. They cannot possibly imagine something that isn't there. Radar can register only solid objects, not light reflections or refractions. Hence saucers are solid objects."

The radar sightings most widely heralded were from the Washing-ton airport, over two independent radar sets. Various airline pilots flying through the saucer areas were asked to check, and most of them drew blanks. Jet planes screamed into the regions, to find them empty. A few pilots, guided by radar bearings, reported seeing "points of light" that withdrew or disappeared. To some persons this was the old game of hide-and-seek, reaffirming the well-known shy-ness of the saucers. To others, this behavior confirmed what seems to be the simplest conclusion, that the saucers do not exist as material objects.

The head of some amateur rocket society requested the Air Force not to shoot at the saucers or do anything that might alienate a friendly intelligence from outside. A German rocket expert reiterated his belief in interplanetary saucers. A radio station in Indianapolis addressed a special broadcast to the saucers, assuring them of our friendliness, guaranteeing them freedom of action, and designating a special air field — near Indianapolis, of course — for the saucers to land.

A Coast Guardsman at Salem, Massachusetts, saw a flash out of the open window, picked up his camera, and shot a picture through the "dirty screen." The photograph showed four bright egg-shaped objects projected against the sky.

A luminous saucer performed aerial acrobatics in the dark sky over Coventry, Rhode Island, causing a traffic jam as motorists stopped to watch — until a spotlight solved the mystery. The saucer was only a flashlight in a plastic bag, hung from eighteen gas-filled balloons and controlled by a long fish pole in the hands of a group of grinning teen-agers who were having the time of their lives.

And the radar saucers continued to zoom over Washington.

To understand the problem, we must know something of the way radar works. Although we have had radar for only a decade, man has occasionally used the basic radar principle for a much longer period of time.

Steamships plying through the Puget Sound in foggy weather or at night navigate by echoes. The time required for a short whistle blast to return from a cliff measures the distance of the reflecting surface. Sound travels approximately 1000 feet per second. An echo that returns 1 second after the blast indicates a reflecting cliff 500 feet away.

Bats use "sound radar" to direct their flight in total darkness. Their supersonic cries, too high in pitch for human ears to hear, bounce from walls or other obstacles. Blinded bats can still fly unerringly. In the early 19th century scientists discovered that covering a bat's ears rendered the animal helpless. One critic wrote caustically in 1809, "Since bats see with their ears, do they not hear with their eyes?"

Radar is a device that sends out short, sharp pulses of radio waves rather than of sound. These radio pulses bounce off solid objects and give echoes that enable us to measure how far away the object is. Radar waves travel with the speed of light — 186,000 miles a second. An echo returning after an interval of 1/1000 of a second has traveled 186 miles, 93 miles out to the object and 93 miles back. The radar automatically measures the delay, and marks the returning signal on the surface of a "scope," which resembles the face of a television tube.

The beam of radio waves rotates like an airport searchlight,

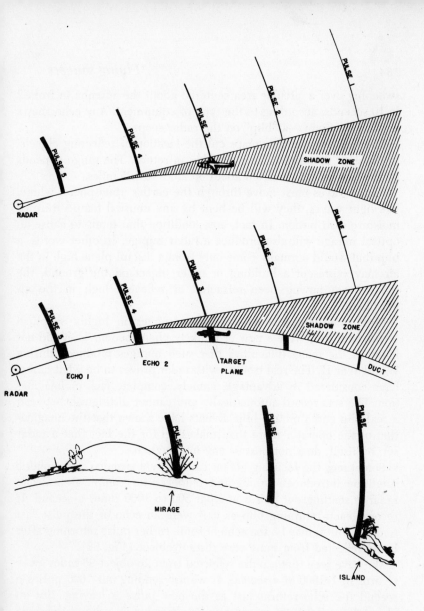

Fig. 82. (a) Transmission of radar pulses under "standard" atmospheric conditions. The pulses do not enter the shadow zone and thus will not be reflected from a plane in that region. (b) A layer of cool air close to the surface forms a sort of duct that transmits radio waves very effectively. (c) If a duct is present, long-delayed echoes can produce ghost images on the radar scope.

Flying saucers

sweeping over a circular area centered about the antenna in from 2 to 10 seconds, according to the type of equipment. Any echo shows as a bright point — a "blip" on the radar scope.

The radar screen thus maps out the location of reflecting objects, to the limit that appreciable signals can return. The range depends on the type of radar — from about 30 miles to 125 miles.

Radar waves must move through the earth's atmosphere, where, like light waves, they will be bent by any unusual temperature or moisture distribution. In fact, any condition that tends to cause an optical mirage will also produce a radar mirage. In other words, a blip that would normally come only from a distant plane high in the air may represent a building or other object on the ground, the radar beam having been refracted or reflected high in the atmosphere.

Most newspapers spoke of radar mirages in highly skeptical terms, as if they were a new or unlikely phenomenon. They did not know of the many difficulties that such mirages produced during World War II. The real trouble with radar proves to be what others have considered its advantage, namely, complete lack of imagination. The sets record automatically and cannot distinguish between a real blip and a mirage blip. Events have shown that the imagination of the operator more than makes up for the fact that a radar set, by itself, does not possess any imagination.

Sometimes the focusing action caused by a peculiar atmospheric condition introduces serious and unlooked-for complications. The radar is sending out pulses at from 500 to 1000 times a second. It records each returning blip as if it were an echo of the pulse last sent out. But it may be the echo of some earlier pulse returning after being reflected from some very distant object (Fig. 82).

We have seen that a pulse reflected from an object 93 miles away returns in 1/1000 of a second. If we are sending out 1000 pulses a second the echo returns just as the new pulse is leaving. But an object 186 miles away would also be returning an echo at the same moment, from the next earlier pulse, and so on for other pulses.

Figure 83 shows schematically a map divided into rings 93 miles across; the observer is at O and A–F are targets at various distances from O. The radar scope would show all these rings superposed

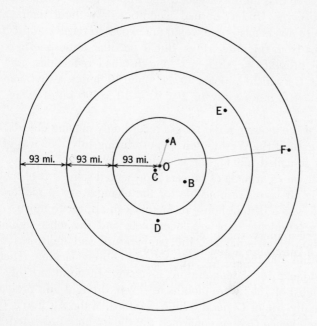

Fig. 83. A schematic map of a region surrounding a radar set at O, with possible targets A–F.

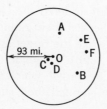

Fig. 84. The radar of Fig. 83 shows all the targets as if they were within 93 miles of O.

(Fig. 84), so that all the targets would appear to be within 93 miles of the observer. Under "normal" conditions — without temperature or moisture inversions — one would not expect to receive appreciable reflections from the outer rings. But if peculiar atmospheric conditions are present, we shall get long-distance reflections, and the image at C, which appears to be only 10 miles away, may be $93 + 10 = 103$ miles away or $2 \times 93 + 10 = 196$ miles away, and so on.

Some of the modern radar scopes record only moving objects. One of those used at the Washington Airport during July 1952 was of this type — a so-called moving-target indicator or MTI. The blips that seemed to be an armada of saucers represented some sort of motion. But if the air layers responsible for the changes are in motion, the image of even a distant house or factory can appear to move.

The meteorologic data are incomplete and the most significant information of all — namely, the temperature and moisture conditions within 100 feet of the ground — is entirely lacking. There is some evidence for a temperature inversion. In addition, July and early August of 1952 were months of severe drought and prolonged heat. Finally, Major General John A. Sanford, of the Air Force Technical Intelligence Center, confirmed the theory here presented: that a sandwich of cold and warm layers of air has caused the saucers, both visual and radar sightings.

During World War II, a cruiser in the Mediterranean suddenly noted a mysterious spot on its radar scope, within the range of its guns. A rapid check on the identification system failed to get any signal return, so the captain ordered the crew to open fire on the mysterious vessel. They checked their gunfire with radar, watching the projectiles seemingly strike the target again and again, without any effect. The expected return of gunfire never materialized. So they started to close in on the target, which stayed where it was like a sitting duck, while they emptied their store of ammunition in a futile effort to sink it.

Finally, curiosity overcame them and they cautiously crept forward, with the target still showing clearly on the screen, but, as they came into position where the target should be, their eyes could see nothing but a broad expanse of ocean. Just as they reached the posi-

Mr. Sanford happens to be one of the Air Force's top saucer debunkers naturally he would confirm this the

tion of the target itself, the mysterious point of light on the radar screen suddenly disappeared. And then someone noticed what had happened. There, on the same bearing as the original ship, was another bright spot at the very edge of the radar screen. They had, somehow or other, been receiving the echo not from the first pulse, but from some earlier pulse, and the mystery was resolved. They had been trying to sink the island of Malta. At last report the island was still afloat.

An unexpected phenomenon makes possible the reception of reflections of signals from very distant objects. The answer, obtained only after much worry and experimentation, proved to be mirage. Radio waves, like light waves, are also subject to bending. And, although the conditions that produce radio mirages are complicated, they have many factors in common with ordinary mirages and the two often occur simultaneously. Cool air close to the earth's surface, surmounted by a warmer layer, is ideal for production of radar mirages as well as optical mirages. Long-range television reception, for example, is best under such conditions.

An incident analagous to that at Malta occurred in Alaskan waters during the later stages of World War II.[1] The Japanese were still in possession of the strategic island of Kiska and our fleet was standing some 600 miles off the Kiska coast, trying to develop a plan for wresting control from the Japanese, when suddenly the radar patrol reported seeing some mysterious vessels operating only 40 or 50 miles away. The crews, thus alerted, went on watch to guard against surprise attack. In spite of various checks, they were unable at the time to decide what it was they had seen. The vessels disappeared as suddenly and as miraculously as they had come.

The ghost fleet, as mysterious as the Flying Dutchman, had a significance that became obvious when our own task force made what they hoped would be a surprise attack on Kiska. They found the island completely deserted. What the radars had disclosed on the earlier date was the Japanese in the process of evacuating Kiska and, had the operators interpreted the radar reports correctly, had they been aware of the vagaries of this instrument, our own fleet would have been in a strategic position to strike a crushing blow at the Japanese.

The failure of the additional radar tests disclosed a glaring fault that later made mandatory the reconversion of all radar sets, so that ghost images could be detected or resolved more readily.

One of the most spectacular and at the same time most frightening experiences came off the coast of Japan, in the vicinity of Nansei Shoto. Our submarines, in 1944, were carrying on extensive operations in Japanese waters, sinking ships and otherwise contributing materially to weakening the Japanese war effort.

As far as radar is concerned, submarines operate at some disadvantage and at considerable peril to themselves. A submarine in enemy waters dared surface only at night. Then, while the air was being replenished and the submarine conditioned, radar reconnaissance was employed to locate possible targets and to check the position of other enemy craft.

During this period I was a Lieutenant Commander in the U. S. Navy, charged with the responsibility of trying to resolve the reports from our submarines about mysterious ghostlike images that seemed to be flitting all over the Nansei Shoto area.

The reports went something as follows: The radar operator, sitting in front of his PPI scope, was checking on possible targets, with the submarine cruising slowly just below the surface and the radar antenna lying just above the surface. At this moment, a remarkable and frightening phenomenon would occur. The radar operator would suddenly become aware of the fact that one — sometimes more than one — of the bright points of light on the radar screen was heading directly toward the submarine, on a course designed to intercept it. If, for the sake of protection, he called for a change in course, the image on the screen would instantaneously change course also and, no matter what the submarine did, short of complete reversal of its path, would tend to steer toward what seemed to be an inevitable collision between the submarine itself and the mysterious ghost object indicated by the glowing point on the radar screen. Its behavior calls to mind that of the foo fighters already discussed.

The radar antenna, we should note, lies either on or just above the surface of the water. And hence as the mysterious object approached the ship, sometimes at a speed from two to three times the normal speed of a surface craft, an officer would scan the sea through the periscope trying to detect this mysterious vessel whose primary aim, so it seemed, was to steer a crash course with the submarine.

No matter what the submarine could do by way of veering course, the speeding image would dodge and parry as skillfully as a shadow boxer. And just when crash seemed inevitable, when everyone expected the mysterious enemy craft to show up in the periscope as well as upon the radar screen, the image would vanish — like the ghost that it was, And thus came its name, the Galloping Ghost of Nansei Shoto.

The basic phenomenon that produced the Galloping Ghost was not very different from others we have already discussed, namely, mirage. A low-lying layer of cold air, close to the surface of the sea, entraps the radar waves, keeping them from going on to higher levels. These radar pulses then bounce around from ship to shore and ship to ship, with remarkable intensity. Sometimes they are reflected more than once by the same moving object, including the submarine that sent them out originally. Thus, a beam that has suffered several reflections will seem to move at the combined speed of all the objects and hence several times faster than we should expect any surface craft to move. Thus, finally, the mystery of the radar ghosts was resolved.

While we were trying to solve the riddle of the galloping ghosts, the possibility of their being flying saucers from Venus or some other world never occurred to us.

Ashore, especially in the desert of North Africa during the night, occasional phantom apparitions of distant troop movements plagued our radar reconaissance. Had we been expecting flying saucers, we should undoubtedly have seen them by the dozens. But in North Africa, in 1943 and 1944, interplanetary space craft were the least of our worries. We were confronted by a real, not an imaginary, enemy. Thus when radar ghost images appeared on our screens, we endowed them with realistic powers and attributed their operation to an enemy we knew well. We did not have to call in the mystical flying saucer as an explanation. But even so, we were getting false information from our radars.

Various committees were set up, charged with the responsibility of carrying out experimental and theoretical programs for the study of radar and other radio problems. I was responsible for the basic programs of such a committee, operating under the Joint Chiefs of Staff. To simulate conditions in the desert of North Africa, we constructed radar testing stations in the arid Southwest. And there indeed we recorded radar mirages like those already described for visual observation. During the day the radar waves, like light waves, would follow paths that were concave upward, and ranges would be limited, sometimes dangerously so. At night, however, we discovered that the hot sands of the desert cooled very rapidly, along with the overlying few feet or few yards of atmosphere, producing the effect of a layer of cold air and a temperature inversion. We have already noted that this layer of cold air produces a strong optical mirage, but it also gives rise to a pronounced radar mirage, bringing images of distant objects apparently close, and causing all sorts of mysterious ghost images.

Thus, our studies established this tendency of the looming mirages to form at night on the desert, a fact that few persons had previously realized. Had I not had prior experience with the propagation committee and communication problems, I doubt whether the relation between radar and optical mirages would have occurred to me. But since the desert areas had taught us the peculiar properties of radar signals over long distances, including the formation of ghost images, I have learned to distrust observations of any unusual reflections — especially observations that might very well be attributed to the mirage effect.

Although I have examined a number of reports of radar saucers, not one seems the least bit convincing. The operators fail to take into account the possibility of mirage and have accepted each observation at its face value, without considering the atmospheric effects of any kind.

Radar is an extremely valuable military protection. Under some conditions, we should much rather investigate an occasional spurious saucer than fail to make proper check. But when anyone argues that some mysterious images, as detected on the desert at night, are due to flying saucers, I do not even stop to apologize for my skepticism. Nearly everyone who has had any appreciable experience with radar realizes its limitations, despite its importance.

We should not be frightened by occasional mysterious appearances for which we have no simple and immediate explanation. That such occurrences sometimes arise no more invalidates radar as a fundamental instrument than the appearance of optical mirages or the phenomenon of flying saucers invalidate the telescope.

20

Interplanetary saucers and space travel

▸▪▪▪◂

The foregoing chapters have explained the facts behind the flying saucers. Many of them have proved to be extraneous objects like newspapers, balloons, or distant airplanes. Others have been searchlight or automobile-headlight reflections on a thin layer of cloud or haze. The most puzzling and by far the most frightening of all saucer phenomena are those that have come from reflections and refractions from drops of water, ice crystals, or even from air itself. Thus, all reports of saucers, those from the air or ground, those seen at night or during the day, those detected visually or by radar, result from unusual and unfamiliar conditions in the atmosphere.

Our position is a little like that of the policeman who, coming home late one night, saw a dim figure ahead of him in the hall. He called "Hands up!" as he reached for his gun. He saw his antagonist also reach for his gun, so he quickly fired just as his opponent fired back at him — to the accompaniment of crashing glass. He had seen his own image in the hall mirror.

As further evidence for the unreality of saucers, I have shown that they are in no sense sacred to any part of the world, although, to the extent that their appearance depends on local meteorological conditions, certain types of saucers may be localized, like the nighttime saucers in the desert.

Moreover, these objects have appeared throughout the ages and have often frightened our ancestors or caused a wave of superstitious fear. Had I chosen to do so, I could have multiplied by a factor of ten the evidence from history.

I have further shown that the American public is being exploited by those who wish to keep up the illusion of interplanetary saucers. People like to read this science-fiction stuff and will pay money to do so, but they will read it more avidly if they suppose it to be real. It is high time that we got some common sense!

Even as I demonstrate the unreality of interplanetary saucers, there are still the many addicts, the die-hards, those who want to believe under any circumstances, those who find believing enjoyable, who are attacking me, sometimes in a simple but often in a vicious manner.

The persons who fall into this category have only one remaining argument that has any validity at all. They ask me to survey the enormous technical advances, particularly of the last ten years — advances that have included atomic power, the V-2 rocket, and the guided missile. Many well-known scientists have seriously discussed the possibilities of travel into space or of setting up an artificial satellite to circle the earth indefinitely as an intermediate step in the bigger problem of space travel. In fact, one special government-sponsored agency, "Project Rand," has released some of their studies of the problem.

Many of the world's leading scientists agree that we could, in a matter of five or ten years, put a projectile from earth into interplanetary space, set up a satellite station, and perhaps even make a visit to the moon. All that would be needed is the allocation of some four or five billion dollars, and the concerted efforts of many scientists and engineers.

For us, then, interplanetary flight seems close — and relatively easy of attainment.

However, the addicts of the flying saucers then ask what seem to be entirely reasonable questions: "Why should the earth be the only inhabited planet? Is it not within reason to suppose that there may also be intelligent beings on the planets Mars or Venus? And, if we are contemplating interplanetary space travel, why should they not also be doing the same? Perhaps they have already solved the problem. Why should they necessarily be behind us in their stage of development?"

These questions *are* reasonable, but they are somewhat beside the point of flying saucers. For suppose we knew that Venus, say, had highly intelligent inhabitants, and that the Venusians had solved the problem of leaving their planet and getting out into space; it would by no means follow that the flying saucers we are seeing in our own atmosphere must of necessity be some of their interplanetary projectiles.

And then, if I were to deny that Venus and Mars were inhabited, those who stand behind the saucer myth come up with another question. "In our Milky Way alone there are some hundred billion (100,000,000,000) stars. Is it not reasonable to suppose that many of these stars have planets and that these planets, in turn, are inhabited by intelligent beings, many of them far in advance of us?"

Here is a rather interesting point and, at first sight, the proposition seems not at all unlikely. Since we have no scientific data with reference to planets or habitable places outside of our own solar system, I should be willing to accept tentatively the truth of the above proposition. Of course, I do not know that it is correct, but I see no strong reason against the idea that planets inhabited by super-beings should not exist in great abundance.

There seems, however, to be an implication that the more such planets there were in space, the more likely we would be to encounter interplanetary beings hovering around the earth. That is an argument I am not willing to accept. At the risk of being accused of disloyalty to the planet earth, I ask what reason we have to suppose that the earth is so much superior to many of these other planets, from the political standpoint as well as from the planetological. Or, to phrase the answer in another way, if our earth is such a paradise, and if curious beings from another world have been exploring it for more than two thousand years, are they not rather dumb if they have not found out yet what we are like down here and made up their minds whether they want to visit us or not? Well, then, I ask, if these flying saucers represent potential interplanetary tourist trade, where is everybody? Can you imagine us Americans, for example, traveling millions or billions — or perhaps even millions of billions — of miles through space, without making some attempt to communicate with what are obviously friendly people, just as we reach our destination?

If, 10 years or 500 years from now, space ships from the earth begin to swing around the planet Venus and find that it is inhabited would we not want to get in immediate touch with these people, to learn from them if they are indeed more intelligent than we are, to study them if they are less highly developed? This game of "cosmic hide-and-seek" that the flying saucers appear to engage in does not carry much weight, and seems to be inane for a civilization allegedly much more advanced than ours.

Another point about the enormous size of the universe and the postulated numbers of inhabited planets deserves further analysis. If, for example, there were only two inhabited planets in the universe, say Venus and the earth, then we should expect to get all of whatever cosmic tourist trade develops. But the more habitable planets there are, the smaller will be our percentage of the tourist trade. For example, if there were a million planets, each one inhabited and each one sending exploring expeditions into space, we should have to compete with all of the 999,999 other planets for our share of the tourist trade. Increasing the number of planets, therefore, in no way has increased our chances of getting interplanetary or interstellar visitors. Hence the argument fails completely, as far as its relation to flying saucers is concerned.

Even so, we find it interesting and perhaps profitable to speculate on the possibility of life elsewhere in the universe. For though I maintain that the flying saucers of today are only lights and reflections, I am by no means insisting that this will always be so. Someday a real interplanetary saucer may reach the earth. I do not know whether that saucer will arrive tomorrow or whether it will not come before a million years have elapsed.

But when that saucer lands, I predict that there will be no doubt about it or its reality. If its operators survive the landing — and we may reasonably assume that they would not undertake such a trip without having proved conclusively to themselves that their space ship could be controlled — there will be no doubt about the landing. There will be no game of hide-and-seek, or of landing and then dashing away when we come up to greet them.

And if we ourselves should undertake trips into space, where would we most likely go and what would we expect to find? First, let me point out the basic problem of economics — economics of time as well as of money. I can conceive of our wanting to explore the solar system, of setting up an artificial satellite, of moving on to the moon and there providing a station on the way to Mars or Venus.

Such exploration, I maintain, will be expensive. But we shall bring a great deal back in return for the expenditure of money and scientific effort. The scientific knowledge alone to be gained from expeditions into space may very well justify them economically — as long as we do not attempt to move outside the solar system.

The average person has the most limited concept of dimensions in the universe. Although radio, rockets, jet planes, and the potential power of the atom have shrunk the earth considerably, it still looks pretty big to the average person. A globe 8,000 miles in diameter and weighing 6,000,000,000,000,000,000,000,000 tons is by no means negligible in the eyes of an earth-dweller. But in the vastness of interstellar space, the earth is like a peanut floating on the ocean.

Even that simile overestimates the importance of the earth. Rather, visualize the earth as a very small pea. Then, if the nearest of all the stars in the sky should have a similar planet, that planet would also be a pea, about 8,000 miles — the diameter of our earth — away from us. Even under the most favorable circumstances that we can envisage, interstellar space is empty and the distances between stars, with any possible planetary systems that they may possess, are enormous compared with distances in our own solar system. For, on this same scale, Mars would be a small seed, only 50 feet away from the pea that represents the earth.

Writers of science fiction glibly talk about trips to distant stars, made at the speed of light. This is all very well in a story, but few people have considered how much energy would be necessary to bring a rocket up to a reasonable percentage of the speed of light. Compared, say, with bringing the speed up to 7 miles a second, the value necessary to get a projectile outside the pull of the earth's gravitation, the fuel expenditure for a 10-ton rocket would be that obtainable from 100 tons of gasoline and oxygen. Although saucer devotees rarely mention such difficulties, the fuel problem is real indeed. We have already seen that the magnetic idea is sheer nonsense. Another widely publicized but equally ineffective suggestion is the possibility of using radiation pressure. Sunlight does exert a small pressure on anything it strikes. But this pressure is usually negligible compared with the force of gravitation. For example, sunlight falling on the entire George Washington bridge across the Hudson River exerts about the same pressure that a fly does, when it stands in the middle of the bridge.

Another difficulty is the time requirement. A common misunderstanding, based on the theory of relativity, has fostered the belief that if we were to travel with the speed of light we should return no older than we were when we left, because time ceases to flow for objects moving at the velocity of light. This is true, as long as we move in one direction. But if we turn around to come home, we undo the effect completely. If we traveled at the speed of light to the very nearest star, visited the planet there briefly (if there is one), then turned around and came home, we should take a minimum of 8 years for the round trip.

Before undertaking a journey to the stars, I should think that anyone would require a reasonable guarantee that the place he was visiting possessed certain minimum requirements in the way of facilities. At the very least he would want to know that the planet existed. Otherwise, he could get all the sensations of space travel, if that is the object, just by swinging a few million miles out beyond the earth.

But even with our present knowledge, we can make reasonable guesses about the future of space travel. What will it be like? What can we learn from it? And what are the various hazards?

To treat these three questions adequately would require a book — a full book on a subject other than flying saucers. But it is of some interest to skim the problems briefly.

The first step toward interplanetary travel, many scientists agree, is the establishment of a space station, an artificial satellite from 500 to 1000 miles above the surface of the earth. Travel to the moon or travel to Mars or Venus will probably require bigger rockets or more powerful rocket ships than we shall find it convenient to launch from the surface of the earth under ordinary conditions. A projectile the size of a small cruiser is somewhat impractical to take through the thick atmosphere of the earth.

We shall start our project of space travel in a more modest way, hoping to achieve our ultimate objective in stages rather than all at once. Our first requirements will be largely experimental, building more powerful rockets until finally we can put an unmanned but guided missile into an orbit outside the earth's atmosphere. The knowledge gained in these experiments will enable us to build a fleet of perhaps forty or fifty space ships, capable of making the trip out to this artificial satellite.

The next step will be the sending of manned craft, with sizable cargoes, out to the island oasis in interplanetary space. Technicians will take up residence there and, as a first assignment, increase the size of the base until truly we have a sort of floating hotel, complete with all major facilities for scientific experiments, for the residence of a large crew of experimentalists, and additional machine shops for the assembly of craft destined for the survey of interplanetary space.

Then, just as automobile manufacturers of today send their individual components to various assembly stations, we shall send out to the artificial satellite the components necessary for a large and powerful interplanetary space ship, one capable of going to the moon or beyond and then returning to the earth — a space ship whose size competes with that of an ocean-going steamer.

Many years may elapse while the ship is being assembled, until a crew takes over, ready to explore our solar system, sending back reports by radio and television of the remarkable sights seen en route.

The moon will become our first major target for many reasons. It is, of course, by far the nearest of the permanent members of the solar system. Although it promises only the minutest chance of our finding any sort of life on its surface, it offers many advantages to the interplanetary explorer. The motion picture "Destination Moon," previously referred to, presents an excellent picture of some of the hazards of space travel and graphically portrays something of the moonscape that would greet the interplanetary explorer.

He might land under the blazing heat of a noonday sun, but the sky would nevertheless be black. The blueness of our own sky results from the simple fact that air itself is blue in color — blue, that is, if we have enough of it. That is why distant mountain ranges, seen horizontally, appear blue. We are merely glimpsing something of the enormous mass of blue air that lies between us and the distant

Fig. 85. A rocket ship on the surface of the moon.

Fig. 86. Explorers of space standing on the surface of the moon. The ball appearing in the dark sky is the earth.

ridges. Since there is no atmosphere on the moon, there would be no blue sky; moreover, sunlight would not be scattered in all directions, as it is by the air, so that the stars would be visible even in the daytime.

We shall have become well conditioned, by this time, to seeing a black instead of a blue sky, because a space ship that rises even 70 or 80 miles will have left behind it most of the atmosphere and most of the blue sky. Thus the sky will tend to be black and we shall be able to see the Milky Way and many faint stars, despite the fact that the sun is shining at the same time. This is one of the surprising paradoxes of interplanetary astronomy.

The surface of the moon is covered with vast holes or pits in the surface ranging from a few feet across to well over 100 miles in diameter. These are the famous lunar craters, which have probably originated in impacts of large meteors against the rocky surface of the moon. The darker areas that our astronomers once took for bodies of water have proved to be rolling plains. We see mountain ranges and deep valleys apparently formed by explosive action — probably associated with the fall of a giant meteor smashing violently into the solar surface and throwing its fragments hundreds of miles, even tearing down parts of mountain ranges as a result of the tremendous impact.

The moon's surface is jagged and rough, free from most forms of erosion except those associated with the big explosions or with the impact of tiny meteorites. Even if we were to stand in the most level areas of all, the rolling plains, we should see that the surface is marred with small pits and broken up into fragments, as sharp as glass. Walking over the surface of such a region would present hazards to the lunar traveler. It would be like walking over a large plain covered with fragments of broken glass. A fall, even under the low gravitational pull, might be hazardous to one wearing a "space suit." Covering the surface to the depth of at least several inches, and possibly down to several feet, we should find finely powdered dust, produced as a combined effect of explosion and erosion.

The uppermost surface of the moon shows very marked changes in temperature as the sun rises and sets, ranging from that of boiling water in the daytime to about that of liquid air during the night.

If we were to dig our way down through only a few inches of the dust and glassy fragments, we should find a place where the temperature is nearly constant and near the freezing point of water.

To a large extent, the future of interplanetary or even of interstellar exploration will depend upon what we can find on the surface of the moon. We know that it will be completely barren, as far as vegetation is concerned. For the moon has neither water nor atmosphere. There is a remote chance that, within the vast mountain-protected regions around the poles, there may be areas that the sun never touches. Here, we might find vast frozen lakes, which would be an extremely important discovery in itself.

However, the greatest need of all, as our explorations would develop, would be for sources first of energy and second of strategic metals. We would scarcely expect to find coal or oil, since these substances originate in organic life of some sort, but we might find minerals that could be used to produce atomic energy. Would our surveys of mountain ranges or lunar valleys disclose large mineralized areas, especially regions where we could mine uranium? If our exploration revealed that such energy sources exist on the surface of the moon, the next step would be relatively easy and essentially self-supporting: For energy is one of the major requirements of interplanetary exploration, and, as we now know, atomic power is likely to be important in such developments.

Even without atomic power, however, lunar exploration would be profitable if we could locate sources of iron, aluminum, magnesium, tin, columbium, or other strategic metals. At least solar energy would be abundant and perhaps by that time we should have developed on the earth methods of harnessing the sun to our needs. Thus we can expect large-scale engineering developments on the moon, where the primary activity would be devoted to the production of quantities of steel, aluminum, or the various alloys of aluminum, magnesium and similar materials. These, coupled with the other possible advantages of inexpensive power and the extremely low surface gravity of the moon, would make this station but a stepping stone to further exploration of space.

Study of the moon will be important. We should like to know exactly how these hundreds of thousands of craters came into existence. Most astronomers now agree that they originated from the crashes of giant meteors. The objections of those who once argued that similar craters should be seen on the earth have by now been largely answered. We do find such craters, although most of them are a good deal smaller than those we saw on the moon. However, in South Africa there is one fossil crater some 50 miles in diameter — an upheaval of rock on so large a scale that even today we can scarcely picture what happened perhaps millions of years ago, when a giant meteorite may have smashed into the earth and caused such enormous devastation.

The earth, with its great erosive agents — wind and water — still highly active, has seen its terrestrial craters worn down and washed away until only fragments are left. But the moon, devoid of both air and water, has retained the mountains and craters in their primitive state. In fact, about the only major erosive agent still active on the moon is the tendency of meteorites to erode the walls of mountains caused by earlier crashes. Photographs of the lunar surface suggest the devastation that has occurred. Some regions show craters overlapping and crowding upon one another in great profusion, sometimes almost completely obliterating some underlying crater whose presence we feel rather than can prove, through the presence of minor fragments still left standing.

Since the moon is without atmosphere, man cannot hope to walk upon its surface without protection. He would need the widely publicized "space suit," with a plastic dome and heavy rubber coating, that resembles a diver's suit.

And so the moon, which today is important primarily for its tide-raising ability and for the fact that it gives light, may eventually assume a new role, that of the halfway station, an interplanetary airport, a strategic base for the construction of still more powerful ships for interplanetary travel, and perhaps a very important source of strategic minerals that can be brought back to earth on the return trips, so that the interplanetary space ships will carry a pay load both ways.

Ability to reach the moon and study it in detail would open many important scientific questions. The moon has the unusual property that it rotates around the earth at exactly the same rate that it spins on its axis. Thus it always keeps essentially the same face turned earthward. We never see the other side of the moon and indeed we do not know what that side is like, though the chances are at least a thousand to one that it is similar to the side that we now see and have so fully explored with our powerful telescopes. We may expect to see the same profusion of craters, rolling plains, and giant mountain chains. Study of this satellite will throw light on such important scientific problems as the origin and evolution of the universe. Even if these problems are the only ones that interplanetary travel will solve, we shall eventually find that this knowledge will make the exploration well worth while.

And so on to the other planets. What about Mars and Mercury and Venus? What about the giant planets Jupiter, Saturn, Uranus, and Neptune? What about Pluto, the newest member of our solar system — new, that is, in terms of the date of its discovery, 1930? These problems are worthy of a chapter all their own and hence we turn to the final pages of this book on flying saucers.

There is one final point that I wish to make, here namely, that whatever forms these interplanetary ships are likely to take, the one least likely from all standpoints is the saucer. From the standpoint of structural stability or dynamical form, the saucer is least practical. For high-velocity travel in the earth's atmosphere — the medium through which we must pass on our way to the planets — the pointed cylinder, like a rocket, is ideal. It travels with least resistance and is the most stable form for penetrating a gaseous medium at a speed greater than that of sound.

Those who have tried to argue that saucers are so stable have probably recalled childhood memories of sailing flattened tin cans through the air or skipping flat stones on the water. They have forgotten how small an error in the throw will cause the "disk" to wobble or crash. It would be absolutely impossible for an object of such a shape to veer or maneuver as reported. And there is no possible way that such an object could be immune to the high resistance of the earth's atmosphere at its reported speeds of movement. In the vacuum of interstellar space, any shape will work, though a sphere holds the greatest volume for a given surface area and possesses greatest potential stability.

21

Visits to Mars and Venus

▪▪▪

A quick survey of the solar system leaves the astronomer with some very distinct impressions about the possibility of life existing elsewhere than on the earth. A precise answer to this problem is extremely difficult to obtain, however, because even the world's largest telescope is incapable of giving any direct observational information. Thus our conclusions about life in the universe must be based on indirect evidence.

We have tried to make our approach as scientific as possible. The philosophical approach can do little for us. It is not particularly convincing to argue that it would be surprising indeed if the earth were the only inhabited spot in the universe. And the common psychological reaction, that we should like to believe in the existence of life on other planets, is no more helpful.

The four giant planets, Jupiter, Saturn, Uranus, and Neptune, are somewhat inhospitable places on the basis of observational evidence alone. Their atmospheres contain the gases methane and ammonia in considerable quantities. The major constituent of these atmospheres appears to be hydrogen; free oxygen is apparently completely absent.

Moreover, the temperatures of the outer surfaces of these atmospheres are extremely low, ranging from about 220° below zero Fahrenheit for Jupiter to more than 300° below zero for Neptune, although the temperature may increase with depth in the extensive atmospheres that these planets must possess. The figure for Neptune is not far from the value for liquid air. Far below the visible surface we may finally come to a layer of solid material — probably ice-covered rock. One's imagination can perhaps conceive of life existing under such circumstances, but the arguments in favor of such a conclusion would be largely those that one could employ as background for science fiction. The planet Pluto, most distant from the sun of all, appears to be even less likely as an abode of life — a frozen, barren, and airless waste.

At the other extreme, close to the sun, we find the planet Mercury, which apparently rotates as it revolves so as to keep one face perpetually turned toward the sun and the other always turned away. In consequence, the one face is heated to nearly 800°F, at which temperature liquid water would be as rare a commodity as liquid air is to us. With the dark side of Mercury correspondingly cold, no form of life could possibly be expected to exist on its surface.

This sweeping generalization has left us with only two possibilities for the development of life in our solar system. At any rate, if life is to be found anywhere else than on earth, we should certainly expect to find it on Mars or Venus. Although Venus is slightly nearer the sun than we are, the somewhat greater reflectivity of its cloud-covered surface tends to keep it cooler. There is some evidence that suggests that Venus rotates very slowly. The length of its day is unknown, but the planet probably does not rotate in a period much less than a couple of weeks. Thus, the night side of Venus may be fairly cold.

Venus possesses an extensive atmosphere, with carbon dioxide as one of its major constituents. Although carbon dioxide is not a poisonous gas, animal life, as we know it, would be impossible without free oxygen, which apparently does not exist at all. Tests for water are somewhat less accurate. Such measures as do exist, however, indicate that the moisture content of the accessible atmospheric layers above the clouds of Venus is probably extremely low. This observation naturally raises the question what the clouds really are. Some persons have suggested that they consist of dust, wind-blown to a high level by turbulent, convective air currents over the surface of the plant. On this view, Venusians would be suffering from a constant dust storm.

On the other hand, there seems to be some reason for supposing that water could still exist on Venus. In many respects this planet is a twin of the earth, both in size and in the extent, though not the chemical composition, of its atmosphere. Hence, it would be somewhat surprising if one of these planets possessed abundant water while the other was only a barren desert.

Whether or not some form of life exists below those mysterious clouds of Venus we have no way of discerning. There is no scrap of evidence to throw our argument one way or the other. Carbon dioxide, although not conducive to the support of animal life, is a necessity on the earth for the maintenance of plant life. On the other hand, plants use up the carbon dioxide and give off oxygen — just the reverse of the animal process. One can, therefore, also point to the absence of oxygen as evidence that plant life does not exist. But the whole argument is inconclusive.

It is not impossible that the warm seas of the planet Venus may have produced the physical and chemical conditions ideal for the initiation of life. One-celled plants and animals may exist in great abundance. We may reasonably suppose that conditions in the oceans of Venus are not very different from those in the oceans of the earth during primitive times. If life developed in the one, it may very well have developed in the other.

How far this life has extended up the evolutionary scale we have no means of knowing. We must admit that the geologic records of our own planet are not particularly encouraging. When we see the haphazard way in which Nature has developed various forms of life, one after the other, later throwing many of them into the discard, we do not have much confidence that the development of a highly intelligent form of life is either simple or inevitable. Lcok at the dinosaurs and the fossil butterflies with wingspreads of a couple of feet. These were among the more bizarre experiments. Why life first developed in this direction rather than going straight on toward the mammals and man is something we cannot tell.

What sort of evolutionary trends might we find on Venus? Will evolution there turn toward the development of shellfish or crustaceans? Will it go toward the development of seaworms? Will it finally swing to the development of fish and other creatures with skeletons and bony structures? We cannot answer. However, it is somewhat interesting to note that, had we ourselves developed on Venus instead of on the earth, it is not at all unlikely that we might have developed into a race of mermaids and mermen.

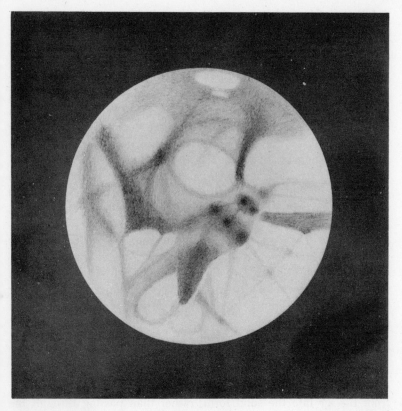

Fig. 87. Drawing of Mars, 11 September 1924.

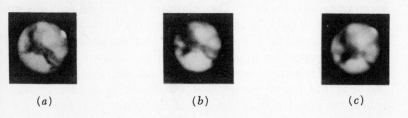

(a)   (b)   (c)

Fig. 88. Photographs of Mars. (a) 29 September 1909; (b) 12 September 1924; (c) 2 November 1926.

Although Venus has undoubtedly received more than its share of attention during the flying-saucer arguments, largely as a result of the University of Denver incident, Mars is the one planet that has, over the years, received far greater publicity as a possible abode of life. And here the evidence is by no means negative.

Although Mars does possess an atmosphere, it is rarefied and sufficiently transparent for us to see the surface beneath. Thus clouds do not plague us as they do in the case of Venus. The outstanding tint possessed by the surface of Mars is red, as its naked-eye appearance suggests. In a large telescope, we see the red disk marked by two charactertistic features: a white button at the pole and gray-green shadows here and there over its surface. In addition to these, the largest telescopes, under best atmospheric conditions, also disclose markings that some scientists have interpreted as a delicate tracery, fine as a spider web, covering the surface of Mars (Fig. 87). These linelike markings are the controversial "canals" of Mars, which Percival Lowell once publicized as being artificial waterways, constructed by intelligent beings to transport water from the Martian poles to the more fertile regions around the equator.

The whitish button at either pole changes in size with the Martian season, to leave no doubt that it is a polar cap composed of ice or snow. Recent evidence indicates that it resembles the hoarfrost that forms inside an electric refrigerator, condensing directly from the air into the solid form, rather than passing through the medium of a liquid stage. As a matter of fact, the polar cap of Mars is a pretty meager affair compared with the vast Arctic and Antarctic caps on the earth. The polar caps of Mars are probably no more than a few inches or at most a few feet thick, for they disappear completely during the course of a single Martian summer.

As spring progresses in one hemisphere of Mars, we note a wave of color that seems to sweep from the equator toward the pole. The gray tint grows greener and stands out in greater contrast against the pastel pink of the rest of the planet. The canals, too, grow darker and show more clearly. Photographs as well as visual observations disclose marked changes in the shading and structure of the dark areas from one year to another, as shown in Fig. 88.

The simplest and probably the correct explanation of these changes is that they are due to some form of vegetation on the surface of the planet.

Well, then, we may ask the question, "Where vegetation exists, is it not also probable that animal life and perhaps human life as well can exist?" This conclusion is drawn a little too fast for the scientist, especially since the argument that tends to favor human life stems from what Lowell professed to have seen in the geometric pattern of the canals. He argued that only artificial waterways would be so regular; any naturally occurring markings would have curves and twists. And so Lowell drew his maps of Mars with essentially straight canals, crossing or switching back from one another, in what he interpreted as a vast irrigation system designed to distribute water over the planet. Later observers, however, have shown that the lines are less straight; most astronomers agree that the canals are not artificial waterways but the remains of river valleys — not the rivers themselves, but the broad, still fertile strip of land in a region that has otherwise reverted to desert. And the dark gray-green areas, originally thought to be oceans, have themselves proved to be vegetation that exists in the beds of ancient seas, seas that have by now dried up.

As to the nature of this vegetation we can only hazard the crudest sort of guess. Precise measurements of color indicate that it probably is not highly organized plant growth, like our own, because there is no evidence of chlorophyll. Instead, it seems to be similar to that of various kinds of lichens. Perhaps some peculiar form of vegetation has evolved in these ancient sea beds from what was the Martian equivalent of terrestrial seaweed. Mars, smaller than our earth, was unable to hold on effectively to either its water or its atmosphere, so that only vestiges of both remain. And if it is difficult for even vegetation to exist on Mars, how much more problematical is the existence of animal life and especially of human life. Many of the arguments discussed in relation to Venus are also applicable here.

What of possible people on Mars? Over the years, imagination has led us to conceive of Martians in many forms. We have already seen how H. G. Wells visualized them as being something like a huge octopus, with armlike tentacles. To my mind, the best model of a Martian was that suggested many years ago by Hugo Gernsback, who is generally credited with being the father of modern science fiction. I am indebted to him for permission to reproduce several figures from the special Mars number of *QUIP*, Mr. Gernsback's

Fig. 89. Male Martian, according to the concept of Hugo Gernsback.

personal Christmas card for 1949. Figure 89 pictures a male Martian, whose characteristics indicate the general trend of evolution on the planet, as conditioned by the physical state of the atmosphere and gravitation. According to Mr. Gernsback, the Martians are

almost 10 feet tall, their huge barrel-shaped upper bodies surmounted by a tremendously ponderous head, shell-like ears almost a foot across, and an elephantine nose 3 feet long. Even more impressive are the stalk-eyes, which project out of their heads and can telescope in or out. These huge eyes are hypnotic in appearance. At the top of the head we discover two huge insectlike antennas – the telepathic organs, which the Martian uses for communication with his fellows. The mouth is like a flattened beak.

A thick, woollike growth covers the entire body, for the sake of warmth. The arms and legs are thin and fragile. Each hand contains eight fingers and the feet possess huge webbed pads. . . The low gravitational force of Mars has prevented its atmosphere from ever being very dense. Therefore, to survive, the Martians had to develop huge lungs; hence the enormous chest, which dominates the entire body. . .

The Martian female is about 6 inches shorter than the male. Her waist is somewhat more shapely, but her outstanding characteristic is the possession of double antennas; she has four of them in contrast to the two of the male. This characteristic enables her to generally out-talk the male and otherwise confuse him. Thus, on Mars, the real rulers are the females.

Thus does Gernsback, in science-fiction form, argue for the case of Mars as a habitable planet. There is one point that the saucer enthusiasts have generally disregarded. If, on Mars or elsewhere, we find beings as intelligent as or more intelligent than we are, if they have developed some sort of vehicle for interplanetary travel, they will almost certainly have developed the radio at some earlier stage of their research.

For many years scientists have discussed the possibility of radio communication with Mars, but we are now in a position where we could easily do it – if there is anyone listening on the other end of the line. Prior to the war, most of our radio communication consisted of long-distance messages over the surface of the earth. We purposely chose wavelengths long enough that they would not penetrate the ionosphere, the earth's radio roof. They bounced around inside between the surface of the earth and the ionospheric roof, escaping into space only by accident. Now we are confident we could put out really powerful signals on short waves – waves that could readily penetrate not only our own ionosphere but also any ionospheric layers that Mars or Venus may possess.

If we are thinking of visiting these planets, if there is any possibility that they may be inhabited by intelligent beings, let us then try sending out signals to them, or at least turning our great receiving antennas occasionally in the direction of these planets and listening for such signals as may come from them directly or indirectly. We might then hear in our receivers the Venusian or Martian equivalents of FM and television. In this way we could begin to check up on the habitability of the solar system, on the possibility of interplanetary communication, and perhaps, through exchange of intelligent ideas, even hasten that day when we ourselves shall be able to leave the earth and explore interplanetary space.

But if we should, at some future date, receive bona fide radio signals from outside the earth, what then? We could absolutely verify their extraterrestrial character [1] and perhaps even determine the actual source by means of direction finders. But could we hope to read the messages and enter into intelligible communication with beings on a distant planet? The archaeologists who read the Maya inscriptions had the advantage of knowing something of their origin, and especially of seeing drawings associated with the writing, to indicate something of the nature of the text.

Let us say that a message has come to us from Mars. It consists of dots and dashes. Phone would be of no advantage and interplanetary television difficult to employ in the early stages of communication, at least. We have recorded the message, have built powerful sending stations with directional antennas. Our own message to the Martians has been repeated, although we know that it is unintelligible to them. But we understand that they hear us. How can we proceed to communicate with beings that have nothing in common with us earth-dwellers?

Nothing in common? That statement is clearly untrue. If we are in communication with one another, both sets of inhabitants possess radios. And along with radios go the various fundamentals of mathematics and the physical sciences, which combined with mathematics, arithmetic first, forms a natural starting point. Let us see if the Martians can count. We send our first message consisting of one dot, two dots, three dots, and so on, up to ten. A six-year-old child should realize that these symbols represent the various numbers. The first test is addition. We select the letter "n" ($- \cdot$) to represent "plus" or "and," and the letter "r" ($\cdot - \cdot$) to represent "equals," "is," or "are." Then we send

$$1 \quad + \quad 1 \quad = \quad 2$$

. —. . .—. ..
.. —. .. .—. ....
.. —. ... .—. .....

and so on. If the Martians understand — and how could they fail? — they will reply in kind, with problems of their own. Note that, in addition to numbers, we have conveyed the abstract ideas of "plus" and "equals."

If we are to proceed with numbers running into the thousands or more, the mere ticking off of dots becomes laborious, though not impossible. To escape such labor we have developed the arabic numerals, the use of zero, and the concept of place. Thus the figure 1 has a different value in the two figures 12 and 120. In the first example, 1 signifies one ten; in the second it signifies ten tens. We use a decimal system. The Martian, perhaps possessing a different number of fingers for primitive counting, might use a system based on eight or sixteen, but any mathematician would immediately recognize another system and convert one to the other. By this method we could communicate our arithmetic to the Martians and learn theirs.

A few abstract numbers, like π — "pi," the ratio of the circumference of a circle to its diameter, 3.14159 — must have the same value on Mars as on the earth. Weights and distances, however, like the distances of planets from the sun, would have no meaning since Martian and terrestrial miles would be different. But *ratios* of distances are independent of the units of measure. Any astronomer who saw the series 4, 7, 10, 16, 52, 100 would recognize them as representing the approximate relative distances from the sun of Mercury, Venus, the earth, Mars, Jupiter, and Saturn. He would still recognize the series even if it were multiplied by any constant. The Martian astronomer, who would undoubtedly be consulting on the transmissions, could not fail to realize its significance. We can imagine the Martians replying, repeating the number "16" several times to emphasize their home planet. We return, with analogous repetition of "10."

We are making progress. Having identified the planets by these numbers, we can then give them some arbitrary symbols different from numbers. And then we send: "Mercury 0, Venus 0, Earth 1, Mars 2, Jupiter 11, Saturn 10." These figures would signify to an astronomer the number of satellites observed for each planet, even if we terrestrials may have missed one or two. And the Martians might repeat the series with a correction "Saturn 11." The first communication of scientific value! We surmise that Martian astronomers, because of better observing conditions and greater proximity to Saturn, have observed eleven satellites. We proceed to compare other planetary data: masses, diameters, rotation times, and so forth. By giving diameters in miles (or kilometers) we can teach the Martians our units of measurement.

Astronomy is not the only science that fits into the Martian picture. The number series 1.008, 4.00, 6.940, 9.02, 10.82, 12.00, . . . for ninety-six numbers provides a starting point, as the relative atomic weights of the successive chemical elements. The number 1.008 identifies hydrogen (H); 12, carbon (C); 16, oxygen (O); and so on. Chemical formulas for compounds — water, HOH (H_2O); acetylene, HCCH (C_2H_2) — can be given, with equations for chemical reactions. The formulas of complex organic compounds might even throw light on the nature of Martian life. We could teach them how to make an atomic bomb more easily than we could tell them how to bake a cake.

There is no obvious limit to the information that could be exchanged. Most irksome would be the delay between sending off a message and receiving the answer. A radio signal that circles the earth seven times in a second will require at least 3 minutes and sometimes as long as 20 minutes to reach Mars, according to the position of the planet in its orbit. I am convinced, for the reasons set forth in the foregoing pages, that if radio signals could be exchanged with any planet, intelligent two-way communication would be possible and would lead to valuable advances in many phases of science.

Let us listen, then, for interplanetary broadcasts. Long before we have real interplanetary saucers we shall be in direct communication with their pilots. Even though we now receive no answer, perhaps we shall eventually get one — millions of years in the future. Remember that the inhabitants of this earth even one century ago could not have discussed intelligently the question of radio communication.

In the meanwhile, should we not adopt a more civilized viewpoint with reference to saucer phenomena. To date, as Lambert [2] has suggested, our attitude toward saucers is not unlike that of a "farm-dog running out to bite the wheels of a passing automobile!"

22

What to do if you see a flying saucer

▸▪▪▸

If you happen to see a flying saucer or what you think might be a saucer, do not be frightened. You should exert every effort to find out exactly what is happening, so that your report will have some meaning.

In my files I have dozens of letters that read something like this: "Several months ago I saw a peculiar light in the sky. It wobbled back and forth and seemed to be almost 20 feet in diameter. If this wasn't a flying saucer, what was it?" Actually, it could have been any one of twenty or more phenomena, as far as the information is concerned. No date, no time, not even a place of observation!

The basic problem in saucers is first to recognize the source of light that makes the saucer visible and second to find out what object or atmospheric condition is sending light to the eye.

Saucers may be self-luminous, that is, they may manufacture their own light; a glowing meteor or a flashlight hung from a balloon are examples. Saucers may be "dull reflectors," like newspapers flying in the wind or clouds that reflect searchlights. These two varieties of saucers have this feature in common: two persons standing some distance apart and indicating where the object seems to be will actually be pointing toward the object that emits or reflects the light and not toward the light source.

Certain saucers are "shiny reflectors," whose mirrorlike surfaces send rays from the sun, moon, or other distant light source into the eye. In this class of saucers fall reflections from metallic surfaces of planes, reflections from ice crystals or water drops, reflections from spider webs, refractions from inequalities of the terrestrial atmosphere, and so on. The directions that two persons will indicate depend more on the distance of the light than on how far away the reflecting surface is. Remember how the rainbow acts!

If you see a saucer, call for someone to check you, as independently as possible. The momentary flash is often due to a source very close to you — a mote in your eye, a spider web, or chance reflection from some distant shiny surface. At night it is usually a meteor.

In any event, try to put yourself where you can repeat exactly what you were doing when you first saw the object. Turn your head from side to side; nod it up and down. Take off your glasses, clean them, and replace them. Move toward the saucer and see if it seems to evade; move away and see if it follows you. If it does, then a mirrorlike reflection is responsible. Stoop down; climb a tree. Note carefully what happens, and then repeat your sequence.

If the saucer seems to veer rapidly toward or away from you, or if it suddenly disappears, its source of luminosity is moving or varying in intensity or you may have moved so that the reflection no longer reaches your eye. Chasing the object or image — as in a plane — is usually the quickest way of losing sight of the saucer. Stop, and leisurely go back to your original post.

Hold your hand at arm's length and spread your fingers. Note how many handbreadths there are between the saucer and the horizon, the saucer and the sun or moon. In many instances the distance will be about 20°, or one normal handbreadth. When that happens you will know you are seeing sundogs or mock suns. Look for the circles or halos associated with this phenomenon.

Still with your hand at arm's length, compare the size of the saucer with your thumbnail or a coin. Note how long it takes for the saucer to move a full handbreadth. Note carefully its shape and any changes of shape. Does the saucer have a color?

Check the weather conditions, sky clarity, color of the sky, visibility of the sun or moon. Later, call your local weather station and ask for a detailed summary of temperature distribution. Especially ask whether temperature inversions are present.

Saucers seen through a window or even through a screen are unreliable. Photographs often show ghosts or fogged patches caused by lens reflection, careless development, light leaks in the camera.

Above all, note exactly where you were when you made the observation. Record all bright sources of light that you can see, mapping their position relative to the saucer. Determine the direction of the saucer. At night, if possible, record the path of the saucer against the stars. Give the exact time and list your name along with the names (and addresses) of confirming witnesses.

REPORT SHEET FOR SAUCER OBSERVERS

Name

Address

Date

Time, duration, and circumstances of sighting (day, night, sunrise, sunset)

Give your exact location, altitude above ground, etc.

Describe the appearance of the saucer(s)

Direction in which you were facing

Weather details and sky conditions, including temperatures and cloud types

Was sun (or moon) shining?

Here draw apparent shape of saucer

Indicate color

Altitude of saucer above horizon (in degrees or in percentage of way from horizon to zenith)

Apparent size of saucer, like a (pea, penny, fingernail, quarter, etc., at arm's length)

Or compare diameter with moon if moon is in sky

Describe motion of saucer

Estimate rate of motion — one hand span at arm's length equals approximately 20°

Did saucer appear to be self-luminous?

To possess a dull finish?

To reflect like a mirror?

To be partially transparent?

The observations confirmed by .... persons.

Identify these persons by name and address

How did saucer behave as you moved in various directions?

Was saucer near sun or moon?

How near? measured in hand spans at arm's length.

Was there a halo around the sun? Describe

If possible, attach detailed weather information from your local station, giving detailed vertical distribution of weather, especially presence of temperature inversions, winds, haze or cloud layers, etc.

General remarks

Check for cobwebs?

Does direction of saucer movement coincide with that of wind?

Could it have been a searchlight playing on a nearly invisible cloud layer?

Fig. 90. Report sheet for saucer observers.

Your basic report sheet might resemble that shown in Fig. 90. Fill it out and send it to the Air Technical Intelligence Center at Wright Field, Dayton, Ohio. They will be glad to get such information. Or, if you prefer, send it to me at Harvard Observatory, Cambridge, Massachusetts, and if it contains any significant information I will forward it to the Air Force.

By the time you have completed the tests outlined above, you will probably have solved the mystery. Your report is none the less helpful.

In any event, remember that Flying Saucers

1. Do exist;
2. Have been seen;
3. Are not what people thought they saw.

Read books by Keyhoe, For The Truth about saucers

Appendix

THEORY OF MIRAGES

The following technical discussion of optical mirages is intended for the scientist who wishes to check certain statements I have made in earlier chapters about lenses of air. It is not necessary for an understanding of the text.

1. *The laws of refraction.* In a vacuum, light travels at the rate of 186,000 miles per second. In air, glass, or any transparent material, light travels at some other speed. Let these two speeds be c and v, respectively. We define the refractive index μ of a substance as the ratio:

$$\mu = c/v. \tag{1}$$

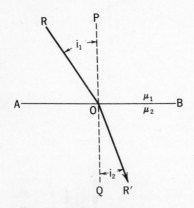

Fig. 91. Refraction of light at an interface AB between two optical materials of different refractive index.

The refractive index of a vacuum, therefore, is equal to unity.

In Fig. 91, let AB represent the interface between two optical materials, with respective refractive indexes μ_1 and μ_2. Let POQ be a line perpendicular to the interface. Suppose that a beam of light, traveling parallel to RO, falls on the surface at the angle of incidence i_1. It is refracted, or bent, at the interface, to the direction OR', which makes an angle i_2 with the perpendicular. A general law of refraction, which determines the path of the light ray, requires that

$$\mu_1 \sin i_1 = \mu_2 \sin i_2 = \text{const.}, \tag{2}$$

a relation termed Snell's law. This is the basic law of refraction, deduced from fundamental principles in most textbooks of elementary optics.

2. *The index of refraction of air* depends on the pressure p, the absolute temperature T, and the wavelength of the incident light. We can write:

$$\mu = 1 + \frac{T_o}{T} \frac{p}{p_o} (\mu_o - 1), \tag{3}$$

where μ_o is the refractive index of air at sea-level pressure ($p_o = 760$ mm-of-mercury) and at 0°C ($T_o = 273°$K). For air, we give the following table of μ_o as a function of wavelength, in Angstrom units.

Color	Letter	Wavelength	μ_o
Red	A	7604	1.0002902
Yellow	D	5896	1.0002919
Green	E	5270	1.0002930
Blue	F	4861	1.0002940
Violet	K	3933	1.0002977

For illustrative calculations, we can use the average value $\mu_o = 1.000293$.

3. *Gravitational equilibrium of the atmosphere.* The mechanical equilibrium of air is governed by the forces acting on a volume element. Consider a volume of gas of density ρ, area 1 cm², and thickness dh (Fig. 92). The mass of this volume element is $\rho\,dh$, and its weight is $g\rho\,dh$, where g is the acceleration due to gravity ($= 980$ cm/sec²).

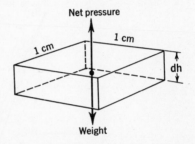

This downward force is counteracted by the pressure of the gas from above and below. The downward pressure on top of the element is p. The upward pressure on the bottom of the element is

$p + (dp/dh)\ dh = p + dp.$

Fig. 92. Equilibrium of a volume element of the atmosphere.

The difference in pressure, dp, balances the gravitational force per unit area, $g\rho\,dh$, or

$$dp = -g\rho\,dh. \tag{4}$$

The minus sign indicates that we count h positive in the upward direction, while gravitation acts downward. We also use the gas law in the form

$$p = \rho k T/m, \tag{5}$$

where m is the mean mass (not the atomic weight) of the atoms or molecules of the gas and k is Boltzmann's constant. This equation, together with Eq. (4), gives us

$$\frac{dp}{p} = -\frac{mg}{kT}\,dh. \tag{6}$$

We can integrate this equation only if we have one additional relation, which specifies T as a function of h. Let us assume that the temperature varies linearly with height from some arbitrary level where we set $h = 0$, $T = T_1$, and $p = p_1$, so that

$$T = T_1\,(1 + ah), \tag{7}$$

where a is a constant. Then integration of Eq. (6) gives

$$\ln \frac{p}{p_1} = - \frac{mg}{akT_1} \ln (1 + ah), \qquad (8)$$

or

$$p = p_1(1 + ah)^{-mg/akT_1}. \qquad (9)$$

From Eqs. (9), (7), and (3), we get

$$\mu = 1 + \frac{T_0}{T_1} \frac{p_1}{p_0} \frac{1}{(1 + ah)^{1+mg/akT_1}}(\mu_0 - 1). \qquad (10)$$

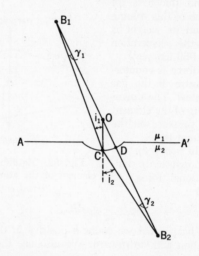

Fig. 93. An air lens resulting from distortion of a temperature inversion.

4. *The vertical lens.* In Chapters 3 and 16 we discussed the mysterious saucer that seemed to accompany a weather balloon in flight. We indicated that it might have been an image formed by a lens of air, resulting from distortion of a temperature inversion. In Fig. 93, we have idealized the problem slightly. We consider an atmosphere consisting of two horizontal layers of refractive indices μ_1 and μ_2, separated by the surface AA', which has a spherical bulge CD whose center is at O. Let B_1 be the balloon and B_2 the position of its image. Let

$$
\begin{array}{lll}
OB_1 = F_1, & \angle OCB_1 = i_1, & \\
OB_2 = F_2, & \angle OCB_2 = \pi - i_2 & \qquad (11) \\
OC = r; & \angle CB_1O = \gamma_1, & \\
& \angle CB_2O = \gamma_2. &
\end{array}
$$

Since OC is a radius of the sphere, it is perpendicular to the surface CD. Thus i_1 and i_2 are the respective angles of incidence and refraction. From Snell's law, Eq. (2), we have

$$\mu_1 \sin i_1 = \mu_2 \sin i_2. \tag{12}$$

Applying the law of sines to the two triangles OCB_1 and OCB_2, we have

$$F_1/\sin i_1 = r/\sin \gamma_1, \tag{13}$$

$$F_2/\sin (\pi - i_2) = F_2/\sin i_2 = r/\sin \gamma_2. \tag{14}$$

The sum of the three angles of triangle B_1CB_2 is equal to 180°, or π. Thus

$$\gamma_1 + \gamma_2 + i_1 + (\pi - i_2) = \pi. \tag{15}$$

We are given the constants of the medium, μ_1, μ_2, and r. We are given the position of the balloon, so that we know F_1. We also assume that if we know γ_1, we are to eliminate the quantities i_1, i_2, γ_2, so as to determine the position of the image, fixed by the parameter F_2.

As long as i_1 and i_2 are small, we can replace the sine by the angle itself. Then Eqs. (12)–(15) take the form:

$$\mu_1 i_1 = \mu_2 i_2, \tag{16}$$

$$F_1/i_1 = r/\gamma_1, \tag{17}$$

$$F_2/i_2 = r/\gamma_2, \tag{18}$$

$$\gamma_1 + \gamma_2 + i_1 - i_2 = 0. \tag{19}$$

Elimination of various quantities gives:

$$i_1 = F_1\gamma_1/r, \tag{20}$$

$$i_2 = \mu_1 i_1/\mu_2 = \mu_1 F_1\gamma_1/\mu_2 r, \tag{21}$$

$$\gamma_2 = r i_2/F_2 = \mu_1 F_1\gamma_1/\mu_2 F_2. \tag{22}$$

Substitution of these expressions in Eq. (19) gives

$$\gamma_1 \left(1 + \frac{\mu_1 F_1}{\mu_2 F_2} + \frac{F_1}{r} - \frac{\mu_1 F_1}{\mu_2 r} \right) = 0. \tag{23}$$

Thus, as long as the angles are small, the factor in parentheses is independent of γ_1. This equation defines F_2 in terms of known parameters. Solving it, we get

$$\frac{1}{F_2} = \frac{1}{r} \frac{(\mu_1 - \mu_2)}{\mu_1} - \frac{1}{F_1} \frac{\mu_2}{\mu_1} \tag{24}$$

To the accuracy required, $p_1 = p_2$ and $T_2 = T_1 + \Delta T$. For μ_1 and μ_2 we can substitute unity, except where the difference occurs. Then from Eq. (3),

$$\mu_1 - \mu_2 = \frac{T_0}{T_1} \frac{p_1}{p_0} \frac{\Delta T}{T_1} (\mu_0 - 1). \tag{25}$$

For an illustrative calculation, we take $T_0 p_1 / T_1 p_0 = 1/3$, and set $\Delta T / T_1 = 0.1$, with $(\mu_0 - 1) = 3 \times 10^{-4}$. Then

$$\frac{\mu_1 - \mu_2}{\mu_1} = \delta \sim 10^{-5}. \tag{26}$$

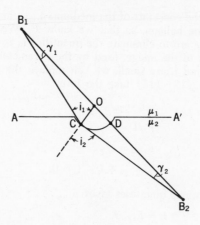

Fig. 94. Air lens, at large angle of incidence.

Equation (24) becomes

$$\frac{1}{F_2} = \frac{\delta}{r} - \frac{1}{F_1} \tag{27}$$

To get the focal length of this lens we set $F_1 = \infty$. Then

$$F_1 \sim 10^5 r. \tag{28}$$

Thus the effective focal length of an air lens of this type is 10^5 times its radius of curvature. Hence, if r were 1 foot, say, F_2 would be 10^5 feet or 20 miles. Thus, vertical lenses cannot produce the observed effect under the assumed conditions, with i_1 small.

We must extend the theory to include the extreme of large angles, under the conditions shown in Fig. 94. Equations (12)–(15) still apply, but now we take

$$i_2 = \frac{\pi}{2} - \epsilon, \tag{29}$$

where ϵ is small. Then

$$\sin i_2 = \cos \epsilon = 1 - \epsilon^2/2, \tag{30}$$

From Eq. (26),

$$\mu_2/\mu_1 = 1 - \delta; \tag{31}$$

from Eq. (12),

$$\sin i_1 = (1 - \delta)(1 - \epsilon^2/2) = 1 - \delta - \epsilon^2/2. \tag{32}$$

whence

$$i_1 \sim \frac{\pi}{2} - (2\delta + \epsilon^2)^{\frac{1}{2}}; \tag{33}$$

from Eq. (13).

$$\sin \gamma_1 = \frac{r}{F_1}(1 - \delta)(1 - \epsilon^2/2), \tag{34}$$

whence

$$\gamma_1 \sim \frac{r}{F_1}(1 - \delta - \epsilon^2/2); \tag{35}$$

similarly, from Eq. (14),

$$\gamma_2 \sim \frac{r}{F_2}(1 - \epsilon^2/2); \tag{36}$$

then, from Eq. (15),

$$\frac{1}{F_2}(1 - \epsilon^2/2) = -\frac{1}{F_1}(1 - \delta - \epsilon^2/2) + \frac{1}{r}[(2\delta + \epsilon^2)^{\frac{1}{2}} - \epsilon] \tag{37}$$

Thus we finally get, to the accuracy required,

$$\frac{1}{F_2} \sim \frac{1}{r}[(2\delta + \epsilon^2)^{\frac{1}{2}} - \epsilon] - \frac{1}{F_1} \tag{38}$$

Comparing this equation with Eq. (27) we see the effective focal length can be very much greater for the physical situation of large angles of incidence. Setting $\delta \sim 10^{-5}$ as before, and taking $\epsilon^2 = 2\delta$, with $F_1 = \infty$, we have

$$F_2 \sim 500 \, r, \tag{39}$$

so that if r is 5 feet, F_2 is only ½ mile instead of 100 miles, as required by Eq. (28).

The spherical aberration of the lens has in effect reduced the focal length to a practical value. The edge of such a lens can produce a distorted image whose maximum displacement from the true direction of the object is of the order of $(2\delta)^{\frac{1}{2}}$, or about 0.25°. Any light deviation appreciably greater than this value must arise from reflection in fog or haze or refraction by ice crystals. At low elevation, however, the cooperation of the lens effect with mirage effects can result in appreciably greater displacements.

Interference of light between the center and the edges of these imperfect lenses causes the phenomenon of twinkling and also produces the moving shadow bands seen at solar eclipses.

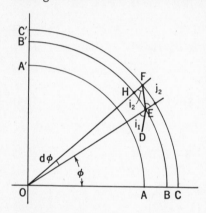

Fig. 95. Path of a light ray through stratified air.

One should note that the upper edge of a temperature inversion may possess a wavy pattern, caused by the natural instability associated with the convective equilibrium that usually exists above this edge. The transient flashes and lights seen from the ground or from planes, and reported as a variety of saucer, are probably due to this effect. As for the vertical balloon, the bubble caused by the balloon's puncturing of the inversion layer may be less significant than natural waves described above. A more refined analysis which allows for the vertical changes of density in a horizontally stratified atmosphere does not appreciably alter the above result.

5. *Mirage theory*. In Fig. 95, let O be the center of the earth, and the AA' a great circle on the surface. We suppose that the atmosphere is stratified uniformly; BB' and CC' represent two layers in the atmosphere, separated by a distance dr. Let DEF be the schematic path of a light ray through this layer. If $DEO = i_1$, the angle of incidence, and $GEF = j_1$, the angle of refraction, Snell's law requires that

$$\mu_1 \sin i_1 = \mu_2 \sin j_1, \tag{40}$$

where μ_1 and μ_2 are refractive indexes on opposite sides of BB'. The ray, after traversing the distance EF, impinges on the next layer CC' at an angle of incidence $i_2 = j_1 - d\phi$. If we set $OE = r_1$ and $OF = r_2$, and apply the law of sines to triangle OEF, we get

$$r_1 \sin j_1 = r_2 \sin i_2, \tag{41}$$

so that we have, in general

$$\mu_1 r_1 \sin i_1 = \mu_2 r_2 \sin i_2 = \mu r \sin i = C, \tag{42}$$

a constant. In the triangle FEH, we have

$$\tan i_2 = HE/HF = r d\phi/dr = \tan i, \tag{43}$$

in general. Since

$$\tan i = \frac{\sin i}{\cos i} = \frac{\sin i}{(1 - \sin^2 i)^{\frac{1}{2}}} = \frac{1}{[(\mu^2 r^2/C^2) - 1]^{\frac{1}{2}}}, \tag{44}$$

the differential equation of a ray becomes:

$$d\phi = \pm \frac{dr}{r[(\mu^2 r^2/C^2) - 1]^{\frac{1}{2}}} \tag{45}$$

We use the double sign to keep ϕ positive whether the ray is concave upward or downward.

To integrate this equation we must know μ as a function of r.

If we confine our attention to rays close to the surface of the earth, that is, within a small range of r, we can simplify this equation. Set

$$r = r_0 + h, \tag{46}$$

$$\mu = \mu_0(1 + bh), \tag{47}$$

$$r d\phi = ds; \qquad C = \mu_0 \cos a, \tag{48}$$

where h is a vertical height measured from some arbitrary radius r_0, b is a constant, ds is a coördinate parallel to the curved surface of the earth, and a is equal to 90° minus the angle of incidence at r_0. Dropping terms of the second order, we find for the differential equation of the ray

$$ds = \pm \frac{dh \cos a}{(\sin^2 a + 2\beta h)^{\frac{1}{2}}}, \tag{49}$$

where

$$\beta = \left(\frac{1}{r_0} + b \right). \tag{50}$$

Integration gives the result:

$$\beta s \sec a = \pm (2\beta h + \sin^2 a)^{\frac{1}{2}} - \sin a, \tag{51}$$

or

$$\beta s^2 \sec^2 a + 2s \tan a = 2h. \tag{52}$$

This is the equation of a parabola, relative to the earth's surface. When β is positive, the parabola is concave upward. For negative β, it is concave downward. The case $\beta = 0$ represents a straight line.

We consider only positive values of h and s. We shall employ signs as follows:

β	a	sign of radical	region
	$+$	$+$	$s \geqq 0$
$+$	$-$	$-$	$0 \leqq s \leqq s_{\text{min}}$
	$-$	$+$	$s \geqq s_{\text{min}}$
	$+$	$-$	$0 \leqq s \leqq s_{\text{max}}$
$-$	$+$	$+$	$s \geqq s_{\text{max}}$
	$-$	$+$	$s \geqq 0$

We have adopted the quantities s_{max} or s_{min} to indicate the distance from the origin where the parabola attains maximum or minimum height above the ground. Here the curve will be parallel to the ground, so that

$$\frac{dh}{ds} = \beta s \sec^2 a + \tan a = 0, \tag{53}$$

for

$$s_{\text{max,min}} = -\frac{\sin a \cos a}{\beta} = s_{\text{m,m}}, \tag{54}$$

corresponding to the heights

$$h_{\text{max,min}} = -\frac{\sin^2 a}{2\beta} = h_{\text{m,m}}. \tag{55}$$

Eliminating a between Eqs. (54) and (55) we get

$$s_{\text{m,m}} = [(2h_{\text{m,m}}/\beta)\,(1 - \beta h_{\text{m,m}})]^{\frac{1}{2}} \sim (2h_{\text{m,m}}/\beta)^{\frac{1}{2}}. \tag{56}$$

If h_1 represents the height of the eye above the ground, the distance to a ray that just grazes the ground tangentially is

$$s_1 = (2h_1/\beta)^{\frac{1}{2}}. \tag{57}$$

The angle a_1 of this limiting ray is determined by

$$\sin^2 a_1 = -2\beta h_1. \tag{58}$$

Rays leaving the source at negative angles whose absolute values exceed $|a_1|$ will intersect the ground. If the surface is a smooth body of water, we can have an additional reflection with formation of an inverted image.

The quantity β, from Eqs. (10), (47), and (50), takes the form:

$$\beta = \frac{1}{r_o} + b(\mu_o - 1) = \frac{1}{r_o} - 3 \times 10^{-4}\left(\frac{1}{T_1}\frac{dT}{dh} + \frac{mg}{kT}\right)$$

$$= 1.0 \times 10^{-9} - 3 \times 10^{-4}\frac{1}{T_1}\frac{dT}{dh}. \tag{59}$$

For adiabatic or convective equilibrium,

$$\frac{dT}{dh} = -\frac{mg}{k}\frac{\gamma - 1}{\gamma} = 1.0 \times 10^{-4} \text{ K deg/cm}. \tag{60}$$

where $\gamma = 1.40$, the ratio of the specific heat of air at constant pressure to that at constant volume. Hence, for the convective atmosphere at standard temperature and pressure,

$$\beta \sim 1.1 \times 10^{-9} \text{ cm}^{-1}. \tag{61}$$

These formulas admit of many variations. Let us discuss a specific example for which we assume the temperature to decrease upward at the adiabatic rate for the first 10 meters. At this point we shall assume that a temperature inversion occurs. From 10 meters to, say, 20 meters, the temperature increases upward at the rate 2×10^{-3} K deg/cm. Then, in this second region,

$$\beta \sim -1.1 \times 10^{-9} \text{ cm}^{-1}. \tag{62}$$

From Eq. (56), with $h_{m,m} = 10^3$ cm, we have

$$s_{m,m} = 1.3 \times 10^6 \text{ cm} = 13 \text{ km}. \tag{63}$$

The situation approximates to that of Fig. 96. Let A be the observer's eye, 10 meters above the ground, and B some object $2 s_{m,m} = 26$ km distant, and also 10 meters above the ground.

The distribution of atmospheric density acts like a convex cylindrical lens. We see the point B twice, once from above and once from below, along the respective paths BDA and BCA, appearing in the directions B' and B'', separated by the angle $B'AB'' = 2 \alpha = 10'$, by Eq. (58).

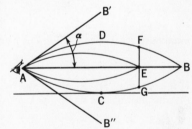

Fig. 96. Mirage formation.

A point intermediate between A and B, such as E, will also show twice, but at slightly smaller angles of separation. Between B' and B'', therefore, will appear images of all the objects along the line AEB. The more distant the object, the greater the magnification. Thus the line FEG will appear to subtend the angle $B'AB''$.

This apparent magnification of distant objects is very sensitive to the position of the eye. A small shift can produce a very rapid change of apparent diameter, which the senses tend to interpret as rapid motion and high acceleration away from the observer.

The cylindrical effect tends to cause tops of mountains or distant clouds to stretch out into long, cigar-shaped images parallel to the horizon. Irregularities of brightness could easily produce the illusion of a wingless plane, with windows where the sky or clouds appear.

For a more general discussion of mirage formation, see J. M. Pernter and F. M. Exner, *Meteorologische Optik* (Vienna and Leipzig: Braumüller, ed. 2, 1922). A less technical discussion appears in M. Minnaert, *Light and Colour in the Open Air*, translated by H. M. Kremer-Priest and revised by K. E. Brian Jay (London: Bell, 1940).

Notes

CHAPTER 2

1. Donald Keyhoe, *The Flying Saucers Are Real* (New York: Fawcett, 1950); Frank Scully, *Behind the Flying Saucers* (New York: Holt, 1950); Gerald Heard, *Is Another World Watching* (New York: Harper, 1950).

CHAPTER 4

1. Kenneth Arnold and Ray Palmer, *The Coming of the Saucers* (Amherst, Wisconsin: Privately printed, 1952).

CHAPTER 5

1. Arthur Conan Doyle, *The Sign of the Four*.

CHAPTER 7

1. *The Observatory*, vol. 39 (1916), pp. 213–215.
2. Numerous letters from observers of the "beam" were published in *Nature*, vol. 27, for 23 November 1882 and the following weeks, and it was upon these that Capron's discussion was chiefly based.
3. *The London, Edinburgh, and Dublin Philosophical Magazine and Journal of Science*, series 5, vol. 15 (1883), pp. 318–339, with 7 figures.
4. *The Times* (London), Saturday 15 October 1859; letter to the editor.
5. *Nature*, vol. 50 (1894), p. 524.
6. *English Mechanic and World of Science*, vol. 88 (1908), p. 211.

CHAPTER 8

1. *Nature*, vol. 48 (1893), p. 77.
2. *Monthly Weather Review* (1898), p. 358.
3. *Saturday Night*, vol. 67 (1952), p. 9.
4. *La Nature*, Supp., communications, 11 November 1899.
5. *L'Astronomie* (1886), p. 309.
6. *La Nature* (1898), p. 127.
7. *Saturday Night*, vol. 67 (1952), p. 9.
8. *The Times* (London), Friday 5 October 1877.

CHAPTER 9

1. Jeremiah 10:2.
2. A. D. White, *History of the Warfare Between Science and Theology* (New York, 1898), vol. 1, p. 196.
3. *The New York Times*, 30 May 1877.
4. *The New York Sun*, 21 September 1877.

CHAPTER 10

1. 2 Kings 11.
2. *Paradise Lost*, Book VI, lines 749–773.

CHAPTER 11

1. Hadley Cantril, with the assistance of Hazel Gaudet and Herta Hertzog, *The Invasion from Mars* (Princeton: Princeton University Press, 1940).
2. *Time*, 7 November 1938, p. 40.
3. *Newsweek*, 7 November 1938, p. 13.
4. *The New Yorker*, 12 November 1938, p. 15.
5. *Newsweek*, 7 November 1938, p. 13.

CHAPTER 12

1. Frank Scully, *Behind the Flying Saucers* (New York: Holt, 1950).
2. The most complete single record appeared in the *Denver Post*, 12 March 1950, in an article by Thor Severson, with a significant follow-up on 19 October. An excellent summary also appeared in the *Rocky Mountain News*, 9 September 1950, when Pasquale Marranzino wrote up an interview with the speaker. These references have been very helpful to me.
3. "Washington Merry-Go-Round." 26 November 1950.
4. *Saturday Review of Literature*, 23 September 1950, p. 20.
5. *Behind the Flying Saucers*, p. 66.

CHAPTER 13

1. Francis Bacon, *Novum Organum*, Aphorisms, L.
2. *Othello*, act 3, scene 3.
3. *King Lear*, act 1, scene 2.
4. I. A. Richards, *Republic of Plato* (New York: Norton, 1942), book 4, p. 79.

CHAPTER 15

1. Pernter-Exner, *Meteorologische Optik* (Vienna and Leipzig, ed. 2, 1922), pp. 252–253.
2. James Glaisher, Camille Flammarion, W. de Fonvielle, and Gaston Tissandier, *Travels in the Air* (London, 1871).
3. *Ibid.*, pp. 276–277.

CHAPTER 16

1. *Travels in the Air*, pp. 297–298.
2. *Ibid.*, pp. 258–261.

CHAPTER 18

1. *Julius Caesar*, act 2, scene 2.
2. H. H. Nininger, *Out of the Sky* (Denver: University of Denver Press, 1952).

3. P. Millman, "An Analysis of Meteor Spectra," *Annals of the Astronomical Observatory of Harvard College*, vol. 82 (1932).

CHAPTER 19

1. D. H. Menzel, *Elementary Manual of Radio Propagation* (New York: Prentice-Hall, 1948), p. 179.

CHAPTER 21

1. The rest of this chapter is adapted by permission from an article on interplanetary communication that I published in *Short Wave and Television* for December 1937.

2. *Saturday Night*, vol. 67 (1952), p. 18.

Index